GAS
CHROMATOGRAPHY

GAS
CHROMATOGRAPHY

Howard Purnell

Lecturer in Physical Chemistry,
University of Cambridge; Fellow of Trinity Hall

John Wiley & Sons, Inc., New York · London

In the short space of ten years, gas chromatography has established itself in laboratories devoted to the study of all the major branches of science and technology. Already it has provided the means for answering many very difficult questions, and it offers every hope of allowing future study of problems hitherto considered too complex even to contemplate seriously. In those instances in which it has merely supplanted existing techniques, it has usually led to substantial improvement and, occasionally, has revealed a need for re-evaluation of existing ideas and theories. It is, therefore, neither wishful thinking nor exaggeration to describe gas chromatography as the most important single analytical tool at our command.

Chromatographic methods have been employed over the years with conspicuous success, although their development has until recently been almost entirely on an empirical basis. This was largely due to the relative experimental inflexibility of liquid-liquid and liquid-solid systems, but, in addition, the mathematical complexity of the existing theory must have been a considerable barrier to its widespread application. The initiation of gas chromatographic methods changed the situation greatly. First, the underlying physical chemistry was much simpler and, second, the comparatively free choice of carrier gas, its flow rate and pressure, and its column temperature and composition made experimental tests of theory readily possible. This situation catalysed interest in chromatographic theory and its application to experiment in a remarkable way. It is significant that almost

PREFACE

all major technical advances of recent years have stemmed from theoretical speculation. Although there is still much to be learned about the details of chromatographic processes, it seems certain that the theoretical picture is already reasonably clear.

Therefore the most profitable use of gas chromatography already demands a reasonable understanding of the basis for the choice of experimental conditions and equipment. In recognition of this situation, this book contains a substantial account of both the theoretical views current at this time and the efforts made to test and profit by them. Emphasis has been given to the theoretical plate concept and the various rate theories because of their proven utility and wide acceptance. In order to clarify and to simplify presentation of the abbreviated, but admittedly still difficult, theories outlined, the book opens with a short section outlining the aspects of physical chemistry that are important in gas chromatography. An added reason for including this material is that only a small percentage of practising chromatographers is likely to be composed of chemists. It is to be hoped, therefore, that this part of the book will serve a dual purpose and will be particularly helpful to those whose major interests are in other areas.

Chromatography is, of course, a means rather than an end, and so, understandably, the greater part of this book is devoted to practical matters. However, I have, as far as possible, discussed these from a quantitative standpoint. Although the particular methods employed may well not be those that ultimately find general favour, they reflect recent trends and at least indicate something of the future. The same may be said of some aspects of the interpretation and practical application of theory. Often what is said can best be described as a reasonable guess. These uncertainties will undoubtedly be cleared up in the relatively near future, if only because of the remarkable rate of advance which we are now experiencing. Their resolution is thus associated with the general sense of enthusiasm and exhilaration which characterises people and events in this field of study. How long the pace and excitement will be maintained is a matter of speculation, but the indications are that the attainment of the steady state is quite far ahead. If this book in any way hastens the process, it will have achieved its purpose.

I want to thank the many workers, editors, and publishers who have so kindly allowed me to reproduce material. I am also heavily indebted to those with whom I have collaborated in research over the years. Their names occur frequently in the text and, although their contribution to the information given and ideas expressed is often undefined, it is immeasurable.

HOWARD PURNELL

Cambridge, England
July, 1962

CONTENTS

Chromatography is an analytical method based on differences in the partition coefficients of substances distributed between a static phase, usually of great surface area, and a moving fluid phase. It is likely that the process has been operative in Nature since earliest times, but its history as a scientific tool is only a little over a half century old. The earliest reported experiments which can be unequivocally regarded as chromatography are those of Tswett (1), who separated the components of plant pigments by passing their solutions through columns of solid adsorbents. It was presumably the formation of the coloured solute rings that suggested the name chromatography, but it would be nice to think that Tswett, whose name, in Russian, means colour, took advantage of the opportunity to indulge his sense of humour. That the name is a misnomer is evident, but despite the fact that in recent years other names have been suggested, the original persists and seemingly always will.

Following on Tswett's discoveries, nothing further was achieved until, after a lapse of 25 years, Kuhn, Lederer and Winterstein (2) rediscovered the technique in 1931, although others—for example, Berl and his associates (3)—came near to developing gas chromatography in their attempts at separation by low-temperature sorption and desorption. From 1931 onwards, the technique flourished, progress was rapid; elution chromatography with a solid adsorbent and a flowing liquid achieved considerable importance, particularly in the fields of organic and biochemistry. However, powerful a tool though it was, there

1
INTRODUCTION

1

was room for great improvement, in particular in the direction of the production of sharper bands of solute. One approach which received attention was the use of rising temperatures during the analysis (4); although these studies achieved little in the way of successful results, they ultimately led to the development of the frontal and displacement development techniques pioneered by Tiselius (5).

In the meantime, however, a revolution had been brought about in 1941 by the work of Martin and Synge (6) who, reasoning that partition isotherms were more commonly linear for the distribution of a solute between two liquids than for its distribution between a liquid and a solid, had shown how it was possible to construct and operate a liquid-liquid system. The extreme simplicity of their ultimate finding that paper strips could be employed in place of columns is, perhaps, one of the most astonishing results in the history of analysis. The tremendous impact of their work in all branches of chemistry needs no elaboration, and it is sufficient to say that paper chromatography now almost certainly constitutes the most powerful weapon in the armoury of organic and biochemists. This fact was recognised in 1954 by the award of the Nobel prize to the inventors.

It must by now be well recognised that in their original paper Martin and Synge pointed out that the flowing liquid could, with advantage, be replaced by a gas. Another ten years elapsed before this proposition was put to the test, again by Martin, but this time in collaboration with A. T. James (7). In the intervening period Claesson (8, 9), Clough (10), Turner (11), Turkel'taub (12) and Phillips (13) had all made contributions to the frontal and displacement methods of gas chromatography, but with little more than limited success. The neglect of Martin and Synge's suggestion that elution gas chromatography might be possible is, therefore, difficult to understand, even if the intervention of the war is taken into account. From the moment that the successful experiments of James and Martin were described, however, interest in techniques other than elution waned abruptly, and there began a period of development in elution gas chromatography almost unparalleled in scope in any other field. Within a short time a number of important papers, which set the seal on the technique, appeared. Among those in gas-solid chromatography the most prominent were by Cremer and Mueller (14), Zhukhovitskii, Zolotareva, Sokolov and Turkel'taub (15), Janak (16), Ray (17) and Patton, Lewis and Kaye (18). In the field of gas-liquid chromatography important contributions came from James and Martin (19), James and Phillips (20), Ray (17), and Bradford, Chalkley and Harvey (22). Between them these workers established the fact that the apparatus requirements for gas chromatography were negligible in comparison to those of existing techniques, while the range of analyses performed covered mixtures of most of the simpler gases and vapours. By the end of 1955, elution gas chromatography had arrived in most laboratories.

In the very nature of things it was to be expected that gas chromatography would find its widest application in analytical chemistry. Nowadays, when the literature contains more than two thousand papers, the analysis of complex mixtures of hydrocarbons, combustion products, engine exhaust fumes, amino-acid residues from polypeptides and proteins, plasma cholesterol fatty acids and esters, to name only a few, are carried out more or less on a routine basis. Simpler mixtures are regularly analysed in connexion with the control of plant processes in many countries, while ambitious steps towards plant automation via gas chromatography are reported from time to time. In the laboratory, both in industry and in schools and Universities, most current research programmes are based on gas chromatographic analysis and, in fact, the erstwhile established techniques of mass spectrometry, infra-red and ultra-violet spectroscopy have been almost entirely superseded. It is, perhaps, only in the field of isotope analysis that mass spectrometry still reigns, but even here its authority is presently being challenged.

Another aspect of gas chromatography which is growing slowly is that of the isolation of pure materials. Preparative scale work is mainly carried out with samples of a gram or less and with columns of large dimensions. While the separations achieved at this time are less spectacular than those obtained in small scale operation, as more and more attention is paid to the problem the method will undoubtedly become more effective. In the author's opinion, gas chromatography can and will compete with distillation in the purification of substances occurring in small quantities in other substances of similar boiling point. A remarkable example of the potentialities of the method is afforded by the recent account by Moore and Ward (21) of the preparation of pure *ortho* and *para* hydrogen. This has never before been achieved and appeared previously to be impossible. Its impact in the field of gas kinetic studies may well be considerable. An approach instituted by Freund, Benedek and Szepesy (23) in which the column packing moves against the gas stream, is highly promising, since the take-off can be made continuous and there are indications that very soon considerable developments in this direction can be expected. When this expectation materialises we may anticipate a widespread generation of interest in preparative scale chromatography.

The third important application of the technique lies in the possibility of its use as a research tool in purely academic physico-chemical studies. James and Martin indicated early how gas-liquid chromatography could provide information about molecular structure while Hoare and Purnell (24, 25) pointed out how vapour pressures, boiling points, latent heats,

heats of solution and mixing, and activity coefficients might be measured. Littlewood, Phillips and Price (26) also measured heats of solution, and, thence, the corresponding free energies and entropies. Purnell (27) has discussed the regular variation of these quantities with molecular structure which is often observed while Pierrotti, Deal, Derr and Porter (28) have demonstrated that gas chromatography may provide a valuable and more rapid method of studying the interaction of solute and solvent than do conventional methods.

Gas chromatography also offers the possibility of measurement of physical quantities in an altogether different field. The introduction of theories such as those of van Deemter, Zuiderweg and Klinkenberg (29) and Golay (30) have shown that in the near future, when, it is hoped, more will be known about the processes occurring in chromatographic columns, it may be possible to measure diffusion rates both in the gas and liquid phases. Such measurements are not easily made by conventional means; thus, it will be worthwhile to persevere in these studies.

While, as yet, this last aspect of gas chromatography has received little attention, it may be expected with every confidence that some day the technique will take an established place among purely physico-chemical methods.

THE RELATION OF GAS CHROMATOGRAPHY TO OTHER ANALYTICAL METHODS

Most physical methods of analysis employ some facet or other of the distribution process, since this is merely a statement of the general law of equilibrium. Gas chromatography has particularly close affinities with ion exchange methods, distillation and counter-current extraction.

Ion exchange columns undoubtedly fall within the scope of the definition of chromatography given on the first page. Distillation and counter-current extraction, however, differ from chromatography in that, in each, both phases are moving and, in neither is the surface area one phase exposes to the other great in the chromatographic sense. Nevertheless, the theory of chromatography and distillation are, in many respects, very similar. In particular, they share the concept of the fundamental act, that is, the equilibration between phases which is repeated over and over again. Where they differ entirely is in the fact that, by its nature, chromatography cannot be anything but a batch process while counter-current methods can be made continuous. On this basis, the preparative chromatographic apparatus described earlier (23) cannot be considered to be truly chromatographic.

As is seen later, the numerical efficiencies required to bring about a given separation are much higher in chromatography than in distillation. This is because, in distillation, the column is used many times over in producing the final equilibrium state while, in chromatography, the materials pass straight through the column, which is only used once. However, the numerical efficiencies in chromatography are often very much easier to realise than those in distillation since, for example, a chromatographic column 100 or even 1000 ft. long can be handled perfectly easily, while a distillation unit only 10 ft. high may well offer exceptional difficulty in operation and construction.

REFERENCES

1. Tswett, M., *Ber. deut. botan. Ges.*, 1906, **24**, 316, 384.
2. Kuhn, R., A. Winterstein and E. Lederer, *Hoppe-Seyler's Z. physiol. Chem.*, 1931, **197**, 141.
3. Berl, E., and E. Wacherdorff, *Z. angew. Chem.*, 1924, **37**, 205.
4. Eucken, A., and H. Knick, *Brennstoff-Chem.*, 1936, **17**, 241.
5. Tiselius, A., *Arkiv. Kemi Mineral. Geol.*, 1940, **14B**, 5; 1943, **A16**, 11.
6. Martin, A. J. P., and R. L. M. Synge, *Biochem. J.*, 1941, **35**, 1358.
7. James, A. T., and A. J. P. Martin, *Biochem. J.*, 1952, **50**, 679.
8. Claesson, S., *Arkiv Kemi Mineral. Geol.*, 1946, **23A**, 133.
9. Claesson, S., *Arkiv Kemi Mineral Geol.*, 1946, **24A**, 7.
10. Clough, K. H., *Petrol. Engr.*, 1955, **27**, 686.
11. Turner, W. C., *Natl. Petrol. News*, 1943, **35**, 234.
12. Turkel'taub, N. M., *Zhur. Anal. Khim.*, 1950, **5**, 200.
13. Phillips, C. S. G., *Disc. Faraday Soc.*, 1949, **7**, 241.
14. Cremer, E., and R. Mueller, *Z. Elektrochem.*, 1951, **55**, 217.
15. Zhukhovitskii, A. A., O. V. Zolotareva, V. A. Sokolov, and N. M. Turkel'taub, *Doklady Akad. Nauk, U.S.S.R.*, 1951, **77**, 435.
16. Janak, J., *Chem. listy.*, 1953, **47**, 464, 817, 1184.
17. Ray, N. H., *J. Appl. Chem.*, 1954, **4**, 21, 82.
18. Patton, H. W., J. S. Lewis and W. I. Kaye, *Anal. Chem.*, 1955, **27**, 170.
19. James, A. T., and A. J. P. Martin, *Analyst*, 1952, **77**, 915.
20. James, D. H., and C. S. G. Phillips, *J. Chem. Soc.*, 1953, 1600; 1954, 3446.
21. Moore, W. R., and H. R. Ward, *J. Amer. Chem. Soc.*, 1958, **80**, 2909.
22. Bradford, B. W., D. Harvey and D. E. Chalkley, *J. Inst. Petroleum*, 1955, **41**, 80.
23. Freund, M., P. Benedek and L. Szepesy, *Vapour Phase Chromatography*, 1957, Butterworths, London (editor D. H. Desty), p. 359.
24. Hoare, M. R., and J. H. Purnell, *Research*, 1955, **8**, S41.
25. Hoare, M. R., and J. H. Purnell, *Trans. Faraday Soc.*, 1956, **52**, 222.
26. Littlewood, A. B., C. S. G. Phillips and D. T. Price, *J. Chem. Soc.*, **1955**, 1480.
27. Purnell, J. H., *Vapour Phase Chromatography*, 1957, Butterworths, London (editor, D. H. Desty), p. 52.
28. Pierrotti, G. J., C. H. Deal, E. L. Derr and P. E. Porter, *J. Amer. Chem. Soc.*, 1956, **78**, 2989.
29. van Deemter, J. J., F. J. Zuiderweg and A. Klinkenberg, *Chem. Eng. Sci.*, 1956, **5**, 271.
30. Golay, M., *Gas Chromatography*, 1958, Butterworths, London, (editor, D. H. Desty), p. 36.

THE
PHYSICO-CHEMICAL
BACKGROUND
OF GAS
CHROMATOGRAPHY

THE PARTITION COEFFICIENT

A system is in equilibrium when its entropy is a maximum or its energy a minimum. Thus, in terms of the Gibbs free energy, we may write as the condition of equilibrium

$$(dG)_{T,P} = 0$$

If two immiscible phases A and B are in contact and some substance, miscible with both, is added it will be distributed between the two phases, equilibrium being attained when its free energy is the same in each. Stating this in terms of the partial molar free energy or chemical potential μ of the distributed substance, we have

$$\mu_A = \mu_B$$

Since

$$\mu = \mu^0 + RT \ln a$$

where a is the activity of the distributed substance in a given phase while μ^0 is its standard chemical potential, that is, μ at $a = 1$,

$$\mu_A{}^0 + RT \ln a_A = \mu_B{}^0 + RT \ln a_B \tag{2.1}$$

The activity is not always known and, at least approximately, can be replaced by concentration c. Making this substitution and rearranging equation 2.1 leads to

$$\ln \frac{c_A}{c_B} = -\frac{(\mu_A{}^0 - \mu_B{}^0)}{RT}$$

or

$$\frac{c_A}{c_B} = K = \exp\left(-\frac{\Delta\mu^0}{RT}\right) \tag{2.2}$$

K, the partition coefficient or distribution ratio, should be constant at constant temperature since $\Delta\mu^0$ has a fixed value and a plot of c_A against c_B (the partition isotherm) should be linear and of slope K. If this linearity is maintained up to

2

SOLUTION, ADSORPTION AND PARTITION

the point where the phases are saturated it is clear that for a two liquid phase system, for example, K represents the ratio of the saturated solubilities. K can, in fact, often be estimated successfully from solubility data.

No stipulation as to the nature of the two phases has as yet been made; thus, it follows that, since a solid-solid system is clearly impossible and since a gas-gas system is precluded by the need for immiscibility, we can envisage only the following types of partitioning system:

    1. Liquid-liquid   2. Gas-liquid
    3. Liquid-solid   4. Gas-solid

Partitioning systems of types, 1 and 2, make use of solution processes while those of types, 3 and 4, involve adsorption.

Liquid-Liquid and Gas-Liquid Systems. It is well known that such systems very often obey the partition law, particularly when the solutions involved are very dilute. Occasionally, however, curved isotherms, that is, plots of c_A against c_B, are met with. These may arise from the fact that the activity of the distributed material may be concentration dependent to different extents in the two immiscible phases, so that K in turn appears to be concentration dependent. In this situation, if K, as is proper, is always expressed in terms of activities, it will of course always be constant, and a linear isotherm would be obtained. Alternatively, if the molecular state of the distributed material differs in the two phases, again curved isotherms may result. For example, there is the case where the substance is monomeric in phase A but completely dimeric in phase B. The formal partition coefficient K is expressed in terms of the concentration of monomer; hence, in phase B the true molar concentration is half the apparent concentration, and equation 2.1 should read

$$(\mu_A{}^0)_M + RT \ln c_A = (\mu_B{}^0)_D + \tfrac{1}{2}RT \ln c_B$$

whence, the true partition coefficient for the system, K', is given by

$$K' = \frac{c_A}{c_B{}^{1/2}}$$

From this it follows that since

$$K = \frac{c_A}{c_B} = \frac{K'}{c_B{}^{1/2}}$$

$$c_A = K' c_B{}^{1/2}$$

An illustration of behaviour of this sort is afforded by the distribution of acetic acid between benzene and water. The acid is highly associated to double molecules in the benzene but is completely monomeric in water, ionization being negligible. Figure 1 shows plots of both c_{benzene} and

$c^{1/2}_{\text{benzene}}$ against c_{water}, the experimental temperature being 20°C. There is clearly marked curvature of the first power plot but that involving the use of the square root of the concentration in the benzene layer is linear. The broken line illustrates the fact that as the solutions become progressively more dilute a curved isotherm approaches linearity. That the square-root plot, although linear, does not pass through zero indicates that there is not

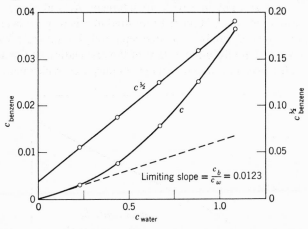

FIG. 1. Partition isotherms for the distribution of acetic acid between benzene and water at 20°C. The curvature of the normal plot (c_b against c_w) results from association in the benzene.

complete dimerisation of the acid in benzene, and a more general treatment of the problem must be developed to allow for this. Suppose that the substance in question is incompletely dimerised in phase B, then there is a partition coefficient K_1 relating the concentrations of monomer in both phases defined by

$$K_1 = \frac{[c_B]_M}{[c_A]_M}$$

In phase B the equilibrium between monomer and dimer can be defined by an equilibrium constant K_2, thus

$$K_2 = \frac{[c_B]_M^{\,2}}{[c_B]_D}$$

The total concentration in phase B, c_B, is

$$c_B = [c_B]_M + 2[c_B]_D$$

and substituting for $[c_B]_D$ from the expression for K_2 yields

$$c_B = [c_B]_M + \frac{2}{K_2}[c_B]_M^{\,2}$$

Dividing through by c_A gives the formal partition coefficient K,

$$K = \frac{c_B}{c_A} = K_1 + \frac{2K_1}{K_2}[c_B]_M = K_1 + \frac{2K_1^2}{K_2}c_A \qquad (2.3)$$

The subscript M and the bracket can be dropped from c_A since, in phase A, all the material exists as monomer. It follows that a graph of c_B/c_A against c_A should be a straight line with an intercept K_1 and slope $(2K_1^2/K_2)$. Figure 2 shows the data of Figure 1 replotted in this way. It is an interesting point that since K_1 can be evaluated separately it is possible from Figure 2 to measure the equilibrium constant of the association of the acid. This point is made since, although for analytical purposes in chromatography it

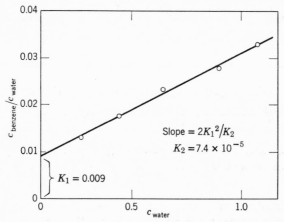

FIG. 2. Data of Figure 1 replotted in the form c_b/c_w against c_w. The linearity demonstrates the occurrence of dimerisation of the acid in benzene, and the slope and intercept can be used to evaluate the equilibrium constant of dimerisation.

is always advisable to use systems with linear partition isotherms, it seems possible that in the near future chromatography may well be employed in the measurement of equilibrium constants. These need not necessarily be restricted to association (or dissociation) but could, of course, be extended to the case where chemical reaction occurs in one phase either between the distributed material and the phase itself or with some additive.

The particular case of acetic acid distribution discussed here is an interesting one, since it is possible also to speculate on what may occur if the distribution were between the gas phase and a liquid. In the vapour phase, acetic acid is considered to be almost completely dimerised more or less up to the boiling point. Thus, if, below this temperature, it were partitioned between the vapour and a non-polar liquid such as benzene or squalane, the molecular state of the acetic acid would be, in both phases, the same and a linear isotherm should result. At very high temperatures when the vapour would contain some monomer, curvature of the isotherm could be expected, this curvature being towards the non-polar solvent axis as in Figure 1. If, on the other hand, the acid were partitioned between the vapour phase and a polar liquid at reasonably low temperatures, the situation would be reversed, with dimers in the vapour and monomers in the liquid. This should give an isotherm curving in the opposite way to that in Figure 1. This form of behaviour has been suggested by James and Martin (1) to be responsible for the very asymmetric gas chromatographic peaks often obtained with fatty acids.

Liquid-Solid and Gas-Solid Systems. Systems of this type do not usually give linear partition isotherms. The classical isotherm attributed to Freundlich is written

$$\frac{w}{m} = kp^{1/n} \tag{2.4}$$

where w is the weight of gas adsorbed by m grams of adsorbent at a gas pressure p; n is almost always greater than unity so that the amount of gas adsorbed increases less rapidly with pressure than would be the case in a system obeying the distribution law wherein n = 1. This isotherm is applicable over restricted pressure ranges only but it is sometimes useful as a method of interpolation. In fact, the equation finds more use in the study of adsorption out of solution, when p is replaced by concentration c, than in gaseous adsorption.

A more satisfactory approach is that of Langmuir in which adsorption is treated as a kinetic problem. Provided the adsorbed molecules form only a monolayer it is readily shown that

$$\frac{w}{m} = \frac{k_1 k_2 p}{1 + k_1 p} \tag{2.5}$$

where k_1 and k_2 are constants for a given system. The equation can be written in the alternative form

$$\frac{p}{(w/m)} = \frac{1}{k_1 k_2} + \frac{p}{k_2}$$

The ratio $p/(w/m)$ is a form of partition coefficient, and clearly a plot of this function against p should be linear. Many, but by no means all, systems show behaviour in accord with this equation.

The complexity of adsorption phenomena can be traced to a number of causes. It is believed that two distinctly different mechanisms can operate, the one physical in origin and the other chemical. The physical forces at play are van der Waals (dispersion) forces and these become most important at low temperatures. They are relatively weak and are non-specific in that they are experienced by all substances. The associated heats of adsorption are generally small and comparable with the heats of vaporisation of the adsorbed material. Further, the equilibrium involved is readily and rapidly reversible, and probably the adsorption requires a negligible activation energy.

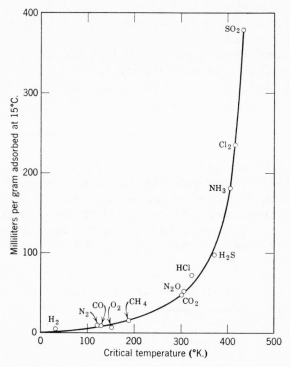

FIG. 3. Illustration of the extent of adsorption of permanent gases at 15°C. by active charcoal as a function of critical temperature.

When chemical forces are involved, actual chemical bonds may be formed at the adsorbing surface, and the heats of adsorption may be as high as 100 kcal. per mole and vary considerably with the extent of adsorption. This process, chemisorption, is favoured by high temperatures, but sometimes occurs at quite low ones. In the latter event, any activation energy necessary will be very small, whereas in the high temperature adsorption it may be considerable. Since chemisorption involves the binding of surface atoms and, hence, loss of adsorption sites, it may be expected to obey the Langmuir isotherm as is often found to be the case.

The dispersion forces responsible for physical adsorption, however, are non-specific, and so it is evident that adsorption is not restricted to a single layer of molecules but may involve many layers. Since a surface of adsorbed gas molecules is not very different from the original adsorbent surface from the point of view of physical attractions, the process is then in some respects comparable to liquefaction. It is a fact that in the adsorption of permanent inorganic and organic gases at about room temperature the extent of adsorption is determined very largely by the critical temperature, and hence the boiling point. Figure 3 shows a plot of such data for the adsorption of a number of gases by active charcoal at

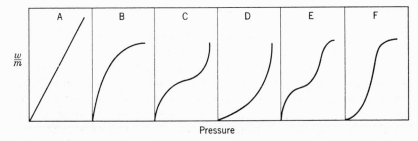

FIG. 4. Qualitative illustration of the various possible forms of adsorption isotherm.

15°C. In the region of physical adsorption it is also generally true that the adsorptive capacity is determined more by the surface area available than by the nature of the adsorbent.

At very low temperatures, and pressures approaching the saturation value, actual condensation may occur since the vapour pressure of a liquid in a capillary is likely to be lower than for a plane surface. In these circumstances the pore structure of the adsorbent may be an important factor in determining the amount of adsorption and the extent of deviation from the distribution law. The narrowest pores will give the greatest amount of capillary condensation.

From published data, the heats of adsorption being usually quite small, it would appear that it is physical adsorption which is the more important in gas-solid chromatography at this time. It is, therefore, worthwhile reviewing the types of adsorption isotherm which have been met with in this field.

Figure 4 illustrates qualitatively the six forms of isotherm which are known. Type A, of course, is an ideal isotherm while B corresponds to one which would fit the classical or Langmuir isotherm equations and thus relates to a monolayer. The flattening off with increasing pressure of adsorbate is a consequence of the approach to saturation of the adsorbent surface. In order to explain isotherms of types C through F, we must extend the Langmuir idea to allow for the formation of multilayers and the participation of capillary condensation. This permits derivation of the well-known Brunauer, Emmett, Teller or BET equation, which can be written

$$\frac{p/p^0}{v_s{}^g(1 - p/p^0)} = \frac{1}{v_m E} + \left(\frac{E - 1}{v_m E}\right)\frac{p}{p^0} \qquad (2.6)$$

p and p^0 are, respectively, the partial and saturation vapour pressures of the adsorbate under the experimental conditions; $v_s{}^g$ is the volume of adsorbate adsorbed while v_m is the volume corresponding to formation of a monolayer; E is defined by

$$E = e^{(\Delta H^a - \Delta H^l)/RT}$$

where ΔH^a is the heat of adsorption of the adsorbate in a monolayer and ΔH^l is the heat of liquefaction of the vapour.

If $\Delta H^a > \Delta H^l$, E is greater than unity and the form of the isotherm is then that of C in Figure 4. If, on the other hand, $\Delta H^l > \Delta H^a$ an isotherm of type D results. Curve E is a modified form of C and is assumed to result from the filling of capillary pores by condensation thus introducing a limit to the adsorption while the isotherm F is similarly derived from D.

It is clear from the above discussion that adsorption is less likely to be of use in chromatographic procedures than is solution since there are so many deviations from the distribution law and so many complexities involved. It is probably for this reason that gas-solid and liquid-solid chromatography have been so much less successful and popular than the liquid-liquid and gas-liquid methods.

What has been said leaves little doubt that the approach to a linear isotherm is facilitated by the use of high temperatures and low partial pressures of adsorbate, and it may be that when more experiments are conducted in these conditions, gas-solid chromatography will become more effective and attractive.

THE SOLUBILITY OF GASES IN LIQUIDS

Ideal Solubility. According to Raoult's law the partial pressure p exerted by a component of a liquid mixture is proportional to the mole fraction x of the substance present in the mixture and to its saturation vapour pressure. In gas liquid chromatography the solvent is assumed to be involatile, and so the total pressure exerted is that by the solute p_1:

$$p_1 = x_1 p_1{}^0 \qquad (2.7)$$

The mole fraction is defined in terms of the number of moles of solute (N_1) and solvent (N_2) by

$$x_1 = \frac{N_1}{N_1 + N_2}$$

which, in reasonably dilute solutions ($N_2 \gg N_1$), reduces to

$$x_1 = \frac{N_1}{N_2} \qquad (2.8)$$

Thus, x_1 represents the solubility of the solute in the solvent in moles per mole. Comparing 2.8 with 2.7 yields

$$\frac{N_1}{N_2} = \frac{p_1}{p_1^0} \qquad (2.9)$$

If w represents a weight and M a molecular weight we can write equation 2.9 as

$$\frac{w_1}{w_2} \times \frac{M_2}{M_1} = \frac{p_1}{p_1^0}$$

or

$$\frac{w_1}{w_2} = \frac{p_1 M_1}{p_1^0 M_2} \qquad (2.10)$$

The ratio w_1/w_2 is, of course, the solubility expressed in grams per gram.

From equations 2.9 and 2.10 we can make several deductions about the ideal solubility of gases in liquids:

a. According to 2.9 all gases at the same value of p/p^0, have the same molar solubility in any solvent.

b. The molar solubility of a gas in any liquid is the same at a constant partial pressure p.

c. The weight solubility of any gas at fixed pressure p depends on the ratio M_1/M_2. It is, therefore, greatest in solvents of low molecular weight.

d. Conversely, the weight solubility of solutes in a given solvent increases with increasing solute molecular weight.

A simple illustration of the magnitude of the difference in the ideal molar solubility between members of a homologous series, for example, is afforded by a comparison of data for methane and hexane. The identity of the solvent is immaterial and if we assume that the temperature is 25°C. and that for both, $p = 0.1$ atm., it is only necessary to evaluate p^0 for each. The value for methane must be extrapolated from the data for very low temperatures. This gives $p^0 \sim 300$ atm. For hexane, at 25°C., $p^0 \sim 0.2$ atm.

Hence from 2.7, we get

$$\frac{x_{\text{hexane}}}{x_{\text{methane}}} \simeq 1500$$

a value which is so great that it is evident that even if the solutions were markedly non-ideal there would still be a vast difference.

The temperature dependence of gaseous solubility follows from equation 2.7. If we assume for convenience that $p_1 = 1$

$$\log x_1 = -\log p_1{}^0$$

and so, since p^0 increases with increasing temperature, x must decrease. Further, by substitution for $\log p^0$ from equation 3.1, we get

$$\log x_1 = \frac{\Delta H^v}{RT} - \text{constant}$$

For an ideal solution, therefore, the energy associated with the dissolution of one mole of solute is equal to its molar heat of vaporisation. Heat must be supplied to vaporise a liquid and so it is liberated when a gas dissolves.

The equations developed up to this point, and the conclusions drawn from them, are restricted to ideal solutions, that is, those which accord with Raoult's law over the whole range of concentration. Few systems are, in fact, ideal or even nearly so, and it is only rarely that equation 2.7 quantitatively describes the solubility of a gas in any liquid. Nevertheless, it is normally the case that the solubility of a gas is proportional to its pressure over quite large ranges of pressure. Henry's law, which describes this behaviour, is usually written

$$\frac{w}{V_s} = kp$$

w is the mass of gas dissolved by the volume V_s of solvent, p is the partial pressure of the gas and k is Henry's constant. In the case of an ideal solution the equation readily reduces to equation 2.7.

Figure 5a shows a diagram of a plot of partial and total pressure against composition for an ideal binary liquid mixture while Figure 5b shows the type of diagram most often encountered in practice. This type of system is said to show positive deviation from Raoult's law, a state of affairs arising from differences in internal pressure, molecular geometry, polarity and polarisability of the two molecular species involved. Negative deviations from Raoult's law, in which the total pressure is less than would be expected, are occasionally encountered and result from very strong interactions between the unlike molecules which may even lead to actual compound formation as, for example, in solutions of CO_2 or NH_3 in water at room temperature. Of importance too in this connexion is the formation of hydrogen bonds. However, the strength of the interaction must be sufficient to overcome the tendency to positive deviation due to the other factors mentioned, and so it is not surprising that negative deviation is relatively rare.

The reason for the generality of Henry's law in contrast to the failure of Raoult's law can be seen from the diagram. While the total pressure plot may exhibit considerable curvature at intermediate concentrations, it becomes approximately linear at $x \to 0$ and $x \to 1$. The tangents to the curve in these regions represent Henry's law, and it is immediately clear that its application is generally limited to dilute solutions.

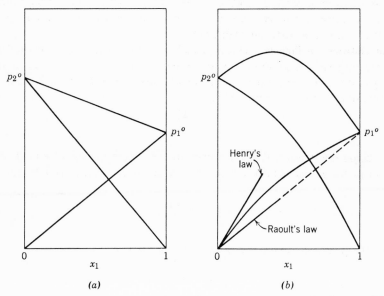

FIG. 5. Plots of partial and total vapour pressures for binary liquid mixtures which (*a*) are ideal, (*b*) show positive deviation from Raoult's law.

The Adsorption of Gases by Solids. It is fairly widely supposed that the adsorption of gases by solids does not obey Henry's law. However, Barrer (2) has pointed out that non-condensable gases such as argon, oxygen and methane very frequently obey Henry's law when physically adsorbed by molecular sieves, alumina, silica gels or charcoals at temperatures above or near room temperature. This behaviour, too, extends over substantial pressure ranges. More readily condensable materials, however, show anomalous behaviour although at high temperatures this may disappear. In general, the more readily condensable the gas, the higher the temperature needs to be for the adsorption to obey Henry's law. A similar view of the extension of Henry's law to gas-solid systems was offered by Emmett (3); Dacey and Fendley (4) have also recently discussed this question. It seems clear from this that the non-applicability of Henry's law to gas-solid systems may not be the complete answer to some of the problems commonly met with in gas-solid chromatography.

THE PRESENTATION OF GAS SOLUBILITY DATA

There are numerous ways of calculating gaseous solubilities. For example, they may be presented in the form of weight of solute per cubic centimeter of solvent as in Henry's law, or, alternatively, as the volume of solute dissolved per cubic centimeter of solvent. For simplicity of calculation in gas chromatography the most desirable method of presentation is in the form of partition coefficients so that it is worthwhile to determine the relationship between the more commonly employed solubility coefficients and the partition coefficient.

The Ostwald Coefficient. This is probably the most widely used method of expressing gaseous solubilities, and the coefficient β is defined as the volume of gas dissolved per cubic centimeter of solvent at the temperature and pressure of the experiment. Thus,

$$\beta = \frac{V_s^g}{V_s}$$

V_s^g being the volume of gas dissolved by the volume V_s of solvent. Considering the gas to be ideal V_s^g may be reduced to its value at N.T.P., $(V_s^g)^0$ and

$$(V_s^g)^0 = \frac{273 p V_s^g}{T}$$

the pressure being expressed in atmospheres, whence

$$\beta = \frac{(V_s^g)^0 T}{273 p V_s}$$

The Bunsen Coefficient. If the volume of gas dissolved is calculated at N.T.P. and not at the experimental temperature we obtain the Bunsen absorption coefficient α and it is clear that

$$\alpha = \frac{273 \beta}{T}$$

The Partition Coefficient. Each of the methods of presenting gas solubility data is a form of a partition coefficient and it is a simple matter to convert them to the true form. The Ostwald coefficient β is given by

$$\beta = \frac{(V_s^g)^0 T}{273 p V_s}$$

and if the gas is ideal and $(V_s^g)^0$ is expressed in cubic centimeters,

$$\frac{(V_s^g)^0}{22,400} = n_s^g$$

that is, the number of moles of gas in solution. Again, if the gas is ideal

$$p = \frac{n_g{}^g RT}{v_g{}^g}$$

$n_g{}^g$ being the number of moles of gas in the gas phase of volume $v_g{}^g$. Thus,

$$\beta = \frac{22{,}400}{273R} \left(\frac{n_s{}^g v_g{}^g}{n_g{}^g V_s} \right)$$

However, $273R = 22{,}400$ when R is expressed in atm. cc. per mole deg., and the term in parenthesis is the partition coefficient expressed in concentrations of moles per unit volume. Hence,

$$\beta = K$$

Concentration could equally well be expressed in grams per unit volume since the molecular weight of the gas occurs in both the numerator and denominator thus giving the same value for K.

The relationship between α and β deduced earlier leads to

$$K = \frac{\alpha T}{273}$$

and, from the definition of Henry's constant k, we have

$$K = \frac{kRT}{M}$$

When data is being converted from k to K it must be remembered that the units of pressure and volume adopted determine the value of R. In the present instance the chosen units are atmospheres and cubic centimeters hence $R = 82.05$ cc. atm. per deg. mole.

Obviously, data relating to the adsorption of gases by solids can be expressed in the form of partition coefficients provided the density of the adsorbent is known.

THE ACTIVITY COEFFICIENT

In order to account for the observed failure of Raoult's law the concept of the activity coefficient is introduced. In this, it is assumed that the true active concentration is not the molar concentration but some fraction or multiple of it defined by

$$a = fx$$

a being the activity and f the activity coefficient. f is described as the rational activity coefficient but when, as is more common, concentrations are given in molalities, the symbol γ is employed.

Modifying the ideal equation 2.7 by introducing the activity concept

$$p = fxp^0 \qquad (2.11)$$

and it follows that the temperature dependence of x at $p = 1$ is given by

$$\log x = \frac{\Delta H^v}{2.3RT} - \text{constant} - \log f \qquad (2.12)$$

It is valuable to inquire immediately into the nature of the activity coefficient and, if possible, to identify it more precisely, since it otherwise remains simply a correction factor and as such has only empirical significance. One approach which has proved valuable is that based on the Gibbs-Duhem equation, which states that at equilibrium

$$N_1 \, d\mu_1 = -N_2 \, d\mu_2$$

where N_1 and N_2 are, respectively, the number of moles of the substances 1 and 2 in a given phase or of a given substance in phases 1 and 2, while μ_1 and μ_2 are the relevant chemical potentials. This equation makes no stipulations about ideal behaviour in the system and is simply a statement of equilibrium conditions. Dividing through by $(N_1 + N_2)$, differentiating with respect to x_1 and knowing that $\mu = \mu^0 + RT \ln p$ gives

$$x_1 \left(\frac{d \ln p_1}{dx_1} \right) = x_2 \left(\frac{d \ln p_2}{dx_2} \right)$$

or,

$$\frac{d \ln p_1}{d \ln x_1} = \frac{d \ln p_2}{d \ln x_2}$$

which is known as the Duhem-Margules equation. This can be solved through use of the empirical equations

$$\ln f_2 = A'x_1 + B'x_1{}^2 + C'x_1{}^3$$
$$\ln f_1 = Ax_2 + Bx_2{}^2 + Cx_2{}^3$$

The coefficients A and A' turn out to be zero, and it is found in practice that powers of x greater than the square are necessary only when one liquid in the mixture is highly associated. The equations thus reduce to the form

$$\ln f_1 = Bx_2{}^2 \qquad (2.13)$$

the coefficients B and B' being equal for symmetrical systems. In gas chromatography, of course, our interest is only in the region where $x_2 \to 1$ and so the symmetry or otherwise of the system is of no consequence.

Thus $f_1 = e^{Bx_2^2}$ so that we may write

$$\log x_1 = \frac{\Delta H^v}{2.3RT} - \text{constant} - \frac{Bx_2^2}{2.3}$$

In the situation that $x_2 = 1$, that is, near infinite dilution of compound 1, equation 2.13 can be written

$$\ln f_1^0 = B \qquad (2.14)$$

whence, in general, equation 2.13 becomes

$$\ln f_1 = x_2^2 \ln \gamma_1^0 \qquad (2.15)$$

This equation was first employed in connection with gas chromatography by Hoare and Purnell (5) who pointed out that in so far as gas chromatography was concerned the solutions involved were effectively always at infinite dilution and the only activity coefficient measurable with certainty was always f_1^0. This view has been re-stated in the recent work of Khan (6).

In dilute solution f_1 and γ_1 become identical; therefore the latter will, for convenience, be used henceforth. We now have

$$\ln \gamma_1^0 = \frac{\Delta G^m}{RT}$$

where ΔG^m is the partial molar excess free energy of mixing. For the special class of regular solutions, for example, where the excess entropy of mixing ΔS^m is zero we see from the relation

$$\Delta G = \Delta H - T \Delta S$$

that $\Delta G^m = \Delta H^m$, the partial molar excess heat of mixing hence, we may write

$$B = \frac{\Delta H^m}{RT}$$

and

$$\ln \gamma_1^0 = \frac{\Delta H^m}{RT}$$

Substituting this value in equation 2.12 gives

$$\log x_1 = \frac{(\Delta H^v - \Delta H^m)}{2.3RT} - \text{constant} \qquad (2.16)$$

The sum $(\Delta H^v - \Delta H^m)$ can be equated to the differential molar heat of evaporation from solution at infinite dilution, $\Delta H_e{}^s$, so that

$$\log x_1 = \frac{\Delta H_e{}^s}{2.3RT} - \text{constant} \tag{2.17}$$

$\Delta H_e{}^s$ is equal, but of opposite sign, to the molar heat of solution ΔH^s.

This equation has been used by a number of workers as the starting point of thermodynamic calculations in gas chromatography (7, 8), but it must be pointed out that its use depends upon the activity coefficient being of the form defined in equation 2.15 and that x_2 must be practically unity, that is, solutions must be highly dilute. If the solutions dealt with are not sufficiently dilute then the heat of solution becomes concentration dependent and consistent results may be difficult, if not impossible, to obtain.

The magnitude of $\Delta H_e{}^s$ depends on the type of deviation from ideality. If we regard the solution of a gas in a liquid as a two stage process involving first the condensation of the gas to a liquid followed by mixing of the two liquids then, when negative deviations are encountered, since these correspond to enhanced intermolecular attractions, heat in excess of the latent heat of condensation will be evolved. In this case, therefore, $\Delta H_e{}^s > H^l$. Positive deviations, on the other hand, correspond to a resistance to mixing; thus, energy must be put into the system to mix the two liquids. Some of the latent heat of condensation will be used up in this process and so $\Delta H^l > \Delta H_e{}^s$.

Occasionally, temperature independent-activity coefficients are encountered in practice. This is often found when studying mixtures of molecules greatly different in size, for example, polymer solutions.

In this situation

$$\Delta G^m = \Delta H^m - T\,\Delta S^m$$

reduces to

$$\dot{\Delta G}^m = -T\,\Delta S^m$$

thus,

$$\ln \gamma_1{}^0 = -\frac{\Delta S^m}{R}$$

The activity coefficient is thus determined only by the entropy of mixing and since such solutions have no heat of mixing they are described as athermal. In gas chromatography there is commonly a great difference in molecular sizes and so it is not surprising that athermal activity coefficients are often encountered as, for example, in the work of Porter, Deal and Stross (7).

Since, in general,

$$\ln \gamma^0 = \frac{\Delta H^m}{RT} - \frac{\Delta S^m}{R}$$

we may write

$$\ln \gamma_t^0 = \frac{\Delta H^m}{RT}$$

and

$$\ln \gamma_a^0 = -\frac{\Delta S^m}{R}$$

Thus,

$$\ln \gamma^0 = \ln \gamma_t^0 + \ln \gamma_a^0$$

or

$$\gamma^0 = \gamma_t^0 \gamma_a^0 \tag{2.18}$$

In the extreme case either γ_t^0 or γ_a^0 is unity, but commonly neither is.

The equations presented are found to be valid in the majority of cases and, as pointed out earlier, it is only when, for example, there is very considerable association of one substance that further modification is necessary. In such circumstances the addition to equation 2.15 of further terms in x_2^3 is usually a satisfactory procedure. This expedient should not, however, affect the situation near infinite dilution.

THE ACTIVITY COEFFICIENT AND MOLECULAR STRUCTURE

The correlation of activities with the molecular structures of the solute and solvent presents difficulties which have, up to this time, been only partially overcome. The theoretical studies of Hildebrand and Scatchard, for example, permit calculation of activity coefficients from energies of vaporisation and molar volumes for the special class of "regular" solutions but the agreement of experimental and theoretical values is only fair. In other types of solutions the theoretical problems are even greater and experiment is far ahead of theory. A number of semi-theoretical studies, such as those of Brønsted and Koefoed (9) and Copp and Everett (10) have led to expressions for the activity coefficient but these again are of limited utility.

The extensive experimental studies of Pierotti and his co-workers (11) have shown that there is often a regular variation of activity with the structure of solute or solvent and because they have shown that their results can be extended to gas liquid chromatographic systems their findings are worthwhile discussing at some length. They employed mixtures often containing one or more polar molecules and interpreted the results on the reasonable basis that only nearest neighbour interactions between molecules are significant and that the molar free energy of mixing, and thus $RT \log \gamma_1^0$, is the sum of all the energies of interaction between different groups in the neighbouring molecules. These assumptions do not differ materially from those made in most theoretical approaches to the study of solutions.

To illustrate the model we may consider the solution of a molecule RX in a solvent designated $R'X'$. Figure 6 shows the possible interactions, indicated by the arrows, to be six in this case. The interactions between end groups of the same molecular type are those between neighbouring molecules. This picture is similar to that postulated later (p. 42) to account for systematic variations in the constants of the vapour pressure equations of pure liquids.

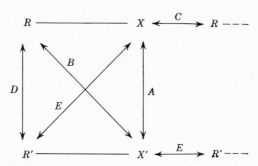

FIG. 6. Molecular interaction scheme as envisaged by Pierotti, Deal, Derr and Porter. *By courtesy of The American Chemical Society.*

In the very simplest cases, Pierotti et al. found that only the interactions $R - R'$ were experimentally significant, a fact which was confirmed by determining activities in mixtures in which only X and X' were varied. Having determined the $R - R'$ interaction, more complex systems were studied systematically so that all the various terms could be separately evaluated. The upshot of the work was the finding that the additive contributions of the various interactions to the molar free energy of mixing could be expressed mathematically as follows:

Group		Contribution
$R - R'$	$=$	$D'(\bar{n} - \bar{n}')^2$
$X - X'$	$=$	A'
$R - X'$	$=$	$\dfrac{B'\bar{n}}{\bar{n}'}$
$R - X$	$=$	$\dfrac{C'}{(\bar{n} + C'')}$
$R' - X$	$=$	$\dfrac{E'}{(\bar{n} + E'')}$
$R' - X'$	$=$	$\dfrac{F'}{(\bar{n}' + F'')}$

$\bar{n}$ representing the number of structural units in the solute, $\bar{n}'$ the number in the solvent and all other terms being constants. The sum of all these terms then equals $\log \gamma^0$. As an example, consider the solubility of n-alkanes in a polar solvent. There is apparently no R-X interaction in the alkanes while the interactions R'-X', X-X' and R'-X are constant since they all involve the solvent, either alone or with the fixed terminal (methyl) group of the alkane. Thus the only variable interactions are R-X' and R-R' and the equation becomes

$$\log \gamma^0 = \text{constant} + B'\bar{n}/\bar{n}' + D'(\bar{n} - \bar{n}')^2$$

Equations of this type were found to give good agreement when the empirically determined values of the constants for, say, pentane, were used to predict values of γ^0 for higher paraffins dissolved in the same solvent. It is an interesting point that an equation very similar to this

$$\log \gamma^0 = D'(\bar{n} - \bar{n}')^2$$

for n-alkanes dissolved in other alkanes in the range C_5 to C_8 was suggested by Brønsted and Koefoed (9) and tested gas chromatographically by Kwantes and Rijnders (12). While the majority of data determined in this way are, at this time, of little value to gas liquid chromatography, the work of Pierotti et al. has shown that, when the appropriate data become available, partition coefficients and, hence, retention volumes (p. 205) may be calculated with considerable success. When more information is obtained, therefore, the application of this method may well become of considerable value to gas chromatographers, particularly since, not only will it be possible to calculate activities for homologues in a given solvent but also for individual solutes in different solvents. With enough information it may, eventually, be possible to draw out calculated chromatograms for various systems and, thus, to minimise the amount of experimental study required.

An important consequence of the work described is that the logarithm of the activity coefficient is often determined by a simple relation involving the number of structural units in the solute molecule. This view has also been advanced by Herington (13) for example. The relationship he proposes, which applies for a homologous series in a given solvent, is somewhat simpler in form than that of Pierotti et al., being

$$\log \gamma^0 = k_1 + k_2 \cdot \bar{n} \tag{2.19}$$

Experimental support for this expression has been deduced from gas chromatographic data by Herington, by Purnell (14) and by Knox (15).

Since, for regular solutions,

$$\log \gamma^0 = \frac{\Delta H^m}{2.3RT}$$

whereas in other situations ΔH^m and ΔS^m are often linearly related, as a corollary to equation 2.19

$$\Delta H^m = k_3 + k_4 \bar{n} \tag{2.20}$$

This relation is similar in form to that discussed later in connexion with heats of vaporisation of pure liquids (equation 3.6) and permits us to assume that in some systems it may be that

$$\Delta H_e^s = k_5 + k_6 \bar{n} \tag{2.21}$$

NON-IDEAL SOLUTION THEORIES

The discussion so far has involved theories of solution which are applicable only to a limited number of systems and, in particular, to those in which the constituent molecules are similar in size. When they differ, as is usual in gas chromatographic solutions, other theories are, perhaps more relevant. These all lead to a result for $\ln \gamma_a$ which can be put in the form

$$\ln (\gamma_a)_1 = \ln \left\{ \frac{1}{1 + (r' - 1)x_2} \left[\frac{1 + (r' - 1)x_2}{1 + (q - 1)x_2} \right]^{z/2} \right\} \tag{2.22}$$

wherein r' is the size ratio of molecules 1 and 2 in the mixture and

$$q = r' - \frac{2}{z} (r' - 1)$$

In the Miller-Guggenheim theory (16), z is identified as the number of nearest neighbour sites to a given segment of molecule while, in the more elaborate treatments of Flory and of Huggins (see for example, 17) it is $r'/(r' - 1)$ times the number of nearest neighbours.

If we define the volume fraction of a component, ϕ, by

$$\phi_2 = \frac{\text{volume of component 2 in mixture}}{\text{volume of components } (1 + 2) \text{ in mixture}}$$

then, since for practical purposes r' is most commonly taken as the molar volume ratio at the temperature in question

$$\phi_2 = \frac{r' x_2}{x_1 + r' x_2}$$

Equation 2.22 can now be re-written in terms of ϕ in the form

$$\ln (\gamma_a)_1 = \ln \left(\frac{1 - \phi_2}{x_1} \right) - \frac{z}{2} \ln \left\{ 1 - \left(1 - \frac{1}{r'} \right) \frac{2\phi_2}{z} \right\}$$

which, in the Flory-Huggins theory, wherein formally $z \to \infty$, reduces to

$$\ln (\gamma_a)_1 = \ln \left(\frac{1 - \phi_2}{x_1}\right) + \left(1 - \frac{1}{r'}\right)\phi_2$$

For the condition of infinite dilution, which is the only one of immediate gas chromatographic interest, this reduces further to

$$\ln (\gamma_a)_1^0 = \ln \frac{1}{r'} + \left(1 - \frac{1}{r'}\right) \tag{2.23}$$

since x_2 and ϕ_2 approach unity.

The theory also leads to an expression for $\ln \gamma_t$ in terms of ϕ which is

$$\ln (\gamma_t)_1 = \bar{\chi}\phi_2^2$$

At infinite dilution this reduces to

$$\ln (\gamma_t)_1^0 = \bar{\chi}$$

The parameter $\bar{\chi}$ is related to the interchange energy Δu through the equation

$$\bar{\chi} = z \frac{\Delta u}{RT}$$

where

$$\Delta u = \tfrac{1}{2}\Delta u_{11} - \Delta u_{12} + \tfrac{1}{2}\Delta u_{22}$$

the subscripts denoting the molecules taking part in the individual interactions. Δu_{11} and Δu_{22} are frequently identified with the latent heats of vaporisation of liquids 1 and 2. At infinite dilution, since z is more or less temperature independent, we can write

$$\gamma_t^0 = e^{\Delta u'/RT}$$

which is of the same form as the expression derived earlier on the basis of the more conventional theory, p. 23. We can conclude finally that the observed activity coefficient at infinite dilution is given by

$$\gamma^0 = \gamma_a^0 \gamma_t^0 = \frac{1}{r'} \exp \left[\bar{\chi} + \frac{(r' - 1)}{r'}\right] \tag{2.24}$$

This relationship can only be expected to hold if $\bar{\chi}$ is small since, otherwise, γ_a^0 and γ_t^0 are not independent, and $\bar{\chi}$ contains an entropy term.

Looking at equation 2.23 we see that the athermal activity coefficient is, in fact, likely to have a small temperature dependence since r' is taken as the molar volume ratio and individual molar volumes do not change in exactly the same way with temperature. However, ignoring this, it is evident that when $r' = 1$, $\gamma_a^0 = 1$ also; in other words, the solution is ideal from the point of view of entropy. Differentiation readily shows that equation 2.23 goes through a maximum value of unity, this is thus the maximum value of $\gamma_a{}^0$. This theory demands that the entropy contribution to non-ideality of solution through size inequality be in the direction of negative deviation ($\gamma_a{}^0 < 1$) and that ΔS^m be always positive. As seen on p. 422, this behaviour has been observed in practice in gas chromatography. Some direct evidence on the applicability of equations 2.23 and 2.24 is available in the work of Ashworth and Everett (18) who made a careful study by conventional static means of fourteen typical gas-liquid chromatographic systems. They concluded that the most satisfactory means of expressing the results was in terms of equation 2.24. While their results cannot be extrapolated to cover all chromatographic systems it seems clearly established that simple solution theories are inadequate in most cases. Thus, it is probable that in future, equation 2.24 and others like it will be more widely used than equation 2.13, for example. Whether or not they prove more useful can only be guessed but their underlying theory is more sophisticated and the basic model is certainly more satisfying.

FUGACITY

Up to this point it has always been assumed that vapours and gases are ideal in the sense that they obey the perfect gas laws. However, this is not strictly so, although in consequence of the low partial pressures employed in gas chromatography it is a reasonable assumption to make in this connection. Account may be taken of gas imperfections if the fugacity of the gas is employed in place of its pressure. However, while vapour pressure data are known for thousands of compounds, fugacities are known only for relatively few. Fugacity corrections for the systems normally employed in gas chromatography are consequently of little importance and, in any event, will normally be within experimental error. It should be remembered, though, that the temperature dependence of the activity coefficient expressed in terms of pressures will contain the temperature dependence of gas imperfection and so, if gas chromatography is used to measure activities in solution it may be necessary to take account of this. When this is done it is sometimes found that an apparent, small temperature dependence of the activity coefficient is eliminated entirely (7).

The fugacity correction can be calculated from the equation

$$f_1 = \gamma_1 x_1 p_1{}^0 = p_1 \exp\left[\frac{(B - V_1{}^m)(P - p_1{}^0)}{RT}\right] \tag{2.25}$$

wherein B is the second virial coefficient of the vapour of mole fraction x_1, of liquid molar volume $V_1{}^m$ and of saturation vapour pressure $p_1{}^0$ at the temperature T. P is the total pressure of the gaseous mixture. $V_1{}^m$ can normally be ignored since it is usually negligible while B can be calculated from P/V data with the aid of an equation of state such as that of Berthelot (see, for example, 6). This approach is not very reliable and may even lead to errors of sign in the quantity ln (f_1/p_1).

REFERENCES

1. James, A. T., and A. J. P. Martin, *Biochem. J.*, 1952, **50**, 679.
2. Barrer, R. M., *Gas Chromatography*, 1958, Butterworths, London (editor, D. H. Desty), p. 122.
3. Emmett, P. H. (see ref. 2), p. 123.
4. Dacey, J. R., and J. A. Fendley, "Structure and Properties of Porous Materials," *Vol. X, Colston Papers*, 1958, Butterworths, London (editors, D. H. Everett and F. S. Stone), p. 142.
5. Hoare, M. R., and J. H. Purnell, *Trans. Faraday Soc.*, 1956, **52**, 222.
6. Khan, M. A., *Gas Chromatography*, 1958, Butterworths, London (editor, D.H. Desty), p. 135; see also E. R. Adlard, M. A. Khan and B. T. Whitham, *Gas Chromatography*, 1960, Butterworths, London (editor, R. P. W. Scott), p. 251.
7. Porter, P. E., C. H. Deal and F. H. Stross, *J. Amer. Chem. Soc.*, 1956, **78**, 2999.
8. Littlewood, A. B., C. S. G. Phillips and D. T. Price, *J. Chem. Soc.*, **1955**, 1480.
9. Brønsted, J. N., and J. K. Koefoed, *danske vidensk. Selsk. Mat.-fys. Medd.*, 1946, **22**, 1.
10. Copp, J. L., and D. H. Everett, *Disc. Faraday Soc.*, 1953, **15**, 268.
11. Pierotti, G. J., C. H. Deal, E. L. Derr, and P. E. Porter, *J. Amer. Chem. Soc.*, 1956, **78**, 2989.
12. Kwantes, A., and G. W. A. Rijnders, *Gas Chromatography*, 1958, Butterworths, London (editor, D. H. Desty), p. 125.
13. Herrington, E. F. G., *Vapour Phase Chromatography*, 1957, Butterworths, London (editor, D. H. Desty), p. 5.
14. Purnell, J. H., *J. Roy. Inst. Chem.*, 1958, **82**, 586.
15. Knox, J. H., *Science Progress*, 1957, **45**, 227.

3

THE
VAPORISATION
OF
LIQUIDS

A pure liquid in a sealed container is in equilibrium with its vapour, the position of equilibrium and, hence, the amount or pressure of the vapour being determined only by the temperature. The pressure characteristic of the equilibrium is the saturation vapour pressure and since this is both a measure of gas phase concentration and a determining factor in the solubility or adsorbability of gases (Chapter 2) it is a quantity of paramount importance in gas chromatography. Kinetically, vaporisation is envisaged as a continuous flight of molecules across a liquid surface in both directions, those which emerge from the liquid being the ones which possess sufficient energy to overcome the attractive force of their neighbours while those which return to the liquid are the ones which, in their random movements in the gas phase, collide with the surface. At equilibrium the free energy dG in both gas and liquid phases must be the same, that is,

$$dG_{\text{vapour}} = dG_{\text{liquid}}$$

whence, since

$$dG = v\,dp - s\,dT$$

where p, v and T have their usual significance and S is the entropy, we have

$$\frac{dp}{dT} = \frac{S_l - S_v}{v_l - v_v}$$

The difference in entropies of liquid and vapour, ΔS, is defined by

$$\Delta S = \frac{\Delta H}{T}$$

ΔH being the molar change in heat content at the temperature T, the heat

32

being assumed to be taken up in a thermodynamically reversible manner. In the case under consideration ΔH is the molar latent heat of vaporisation ΔH^v and so the original equation becomes

$$\frac{(v_l - v_v)\, dp}{dT} = \frac{\Delta H^v}{T}$$

This equation is the well known Clausius-Clapeyron equation which, while useful as it stands, can be put into a form more suitable for application to experiment if a few simplifying approximations are made. The volume of liquid, v_l, can be neglected in comparison with v_v since, for example, at the normal boiling point of water $v_v/v_l \sim 1600$. If also it is assumed that the vapour obeys the perfect gas law, that is, $v_v = RT/p$, we have

$$\frac{dp}{dTp} = \frac{\Delta H^v}{RT^2} \quad \text{or} \quad \frac{d \ln p}{dT} = \frac{\Delta H^v}{RT^2} \tag{3.1}$$

In order to integrate this expression it must be assumed that ΔH^v is a constant, independent of temperature. Integration then yields the familiar equation

$$\ln p^0 = -\frac{\Delta H^v}{RT} + \text{constant} \tag{3.2}$$

It is to be expected that the applicability of equation 3.2 may be limited severely by the assumptions made in the derivation and this is, indeed, often the case; the most important error being introduced with the assumption that ΔH^v is independent of temperature. Nevertheless, very many liquids are found to conform sufficiently well as a result of the cancellation of the errors introduced by the various assumptions made. For example, the latent heat of vaporisation decreases with increasing temperature at about the same rate as does the difference $(v_l - v_v)$.

Some idea of the range of compound types which show behaviour in accord with equation 3.2 can be gained from the following table. These data have been taken at random from the compilation of vapour pressure data by Jordan (1) and are presented in the modified form of equation 3.2,

$$\log_{10} p^0 = C - \frac{A}{T} \tag{3.3}$$

the constants A and C being listed.

Although Jordan's book contains data for many hundreds of compounds, equations are given for only about ninety. Of these, sixty-two are of the form of equation 3.2. When one also considers the enormous diversity of

TABLE 1
VAPOUR PRESSURE DATA

Substance	C	A
Methanol	8.801	2001.5
Butanol	9.136	2442.8
Acetaldehyde	7.821	1447.1
Butyraldehyde	7.959	1768.4
Methylethylether	7.769	1371.7
Dipropylether	7.821	1791.2
Dibutylether	8.002	2106.0
Formic acid	7.858	1860.0
Butyric acid	9.010	2669.0
1-Pentene	7.406	1372.2
Dipentene	7.984	2289.0
Indene	7.919	2291.0
Fluorene	8.059	2957.0
Diphenylmethane	7.967	2735.1
Anthracene	7.910	3093.0
1-4 Dioxan	7.864	1867.0
Methyl formate	7.220	1320.8
Vinyl acetate	8.091	1797.4
Ethyl chloroacetate	8.389	2292.0
Propylene oxide	8.487	1723.0
2-Nitrothiophene	8.334	2680.0
Diethylamine	8.103	1709.1
Triethylamine	8.059	1838.2
Aniline	8.128	2400.0
2-Nitroaniline	8.868	3336.0
Zinc dimethyl	7.521	1486.0
Gallium trimethyl	8.070	1705.0
Tetramethyl lead	7.751	1865.0
Methyl borane ammoniate	7.880	1800.0
Carbon diselenide	7.915	1987.0
Dichloromethylsilane	7.630	1489.0
Ethyl mercaptan	7.672	1463.0

chemical species constituting Table 1 it is obviously reasonable to accept the applicability of this simple equation in the majority of cases.

The Kirchhoff Equation.   The assumption of the temperature independence of ΔH^v which led to equation 3.2 is equivalent to the assumption that the heat capacities of liquid and vapour are equal. This is certainly untrue in many instances, and so any method of allowing for the difference will yield a vapour pressure equation of greater validity than equation 3.2.

If we restrict ourselves to small temperature changes the Kirchhoff equation can be written

$$\frac{d(\Delta H)}{dT} = C_{p\,\text{vapour}} - C_{p\,\text{liquid}} = \Delta C_p$$

and assuming that ΔC_p is constant, independent of temperature, and zero when $T = 0$,

$$\Delta H^v = \Delta H_0^v + \Delta C_p T$$

which, when substituted in equation 3.1, leads to the integrated equation

$$\ln p^0 = -\frac{\Delta H_0^v}{RT} + \frac{\Delta C_p \ln T}{R} + \text{constant} \qquad (3.4)$$

or, in the more general form comparable to equation 3.3,

$$\log p^0 = c - \frac{a}{T} + b \log T \qquad (3.5)$$

When the experimental data are sufficiently precise, equation 3.4 is found to give a better fit than equation 3.1. However, there is no simple way of presenting the data graphically if they accord with equation 3.4 and so recourse to empirical modifications may be necessary in order to produce straight line graphs.

Antoine Equations. Many authors, particularly those whose aim is the practical use of vapour-pressure data rather than their interpretation, overcome the need to employ a Kirchhoff type equation by use of equations of the so-called Antoine type. Essentially, these equations make it possible to present data which are accurately represented by equation 3.4 in a form analogous to 3.2. This is brought about by an artificial change in the absolute zero of temperature and so the general form of the such equations is

$$\log p^0 = \bar{C} - \frac{\bar{A}}{(t + \bar{B})} \qquad (3.6)$$

t is the temperature on the centigrade scale while $\bar{B}$ is some number specific to a substance which generally lies between 200 and 320. When $\bar{B} = 273$, of course, the Antoine equation corresponds exactly to equation 3.2. Some typical values of Antoine constants are listed in Table 2.

The three vapour-pressure equations presented here are only a few of the very many which have been employed from time to time. Partington (2) for example, lists fifty-five such equations, the majority of which are applicable only to specific liquids over restricted ranges of temperature and few having any sound theoretical basis. In so far as the gas chromatographic

TABLE 2
VAPOUR PRESSURE DATA
Antoine Constants

Substance	$\bar{A}$	$\bar{B}$	$\bar{C}$
Ethane	656.4	256.0	6.803
n-Octane	1355.1	209.5	6.924
Ethylene	585.0	255.0	6.746
trans-2-Pentene	1084.0	233.0	6.906
Benzene	1206.0	220.2	6.8975
o-Xylene	1477.5	214.0	7.003
1,2,3-Trimethyl benzene	1646.8	214.0	7.102
Propyl benzene	1491.6	207.2	6.952

use of vapour-pressure equations is concerned, those presented here are the only ones of importance at this time.

Saturation Vapour Pressure and Total Pressure. In gas chromatography the gases and vapours which constitute the mixture under analysis are highly diluted by the carrier gas and the total pressure might be as high as 20 atm. The contribution of the vapours towards this pressure is, of course, negligible, but it is important to determine whether or not the carrier gas pressure in any way affects the saturation vapour pressure of the liquids, since, if this occurred, there would also be changes in the partition coefficients (see Chapter 10) and hence in the time and possibly the order of elution of the vapours analysed.

Dalton's law states that the total pressure in a gas is the sum of the individual partial pressures. Unless strong intermolecular forces become operative in the gas phase there is no reason for a system to deviate from this rule. However, the liquid is compressible and will, therefore, experience changes in molar volume as a result of changes in external pressure. In integrating the Clausius-Clapeyron equation the volume of liquid v_l was neglected in comparison with that of the vapour v_v. If this is not done it becomes possible to evaluate the effect of external pressure on the saturation vapour pressure of a liquid. At equilibrium, at constant temperature

$$v_v \, dp = v_l \, dp$$

As shown above, v_v is determined only by the pressure exerted by the vapour, whereas v_l is dependent upon the total external pressure. Hence, the dependence of saturation pressure upon total pressure P is

$$\frac{dp^0}{dP} = \frac{v_l}{v_v}$$

and substituting for v_v

$$\frac{dp^0}{p^0} = \frac{v_l \, dP}{RT}$$

Integrating this expression between the pressure limits P_1 and P_2

$$\ln \left(\frac{p_1^0}{p_2^0}\right) = \frac{v_l(P_1 - P_2)}{RT} \tag{3.7}$$

We can best assess the effect of total pressure on the saturation vapour pressure by an actual example. Consider water boiling at 1 atm. pressure at 100°C. In these circumstances, $p_2^0 = P_2 = 1$ atm.; $v_l \simeq 20$ ml. and $R = 0.082$ l. atm./mole deg. The effect on p^0 of raising P from 1 to 10 atm. is

$$\log p_1^0 = \frac{2.10^{-2} \times 9}{2.3 \times 0.082 \times 373} = 0.0026$$

Hence $p_1^0 = 1.006$ atm. and the change in its value for a 10-atm. total change is only about 0.6 per cent. In general, therefore, the effect is so small that it is negligible. It is, however, possible that in circumstances where the measurement of gas chromatographic quantities became accurate enough, the effect of carrier gas pressure might necessarily have to be allowed for by application of equation 3.7. It seems likely, though, that if this situation should arise, account would also have to be taken of the fact that the carrier gas solubility would be relatively high and the vaporisation of the liquid out of solution might be complicated by the presence in solution of a fairly large amount of carrier gas. The system would then become a ternary one, in other words the solvent would be effectively impure.

An important consequence of equation 3.7 is that reduction of the pressure for example, has no real effect on p^0 and so there is no justification, on this basis, for attempting gas chromatography at low pressures.

THE TROUTON RULE

When substances are at equal fractions ϕ, π and θ of their critical volume, pressure and temperature, respectively, they are said to be in corresponding states. It is found that the boiling point of liquids is close to a corresponding state and the value of θ is then about 0.6. This is the well known Guldberg rule. Any equation of state containing no more than three independent constants can be cast in a form containing only "reduced" constants such as ϕ, π and θ and so the integrated Clausius-Clapeyron type of vapour pressure equation can be written in the form

$$\ln \pi = k\left(1 + \frac{1}{\theta}\right)$$

which on differentiation becomes

$$\frac{d \ln \pi}{d\theta} = -\frac{k}{\theta^2} = \frac{1}{\pi}\frac{d\pi}{d\theta}$$

and, on rearranging and comparing with the Clausius-Clapeyron equation we find

$$\frac{\Delta H^v}{RT} = \frac{k}{\theta}$$

At the boiling point $T = T_b$ and $\theta = 0.6$ while k is found to be about 7 for most substances (Moelwyn-Hughes, 3). Then

$$\frac{\Delta H^v}{T_b} = \frac{7 \times 2}{0.6} = 23.3 \text{ cal.} \times \text{mole}^{-1} \times \text{deg.}^{-1}$$

That this relationship exists was first shown empirically by Trouton and the rule is known by his name. A more widely applicable rule of a similar sort, put forward by Hildebrand, involves measuring the ratio $\Delta H^v/T$ not at the boiling points of various liquids but at temperatures at which the concentration of their molecules in the vapour is the same. The experimental application of this relation is very considerably more difficult than that of the Trouton rule and so it is the latter which is most often used in practice. Some typical values of the Trouton constant are shown in Table 3.

TABLE 3

TROUTON CONSTANTS

Substance	Constant
Butyraldehyde	23.9
Dipropyl ether	22.5
Naphthalene	23.0
Dipentene	23.6
Fluorene	24.1
Propylene oxide	25.9
Diethylamine	24.0
Mercury diethyl	23.4
Tetramethyl tin	21.2
Ethyl formate	22.8
2-Nitrotoluene	23.4
Aniline	24.2
Acetic acid	25.9
Butyric acid	28.0
Vinyl acetate	24.0
Ethyl chloroacetate	25.2
Methanol	27.9
Butanol	28.7

The majority of compounds have constants between 22 and 24, the most notable anomalies being with compounds such as the alcohols and fatty acids in which hydrogen bonding is known to occur. The calculation of over seventy Trouton constants from data readily available in Jordan's book of vapour pressure data (1) yields an average value of 23 if alcohols and acids are omitted. It is clear that the Trouton constant represents the molar entropy of vaporisation and, as will be seen later, its value goes far in determining the gas chromatographic behaviour of a solute.

SATURATION VAPOUR PRESSURE AND MOLECULAR CONSTITUTION

Studies in gas liquid chromatography have shown that the relationship between the logarithm of the retention volume, (p. 205), which is characteristic of the solute/solvent system, and various physical properties of solutes which are members of homologous series is very frequently linear. Since, as is seen later (p. 209) the logarithm of the retention volume is directly dependent on the logarithm of the saturation vapour pressure of a solute over the solution, it would seem pertinent to enquire into the extent to which the logarithm of the saturation vapour pressures of pure solutes at constant temperature is linearly dependent on their various physical properties. The literature contains relatively few such studies and so it is another important aspect of gas liquid chromatography that its development may result in stimulating interest in this direction and quite possibly it may well provide a rapid and accurate method of obtaining the necessary data.

Figures 1 to 3 illustrate plots of boiling point against the number of carbon atoms contained in the molecule for a wide range of types of homologous series. It is clear that a linear relationship is general. From the graphs it is a simple matter to reduce the data to a linear equation of the type

$$T_b = k_7 + k_8 \bar{n} \tag{3.8}$$

where $\bar{n}$ is, in this instance, the number of carbon atoms in the molecule. Table 4 lists some of these reduced data deduced from the figures shown. This list by no means represents all the types showing this behaviour and the table is merely a representative selection. It should, however, be pointed out that over a very wide range of $\bar{n}$ the individual graphs are generally curved. The data in Table 4 relate to the lower members of series, but similar constants for higher members can be determined.

The generality of the Trouton rule illustrated in Table 3, combined with that of the boiling point equation 3.8 clearly indicates that there must also be a comparable relation between the latent heat of vaporisation and the number of carbon atoms or other structural units. Figure 4 illustrates data

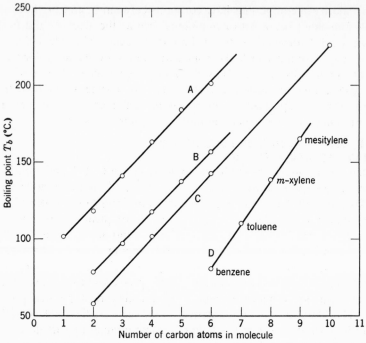

FIG. 1. Plot of boiling point against number of carbon atoms in the molecule for: A, n-fatty acids; B, n-alcohols; C, symmetrical alkyl ketones; D, aromatics.

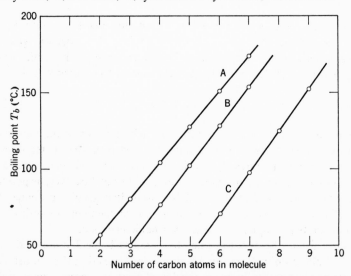

FIG. 2. Plot of boiling point against number of carbon atoms in the molecule for: A, methyl n-alkyl ketones; B, n-aliphatic aldehydes; C, n-paraffins.

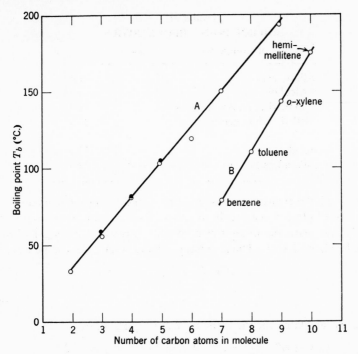

FIG. 3. Plot of boiling point against number of carbon atoms in the molecule for: A, methyl (open circles), and ethyl and propyl (closed circles) esters of lower fatty acids; B, aromatics.

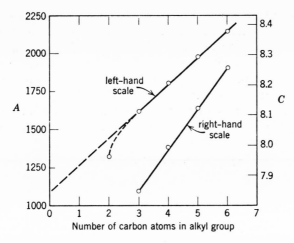

FIG. 4. Plots of the constants A and C of the integrated Clausius-Clapeyron equation against number of carbon atoms in the alkyl group of some n-alkyl formates.

TABLE 4

BOILING POINT REGULARITIES

Class of Compound	k_7	k_8
n-Fatty acids	84	19.6
n-Alcohols	39	19.6
Symmetrical n-alkyl ketones	12	22.0
Methyl n-alkyl ketones	10	23.4
n-Alkyl esters	−14	23.2
n-Aldehydes	−27	25.6
n-Paraffins ($n > 6$)	−95	27.3

for some n-alkyl formates. In this, both the A and C constants of equation 3.3 have been plotted against the number of carbon atoms in each ester molecule and, with the exception of methyl formate, the data lie on a straight line in each case. The equations for these quantities can be written

$$A = k_9 + k_{10}\bar{n} \qquad (3.9)$$

and

$$C = k_{11} + k_{12}\bar{n} \qquad (3.10)$$

The values calculated for the formates from Figure 4 are

$$k_9 = 1090; \quad k_{10} = 178; \quad k_{11} = 7.435; \quad k_{12} = 0.137$$

The constant A, of course, is equal to $\Delta H^v/4.6$, hence, for the formates we can write

$$\Delta H^v = 5014 + 819\bar{n} \text{ cal./mole}$$

Many other homologous series show behaviour of this type and consideration suggests that the Trouton constant for a series is often either a constant, or changes linearly with the number of fundamental structural units. As will be seen later, these conclusions are of considerable importance in elucidating the thermodynamics of gas-liquid, and, to some extent at least, gas-solid chromatography.

Regular changes in the values of the constants a and b in the Kirchhoff type equation have recently been pointed out by Moelwyn-Hughes (3). He has shown that for n-paraffins

$$\Delta H_0^v = 1100 + 1700\bar{n} \text{ cal./mole}$$

and

$$b = 0.5 + 0.94\bar{n}$$

while for n-alcohols

$$\Delta H_0^v = 10,000 + 2200\bar{n} \text{ cal./mole}$$

and

$$b = 2.5 + 1.88\bar{n}$$

Moelwyn-Hughes explains the existence of such relationships on the basis that the intermolecular forces between neighbouring molecules, which determine the saturation vapour pressure, are, at least to a close approximation, the sum of the energies of interaction between individual groups within the separate molecules. On this basis the constant term would represent mainly, but not entirely, terminal group interactions between nearest neighbours while the additive term would represent, in greatest proportion, the interaction of the groups forming the backbone of the

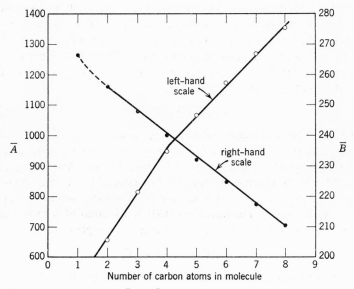

FIG. 5. Plots of the constants $\bar{A}$ and $\bar{B}$ of the Antoine type vapour pressure equations against number of carbon atoms in some lower n-paraffins.

molecule. For this reason, the alcohols, with the strong possibility of hydrogen bonding through hydroxyl groups, would have higher values for the constants than the n-paraffins. This view is similar to that taken by other workers and has been applied to solutions generally and recently in gas chromatography, as described in Chapter 2 in the "building block" model advanced by Pierrotti and his colleagues (4).

The growing use of Antoine type equations in gas liquid chromatography makes it worthwhile to study the possibility of finding regularities in the constants of these equations. Figure 5 shows plots of $\bar{A}$ and $\bar{B}$ against the number of carbon atoms in lower n-paraffins. The plot of $\bar{A}$ appears to consist of two intersecting straight lines while, with the exception of methane, that for $\bar{B}$ is linear over the whole range. Similarly, it is found that there is a regular increment in $\bar{C}$ for each CH_2 group added to the molecule. These plots can be summarised in the equations

$$C_2 \text{ to } C_4 \qquad \bar{A} = 367 + 145\bar{n}$$
$$\text{higher than } C_4 \; \bar{A} = 575 + 100\bar{n}$$
$$\text{higher than } C_2 \; \bar{B} = 271.5 - 7.8\bar{n}$$
$$\bar{C} = 6.76 + 0.02\bar{n}$$

This brief review indicates unquestionably that, irrespective of the form of vapour pressure equation employed, it is very commonly found that the values of the constants in the chosen equation vary linearly with the molecular weight of members of homologous series. Further consequences of the relationships listed earlier are that, since A and C of equation 3.3, for example, are linearly dependent upon the number of carbon atoms in the molecule of a member of a homologous series, so must $\log p^0$. Thus, for a series of homologues at temperature T,

$$\log p^0 = k_{13} + k_{14}\bar{n} \qquad (3.11)$$

Herington, in his discussion of the thermodynamics of gas-liquid chromatography (5) employed this equation and presented comprehensive evidence that it was obeyed for a wide variety of chemical types. Another equation, also employed by Herington, can also be deduced from those presented earlier. The dependence of the boiling point on the number of carbon atoms, for example, as illustrated in equation 3.8, coupled with the generality of Trouton's rule, means that at any given temperature

$$\log p^0 = k_{15} + k_{16}T_b \qquad (3.12)$$

It is not surprising, in view of the other evidence, that, for example Herington (5) and Pierrotti, Deal, Derr and Porter (4) found this relationship to be widely applicable for members of homologous series.

In conclusion we may reconsider the question of the variation of C and $\bar{C}$ in equations of types 3.3 and 3.6. The data contained in Table 1 show that with the exception of alcohols and fatty acids, particularly, the values of C lie almost entirely between about 7.6 and 8.1. Correspondingly, from Table 2 it is seen that $\bar{C}$ lies generally between 6.7 and 7.1. As a generalisation, therefore, we may say that the variation of C or $\bar{C}$ over a wide range of compounds is only about ± 4 per cent. In consequence, no very serious error is introduced if C and $\bar{C}$ are considered to be constant and independent of chemical type. This approximation very considerably simplifies the thermodynamic treatment of gas-liquid chromatography. It must always be borne in mind, however, that the equations developed in this chapter are only of a general nature and that exceptions to the rule will be frequent. It is pertinent at this point to say that these exceptions very often involve substances of high boiling point such as are usually used as solvents in gas-liquid chromatography. Substances such as the alkyl phthalate esters may have Trouton constants as high as 35 and show no regularities of physical properties with molecular weight or structure. Such high Trouton constants are, presumably, to be associated with very low entropies in the pure liquid, the consequence of which is to make the heat of vaporisation great in relation to the boiling point.

REFERENCES

1. Jordan, T. E., *Vapour Pressures of Organic Compounds*, 1954, Interscience, New York.
2. Partington, J. R., *Physical Chemistry*, 1949, Longmans, London, Vol. 1.
3. Moelwyn-Hughes, E. A., *Physical Chemistry*, 1957, Pergamon Press, London, p. 682.
4. Pierotti, G. J., C. H. Deal, E. L. Derr and P. E. Porter, *J. Amer. Chem. Soc.*, 1956, **78**, 2989.
5. Herington, E. F. G., *Vapour Phase Chromatography*, 1957, Butterworths, London (editor, D. H. Desty), p. 5.

4

DIFFUSION
IN
GASES
AND
LIQUIDS

Wherever a concentration gradient exists there will be a movement of molecules to eliminate the gradient. In a pure substance the process is called self-diffusion, while in a multi-component mixture it is termed interdiffusion. The spreading of solute bands in a chromatographic column is largely due to diffusional processes and even those which are not strictly diffusional are formally so similar that they can be treated as such. In consequence, our ideas about band broadening are most often founded on the basic theory of diffusion, and so a knowledge of its fundamentals is of great importance to an understanding of the gas chromatographic process.

The general law of diffusion, known as Fick's law, states that the number of molecules (N) crossing a plane in time t is proportional to the area and to the concentration gradient (dn/dl). That is, for a plane of unit area

$$\frac{dN}{dt} = -D\left(\frac{dn}{dl}\right) \qquad (4.1)$$

The proportionality constant, D, is the diffusion coefficient and the negative sign is introduced in order that D may be positive. This is equivalent to considering the mass transport as being against the concentration gradient. An alternative way of defining D is by means of Fick's second law, which is written

$$\frac{dn}{dt} = D\left[\frac{\partial^2 n}{\partial x^2} + \frac{\partial^2 n}{\partial y^2} + \frac{\partial^2 n}{\partial z^2}\right]$$

for the general case of diffusion in three dimensions, but for one dimensional diffusion, which is the situation of interest in gas chromatography, reduces to

$$\frac{dn}{dt} = D\left(\frac{d^2 n}{dl^2}\right) \qquad (4.2)$$

46

The Coefficient of Self-Diffusion. The significance of D can be readily evaluated if we consider three planes, each of unit area, within a gaseous system, each one mean free path λ removed from the other. If the concentration of molecules in the central plane is n then those in the right and left hand planes are, respectively, $\left(n + \lambda\dfrac{dn}{dl}\right)$ and $\left(n - \lambda\dfrac{dn}{dl}\right)$. Consider now the movement of molecules from left to right, that is, against the concentration gradient as specified by Fick's law.

The net rate of movement from left to right is

$$\frac{d\mathrm{N}}{dt} = -2\bar{v}\lambda\left(\frac{dn}{dl}\right)$$

if $\bar{v}$ is the average component of the velocity in the direction of motion. Comparison with equation 4.1 shows that

$$D = 2\bar{v}\lambda$$

and since $\bar{v}$ can be related to the average velocity of the molecules $\bar{c}$ by the expression $\bar{c} = 4\bar{v}$,

$$D = \tfrac{1}{2}\bar{c}\lambda \tag{4.3}$$

Statistical theory shows that

$$\bar{c} = \left(\frac{8kT}{\pi \mathrm{m}}\right)^{\frac{1}{2}} \quad \text{and} \quad \lambda = (\sqrt{2}\pi n\sigma^2)^{-1}$$

where k is Boltzman's constant, m is the mass of the molecule of collision cross section σ and T is the absolute temperature. Thus, we find that

$$D = \frac{(kT/\pi \mathrm{m})^{\frac{1}{2}}}{\pi n\sigma^2} \tag{4.4}$$

D is thus inversely proportional to n, and hence the pressure, and directly proportional to $T^{1.5}$; the extra power of T deriving from the ideal gas law temperature dependence of n. It is also evident that D diminishes considerably with increasing molecular weight and collision diameter.

The Coefficient of Interdiffusion. Self diffusion plays no part in gas chromatography, of course, and it is with interdiffusion that one has to deal. Nevertheless, the mathematical treatment of interdiffusion is essentially the same as that of self diffusion and so it is instructive and helpful to have considered the latter.

In a two component gas mixture, the concentrations of the component gases being n_1 and n_2 molecules per cc., the sum of the concentrations at any point must be constant if there are not to be pressure gradients, and so

$$\frac{dn_1}{dl} = \frac{-dn_2}{dl} \tag{4.5}$$

If there is a mass velocity of movement u, it must be the same for both species in order again that pressure gradients should not develop. An argument identical with that given for self diffusion leads to

$$\frac{dN_1}{dt} = un_1 - \tfrac{1}{2}\bar{c}_1\lambda_1\left(\frac{dn_1}{dl}\right) \tag{4.6}$$

and

$$\frac{dN_2}{dt} = un_2 - \tfrac{1}{2}\bar{c}_2\lambda_2\left(\frac{dn_2}{dl}\right) \tag{4.7}$$

but since the mass velocity (dN/dt) of the two species must be the same, equations 4.6 and 4.7 are equivalent and so

$$u(n_1 + n_2) = \tfrac{1}{2}\bar{c}_2\lambda_2\left(\frac{dn_2}{dl}\right) + \tfrac{1}{2}\bar{c}_1\lambda_1\left(\frac{dn_1}{dl}\right)$$

The value of u obtained from this can be substituted in either equation 4.6 or 4.7, and using the former we get,

$$\frac{dN_1}{dt} = - \frac{dn_1}{dl}\left[\frac{n_1\bar{c}_2\lambda_2 + n_2\bar{c}_1\lambda_1}{2(n_1 + n_2)}\right] \tag{4.8}$$

(dn_2/dl), wherever it occurred, having been replaced by $-(dn_1/dl)$. Comparing this result again with equation 4.1 we see that the interdiffusion coefficient D_{12} is apparently given by the relation

$$D_{12} = \frac{n_1\bar{c}_2\lambda_2 + n_2\bar{c}_1\lambda_1}{2(n_1 + n_2)} \tag{4.9}$$

or its equivalent in terms of mole fractions, x,

$$D_{12} = \tfrac{1}{2}x_1\bar{c}_2\lambda_2 + \tfrac{1}{2}x_2\bar{c}_1\lambda_1 \tag{4.10}$$

This form of the interdiffusion equation is known as Meyer's formula and an important consequence of it is that the interdiffusion coefficient appears to be dependent upon the composition of the mixture. In fact, in dilute solution, if no other, D_{12} is generally found to be independent of composition and a function only of the total concentration or pressure. In order to get around this difficulty, Maxwell postulated that collisions between like molecules should not influence interdiffusion, and that only collisions between unlike ones need be considered. Adopting this point of view the appropriate values of the mean free paths to be substituted in equation 4.9 are of the form

$$\lambda_1 = \frac{1}{\pi n_2 \sigma_{12}{}^2(1 + m_1/m_2)^{\frac{1}{2}}}$$

σ_{12} being a mean collision diameter [$\frac{1}{2}(\sigma_1 + \sigma_2)$]. The result, known as the Stefan-Maxwell equation, is

$$D_{12} = \left[\frac{1}{\pi\sigma_{12}^{2}(n_1 + n_2)}\right]\left[\frac{2kT}{\pi}\left(\frac{1}{m_1} + \frac{1}{m_2}\right)\right]^{\frac{1}{2}} \qquad (4.11)$$

This equation no longer contains any terms representing composition of the gas and D_{12} depends inversely on the total pressure $(n_1 + n_2)$ as was found for self diffusion. Similarly, the diffusion rate depends upon $T^{1.5}$.

TABLE 1

INTERDIFFUSION COEFFICIENTS (cm².sec.⁻¹) OF
PARAFFINS AT 30°C AND 1 ATM.

Carrier Gas	n-Heptane	2:4-Dimethyl Pentane	n-Octane	2:2:4-Tri-methyl Pentane
Hydrogen	0.283	0.297	0.277	0.292
Deuterium	0.218	0.224	0.208	0.212
Helium	0.265	0.263	0.248	0.253
Nitrogen	0.0740	0.0744	0.0726	0.0713
Argon	0.0658	0.0655	0.0587	0.0599

The equation 4.11 represents the behaviour of gases reasonably well, although it is sometimes found that the temperature dependence may be anywhere between $T^{1.5}$ and T^{2}. In addition, better agreement between experiment and theory is observed if π outside the bracketted term is replaced by $\frac{8}{3}$. It must be remembered that the derivation of equation 4.11 is based on kinetic theory assumptions and these are applicable only to rigid spherical molecules with somewhat unrealistic properties. Thus, the application of theoretical equations to, say, paraffin type molecules which may be linear or even crumpled in the gas phase can only be an approximation. Nevertheless, the experimental and calculated data usually agree quite well, certainly there is no question of orders of magnitude being involved.

Table 1 illustrates the magnitude of D_{12}, the data listed being those obtained by Clarke and Ubbelohde (1) for the diffusion of some paraffins into permanent gases.

The data bear out closely what has already been said. For example, the ratio of D_{12} for n-octane in hydrogen to that in nitrogen is 3.72 which may be compared with the molecular weight ratio $(M_{N_2}/M_{H_2})^{\frac{1}{2}}$ which is close to 3.80. Again, D_{12} for any carrier gas is higher for branched than for straight chain paraffins in most cases. The tabulated data may be used further to illustrate the extent to which equation 4.11 is capable of accurate prediction of D_{12}.

The value of σ for n-octane, calculated from viscosity measurements, is 5 Å, and using this and the accepted value of σ for hydrogen, equation 4.11 yields $D_{12} = 0.276$, in excellent agreement with the value in the table. In principle σ for n-octane ought to be the same in all permanent gases, but Clarke and Ubbelohde found that it ranges from 4.5 Å in helium to 5.55 Å in argon. This apparent variation of σ is a consequence of the simplified approach adopted in the derivation of equation 4.11. However, if an average value of 5 Å were chosen then, clearly, the calculated value of D_{12}

TABLE 2

TEMPERATURE DEPENDENCE OF DIFFUSION
COEFFICIENTS OF GASES AND VAPOURS

Diffusing Gas	Carrier Gas	$D_{12}{}^0$ cm.²/sec.	m'
Oxygen	Nitrogen	0.181	1.75
Hydrogen		0.674	1.75
Hydrogen	Air	0.611	1.75
Carbon dioxide		0.138	2.00
Methanol	Hydrogen	0.5059	1.75
Acetic acid		0.4163	2.00
Ethyl acetate		0.2730	2.00
Diethyl ether		0.2964	2.00
Benzene		0.2948	1.75

for any of the carrier gases cited would still be correct to ± 20 per cent. This value probably represents the extent of agreement which can be hoped for and so it is evident that theoretical values of diffusion coefficients must be used with caution if other data are to be derived from them and it is undoubtedly safest to employ measured coefficients when such data are needed in gas chromatographic studies.

If diffusion data at several pressures and temperatures are known the results for gases can be compactly presented in the form of an equation such as

$$D_{12} = D_{12}{}^0 \left(\frac{T}{T_0}\right)^{m'} \frac{p_0}{p} \qquad (4.12)$$

which follows from 4.11 wherein, theoretically, $m' = 1.50$. It is usual to take T_0 as 273°K. and p_0 as 1 atm. The pressure dependence of D_{12} is almost always the inverse first power dependence specified by equation 4.11, but, as mentioned, the temperature dependence varies from system to system, and m' does not always have the predicted value. Table 2 lists some values of $D_{12}{}^0$ and m' taken from International Critical Tables which illustrate the above points.

Not all authors, however, are agreed on the variable value of m' in equations 4.11 and 4.12. Gilliland (2), for example, reviewed a large proportion of the data in the literature up to 1934 and concluded that 4.11, written in the simpler form

$$D_{12} = \frac{A'T^{3/2}}{\sigma_{12}{}^2 P}\left(\frac{1}{M_1} + \frac{1}{M_2}\right)$$

wherein P represents pressure in atmospheres and A' is a constant, adequately described the behaviour of the majority of systems. Since σ_{12} is not always known experimentally, he calculated its value in many instances from the approximate proportionality of σ to the cube root of the molecular volume at the normal boiling point. Thus

$$\sigma_{12} = \tfrac{1}{2}(\sigma_1 + \sigma_2) = \tfrac{1}{2}[(v_1{}^m)^{1/3} + (v_2{}^m)^{1/3}]$$

whence,

$$D_{12} = \frac{B'T^{3/2}}{P[(v_1{}^m)^{1/3} + (v_2{}^m)^{1/3}]^2}\left[\frac{1}{M_1} + \frac{1}{M_2}\right] \tag{4.13}$$

B' being a new constant. Its value was found experimentally to vary between 0.0037 and 0.0047 for the substances studied and Gilliland recommended an average value, 0.0043. The molecular volumes have generally to be calculated from Kopp's law tables of atomic and bond volumes and so it is clear that the use of 4.13 involves several approximations in excess of those which may be necessary in the use of 4.11. It is likely, therefore, to be less reliable, a point which is made since 4.13 has several times been used to estimate D_{12} for gas chromatographic purposes (3, 4).

Sutherland type equations, in which an apparent temperature dependence of σ is corrected for by use of a function

$$\sigma_{12} = \sigma_{12}{}^0\left(1 + \frac{C'}{T}\right)^{1/2}$$

are commonly used to represent viscosity and diffusion data, but, for diffusion, are generally less useful than 4.11. However, particularly in the case of viscosity, much of the available data is in this form, and may have to be used. If the constant C' is unknown it may be calculated from the approximate relationship with the boiling point,

$$C' = 1.47T_b$$

According to the Guldberg rule (p. 37), the boiling point and critical temperature are related by $T_b = 0.6T_c$, so that $C' = 0.882T_c$. Experimentally this is often found to be true and values of C' may therefore be calculated from T_b with a certainty about as great as that inherent in the calculation of T_c from T_b.

A further alternative way of expressing the temperature dependence of D_{12} is in the familiar logarithmic form

$$\log D_{12} = -\frac{E}{2.3RT} + \text{constant} \tag{4.14}$$

in which E represents an activation energy of diffusion—usually very small. For diffusion in polymeric liquids, however, E may be as high as 8000 cals/mole. This form of equation finds more use in studies of diffusion in liquids than in gases, and has been used occasionally in connexion with gas chromatography (5, 6).

Diffusion and the Viscosity of the Medium. By arguments analogous with those used in deducing the value of the self-diffusion coefficient given by equation 4.3, the coefficient of viscosity can be shown to be given by

$$\eta = \tfrac{1}{2}\rho\lambda\bar{c}$$

where ρ is the density. Thus,

$$\frac{\rho D}{\eta} \equiv 1$$

Experimentally the ratio for gases is found often to be 1.39, and even if π is replaced by $\tfrac{8}{3}$ in equation 4.11, the theoretical ratio, 1.18, still falls short of that commonly found. Nevertheless, it is clear that for gases a quantitative relationship between D and η exists and qualitatively, even for liquids, it will be safe to assume that diffusion will be slow in a medium of high viscosity and even to calculate an approximate diffusion coefficient from viscosity data which are easier to obtain and hence, more abundant.

DIFFUSIONAL SPREADING AND THE EINSTEIN EQUATION

It is evident from the equations discussed that at constant pressure and temperature for a given system the extent to which molecules diffuse away from a source is determined only by the time available. Since all the processes occurring in chromatographic columns are either diffusional or formally similar, it is important to know the quantitative relation between time and extent of diffusion.

The first steps in this are to set up again the one dimensional form of the equation corresponding to Fick's second law, equation 4.2,

$$\frac{dn}{dt} = D\left(\frac{d^2n}{dl^2}\right)$$

for which an acceptable solution is

$$n = \frac{A}{t^{1/2}} e^{-l^2/4Dt} \tag{4.15}$$

as can readily be verified by differentiation. The term A is an arbitrary constant which can be eliminated as follows. The total quantity of diffusing material, m, is given by

$$m = \int_{-\infty}^{\infty} n \, dl \qquad (4.16)$$

If we now write

$$y^2 = \frac{l^2}{4 \, Dt}$$

then

$$dl = 2(Dt)^{1/2} \, dy$$

and, if we rewrite equation 4.15,

$$n = \frac{A}{t^{1/2}} e^{-y^2}$$

Equation 4.16 becomes

$$m = 2AD^{1/2} \int_{-\infty}^{\infty} e^{-y^2} \, dy \qquad (4.17)$$

which, on integration, gives

$$m = 2A(\pi D)^{1/2}$$

We thus find that

$$A = \frac{m}{2(\pi D)^{1/2}}$$

and, if we insert this value in equation 4.15

$$n = \frac{m}{2(\pi Dt)^{1/2}} e^{-l^2/4Dt} \qquad (4.18)$$

As will be seen later, this equation is very similar to that deduced by Glueckauf (7.27), in connexion with the theoretical plate theory of chromatography, and it suggests that the theoretical plate concept is equally valid for diffusional spreading as for the partition process. Equation 4.18 represents a Gaussian distribution, of course, and Figure 1 illustrates the use of the equation to construct plots of n/m against l for various values of Dt, D being assumed to be 0.1. The width of the curves is determined entirely by the product Dt. Thus, for example, the same curve is obtained for $D = 0.1$, $t = 10$ as for $D = 10$, $t = 0.1$.

The maximum value of n derived from equation 4.18 is

$$n_{max} = \frac{m}{2(\pi Dt)^{1/2}}$$

hence we may write

$$n = n_{max} e^{-l^2/4Dt}$$

If we now make

$$n = n_{max}/e$$
$$e^{-1} = e^{-l^2/4Dt}$$

and

$$l_e^2 = 4Dt \qquad (4.19)$$

The term l_e represents the Gaussian band half width at the $1/e$th height of the band. From the properties of the Gaussian distribution we know that

$$l_e = (\sqrt{2})l$$

where l, the standard deviation, is the half band width at the inflexion point. Thus

$$l^2 = \frac{l_e^2}{2} = 2Dt \qquad (4.20)$$

which is commonly known as the Einstein equation.

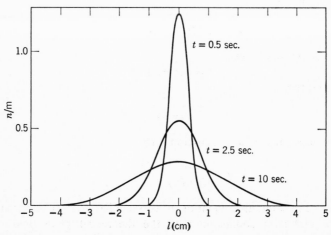

FIG. 1. Concentration profiles resulting from the diffusion of a substance away from the source over different periods of time. The curves would also represent the profiles of substances of different diffusion coefficient diffusing for different periods of time defined by the fact that Dt is constant for a given curve.

The actual magnitude of diffusional spreading likely to be met with in practice can be estimated by a simple calculation. From Table 1 we see that, for n-octane in nitrogen at 30°C. and 1 atm. pressure, $D_{12} = 0.0726$ cm.^{2}/sec. while in hydrogen it is 0.277 cm.^{2}/sec. Thus, in nitrogen, in 60 sec.,

$$l = (2 \times 0.0726 \times 60)^{1/2} = 2.9 \text{ cm.}$$

while in hydrogen in the same time

$$l = (2 \times 0.277 \times 60)^{1/2} = 5.8 \text{ cm.}$$

The gaussian band half widths at the inflexion point are, to all intents and purposes, about one-sixth of the effective total spread, hence, for example, n-octane, 60 sec. after introduction as a plane into hydrogen, will be found over a distance of about 30 cm. around the point of introduction. Supposing that n-octane is eluted by hydrogen from a gas chromatographic column at a flow rate such that it spends 60 sec. in the gas phase, then, immediately before leaving the column it is obviously spread over 30 cm. of column, and if the column is only a metre long, as is often the case, it occupies 30 per cent of the column. This spread, due to gaseous diffusion only, clearly represents the minimum band width.

As was pointed out earlier, the equations derived apply equally to the gas and liquid phases. As might be expected, diffusion in liquids is very

TABLE 3

DIFFUSION COEFFICIENTS IN SOLUTION AT 15°C.

Diffusing Species	Carrier Liquid	$10^5 \times D_{12}$ cm.^{2}/sec.
Acetic acid	Methanol	1.54
Ethyl acetate		2.10
Diethyl ether		2.00
Benzene		2.12
Acetic acid	Benzene	1.92
Diethyl ether		2.21

considerably slower than in gases. Table 3 lists some data taken at random from International Critical Tables and comparison with those in Table 2 reveals the extent of the difference between diffusion in the two phases.

Considering the values of D_{12} for acetic acid in hydrogen and in liquid benzene we see that the ratio is about 2×10^4. Putting the values into the Einstein equation we find that the ratio of distances diffused in equal time is about 140. This factor would suggest that in gas chromatography, where molecules may either be in solution or in the gas phase, longitudinal band spreading in solution would be of negligible significance compared to that occurring in the gas phase. However, molecules generally spend more time in solution than in the gas if chromatographic separation is to be achieved, but a simple calculation shows that even this is unlikely to be important. As is seen later the ratio of time spent in the two phases

$$\frac{t_{\text{liq}}}{t_{\text{gas}}} = \frac{l_{\text{liq}}^2 D_{\text{gas}}}{l_{\text{gas}}^2 D_{\text{liq}}} = K \frac{V_l}{V_d}$$

where K is the partition coefficient, V_l is the volume of solvent in a column, and V_d is the free gas volume. V_l/V_d is rarely greater than 0.2 and so for l_{liq} to be equal to l_{gas}, since $D_{\text{gas}}/D_{\text{liq}} \simeq 2 \times 10^4$ for the example considered, $K = 10^5$. Such an enormous value of K would be of little value chromatographically, since the time taken to carry out an analysis would be much too great for convenience. In fact, practically, it seems certain that we do not approach the above value by nearly two orders of magnitude. However, the fact that, at high values of K, longitudinal diffusion in solution may contribute to solute band spreading should not be overlooked completely.

The data used in the example relate to fairly small molecules and so it is unlikely that larger values of D_{12} will be met with in practice, particularly in gas chromatographic systems where the solvent is normally of high molecular weight. Even at high temperatures it does not seem likely that values of D_{12} greater than 10^{-4} cm.^{2} sec.$^{-1}$ will be met with, and $10^{-6 \text{ to } -7}$ cm.^{2} sec.$^{-1}$ is a more probable value.

Since we may neglect longitudinal diffusional spreading of material in solution in comparison to that in a gas, it follows that we must consider the implications of this view with respect to lateral diffusion, that is, movement at right angles to the direction of flow in chromatographic systems. In order to achieve the best possible effect in a chromatographic column it is necessary that there should be mass equilibrium at all points and times. This may not be possible if diffusion in the liquid phase is slow. We may again use the example of acetic acid diffusing in hydrogen and liquid benzene. Now we have a situation in which the time of contact is the same for both phases, and so

$$\frac{t_{\text{liq}}}{t_{\text{gas}}} = \frac{l_{\text{liq}}^2 D_{\text{gas}}}{l_{\text{gas}}^2 D_{\text{liq}}} = 1$$

Hence, since the ratio of diffusion coefficients is 2×10^4, $l_{\text{gas}}/l_{\text{liq}}$ must be about 140 if equilibration of material in a static gas phase is to be as important as that in the liquid phase. The thickness of a liquid film in a gas chromatographic column is anyone's guess, but might lie between 10^{-4} and 10^{-2} cm. The layer of gas in contact with the liquid must be approximately the same as the diameter of the solid particles in the column packing, that is, between 1.5 and 6.0×10^{-2} cm. Hence, we may conclude that the form of mass transport in the gas phase discussed is only of importance relative to that in the liquid phase when we are dealing with columns in which the liquid film is very thin and particle size relatively great. A more significant gas phase mass transfer problem arises because of the non-uniform velocity gradient across a gas flowing in a tube, a phenomenon which is discussed in Chapter 5. This may be of sufficient consequence that the net gas phase mass transfer resistance becomes comparable with that in the liquid phase, and it is not inconceivable then that when lean packed chromatographic columns or capillaries are used, liquid films may be so thin and gas layers so thick that resistance to mass transfer in the gas phase may be the dominant factor.

REFERENCES

1. Clarke, J. K., and A. R. Ubbelohde, *J. Chem. Soc.*, **1957**, 2050.
2. Gilliland, E. R., *Ind. Eng. Chem.*, 1934, **26**, 681.
3. Keulemans, A. I. M., and C. G. Verver, *Gas Chromatography*, 1957, Reinhold, New York, p. 142.
4. van Deemter, J. J., F. J. Zuiderweg, and A. Klinkenberg, *Chem. Eng. Sci.*, 1955, **5**, 271.
5. Littlewood, A. B., *Gas Chromatography*, 1958, Butterworths, London (editor, D. H. Desty), p. 30.
6. Purnell, J. H., *Ann. N.Y. Acad. Sci.*, 1959, **72**, 592.
7. Glueckauf, E., *Trans. Faraday Soc.*, 1955, **51**, 34.

5
THE
FLOW
OF
GASES

There are three regimes of flow in fluids. At very low pressures when the mean free path is great there is diffusional or Knudsen flow. At higher pressures and low velocities, flow is streamlined, while at high velocities the flow becomes turbulent. In gas chromatography, pressures are too high and velocities too low for anything but streamlined flow, and so only this form of motion need be considered here, whether it be for open or packed tubes.

Capillary Flow. The recent emergence of capillary columns makes it worthwhile to recapitulate briefly something of the theory of fluid flow in such systems. The basis of the theory is to assume that the viscous force acting on a cylinder of radius r of fluid of viscosity η coaxial with and within the capillary, $[2\pi r L\eta(du/dr)]$, is equal and opposite to the hydrostatic force $[\pi r^2 \Delta p]$ over the length (L) of this cylinder, Δp being the pressure drop. Then,

$$\frac{du}{dr} = -\frac{\Delta pr}{2\eta L}$$

Thus, the velocity gradient across the tube is negative and zero at the centre ($r = 0$). Assuming that the velocity u is zero at the wall where r is the capillary radius r_0, we can integrate the above equation and

$$u = \Delta p \frac{(r_0^2 - r^2)}{4\eta L} \qquad (5.1)$$

while at the centre, where u is a maximum and $r = 0$ we have

$$u_{\max} = \frac{\Delta pr_0^2}{4\eta L} \qquad (5.2)$$

whence

$$u = u_{\max}\left[1 - \frac{r^2}{r_0^2}\right]$$

58

Figure 1 shows the velocity distribution across the cylinder calculated from equation 5.1, and it requires little imagination to realise that the form of this distribution may be important in any form of chromatography, since while the low velocity near the capillary wall will help equilibration between phases it also means that molecules in the centre of the fluid stream will pass through a column much more rapidly than those at the wall unless there is a very rapid exchange of positions.

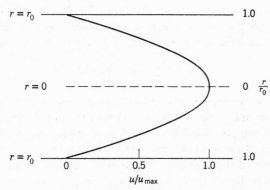

FIG. 1. The form of the velocity distribution across a cylinder of radius r_0. The flow is streamlined.

The conversion of equation 5.1 from fluid velocity to volume flow rate (F) is brought about simply, since

$$F = \int_0^{r_0} 2\pi r u \; dr$$

and

$$F = \frac{\pi \, \Delta p r_0^{4}}{8\eta L} \tag{5.3}$$

which is Poiseuille's equation. This equation holds over the wide range of conditions between the region of diffusional flow and the point when turbulence sets in. This point is, in fact, difficult to attain with gases and it is probable, as pointed out by Golay (1) that the velocities employed in gas chromatography are as much as two or more orders of magnitude below those at which turbulence would occur.

Flow Through Packed Columns. The fundamental law governing the flow of fluids through unconsolidated packed beds is known as Darcy's law and states that the velocity of flow is proportional to the pressure gradient (dp/dl) causing flow.

$$u_a = -B_1 \frac{dp}{dl} = B_1 \frac{\Delta p}{L} \tag{5.4}$$

B_1 is the *permeability coefficient* which can be replaced by the more satisfactory *specific permeability coefficient* B_0 if allowance is made for fluid
viscosity.

$$u_a = \left(\frac{-B_0}{\eta}\right)\left(\frac{dp}{dl}\right) = \left(\frac{B_0}{\eta}\right)\left(\frac{\Delta p}{L}\right) \tag{5.5}$$

The velocity u_a is calculated by dividing the volume flow rate by the cross-
sectional area of the bed or column and does not take into account the fact
that the free cross section which is available for flow is a fraction of this.
This fraction, the porosity ϵ, is defined as the total inter granular free space
per unit column volume and so the true fluid velocity $u = u_a/\epsilon$ whence

$$u = \left(\frac{-B_0}{\epsilon\eta}\right)\left(\frac{dp}{dl}\right) = \left(\frac{B_0}{\epsilon\eta}\right)\left(\frac{\Delta p}{L}\right) \tag{5.6}$$

It can readily be deduced that B_0 has the dimensions cm.^{2} and its value can
readily be determined experimentally. However, since in gas chromatography it is gas and not liquid flow which is of interest the problem of the
compressibility of the medium must be considered. For there to be flow at
all, a pressure gradient must exist and so there will be a continuous expansion of gas as it moves along the column. To take this into account we
start with Boyle's law,

$$pV = p_oV_o$$

or,

$$pOu = p_oOu_o$$

thus,

$$u = \frac{p_ou_o}{p}$$

In this instance the subscript o may be taken to represent conditions at the
outlet end of the column or bed, O being cross-sectional area. Substitution
in equation 5.6 gives

$$u_o = -\frac{B_0}{\epsilon\eta p_o} \cdot p\frac{dp}{dl} \tag{5.7}$$

Since $p = p_i$ when $l = 0$ and $p = p_o$ when $l = L$ we can write the integral

$$\int_0^L dl = -\frac{B_0}{u_o\epsilon\eta p_o}\int_{p_i}^{p_o} p\,dp \tag{5.8}$$

which gives

$$u_o = \frac{B_0}{\epsilon\eta L}\frac{(p_i^2 - p_o^2)}{2p_o}$$

or,

$$u_o = \left(\frac{B_0}{\epsilon\eta L}\right)\left[\frac{(p_i + p_o)}{2p_o}\right](p_i - p_o) \tag{5.9}$$

The bracketted term is the ratio of the arithmetic average pressure $\bar{p}_a$ to p_o while the last term is Δp. Hence, we can write

$$u_o = \frac{B_0 \, \bar{p}_a \Delta p}{\epsilon \eta L p_o} \tag{5.10}$$

The evaluation of B_0 from experimental data is thus carried out either by plotting $\dfrac{u_o p_o}{\bar{p}_a}$ against Δp or u_o against $\dfrac{\bar{p}_a \, \Delta p}{p_o}$, the slope of the graph in either case being $\dfrac{B_0}{\epsilon \eta L}$. If it is desired to correlate flow data for columns

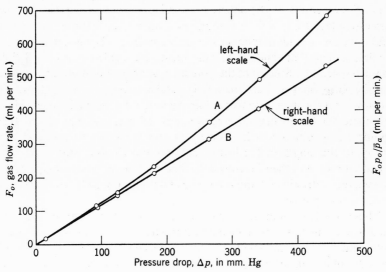

FIG. 2. Plot of A the volume flow rate, F_o, of nitrogen against Δp for a column of 150 cm. × 0.4 cm. packed with 30 to 40 B.S.S. mesh Sil-O-Cel and B of $F_o p_o / \bar{p}_a$ against Δp for the same column.

containing particles of the same size but of different lengths and used with different gases, $\dfrac{u_o \epsilon \eta p_o}{\bar{p}_a}$ can be plotted against $\dfrac{\Delta p}{L}$ when a line of slope B_0 should be obtained. It may be pointed out that $u_o \epsilon$ corresponds to the outlet velocity u_a calculated as though the column contained no packing, a fact which simplifies the calculations somewhat. If it is desired to deal with volume flow rate rather than velocity, this is quite simple, since $F_o = u_o \epsilon O$. Figure 2 shows plots of volume flow rate of nitrogen through a 4-ft. column of 30 to 40 mesh Sil-O-Cel firebrick, the containing tube being of stainless steel of internal diameter 5/32 in. One plot is a simple one of F_o against Δp while the other is a graph of $F_o p_o / \bar{p}_a$ against Δp. The former shows the expected curvature while the latter is straight.

The Structure of Packed Beds. The materials conventionally used to pack gas chromatographic columns are, with the exception of glass beads, irregular in shape. The actual structure of the intergranular space is, thus, likely to be extremely complex in nature. Even with uniform spherical particles the shape of the free space is difficult to define and depends very much on the way in which the spheres pack together. For example, spheres in the most dense possible arrangement have $\epsilon = 0.26$ while in cubic packing they have $\epsilon = 0.476$. However, in the latter array, the porosity is not uniform but varies continuously from plane to plane; in that of the centres of the spheres $\epsilon = 0.215$ while in the plane between successive layers $\epsilon = 1.0$. It is found experimentally that uniform spheres often pack in a random manner in which $\epsilon = 0.38$. The generality of this finding is such that random packing must be considered to be a definite mode of packing. Studies of the porosities of beds of non-uniform spheres and irregular shapes most frequently yield a value of $\epsilon = 0.38$ and this suggests that for such systems random packing is the normal mode. This is fortunate for the theory since randomness of packing implies that there should be no differences in porosity of successive planes taken at right angles to the length of the bed or column and the fractional free cross-sectional area will then be constant. The packing can in consequence be considered isotropic and any theory need not attempt to take into account variations in porosity.

There are few published data for porosities of gas chromatographic columns at this time. Bohemen and Purnell (2) have made measurements with columns containing Sil-O-Cel firebrick as the support material and observed a minimum porosity of 0.345. Over a fairly wide range of particle sizes packed in many columns with and without solvent they found that $\epsilon = 0.42 \pm 0.03$. This result is in excellent agreement with the concept of random packing and with data obtained for packed beds in general (see for example Carman, 3), and is also in accord with the theoretical prediction of Alder (4) who calculated the radial distribution function of spherical molecules in random close packing and found $\epsilon = 0.42$.

In order to attempt to elucidate the precise meaning of the specific permeability coefficient it is necessary to make some assumptions about the inter-relation of flow velocity, structure of the intergranular space and particle size. In order to simplify the mathematics of the problem it is usual to assume that a packed column can be taken as equivalent to a bundle of capillaries of uniform size. In this case, Poiseuille's law can be considered to apply and since random close packing is the rule it is reasonable to suppose that all beds of similarly shaped particles of the same porosity will be geometrically similar, and thus have the same proportionality constant between velocity of flow and particle diameter. Thus

$$u \propto d^2$$

The Hydraulic Radius. A concept which has proved to be of great help in the study of flow through packed beds is that of the hydraulic radius, r_h, which is defined by

$$r_h = \frac{\text{volume filled with gas}}{\text{surface area of particles in contact with gas}}$$

For a circular pipe, for example,

$$r_h = \frac{\pi r^2 L}{2 \pi r L} = \frac{r}{2} = \frac{d}{4}$$

Thus, $2r_h$ can be regarded as a mean pipe radius and if we define S as the total surface area of solid particles exposed to gas in 1 cc. of bed we can see that

$$r_h = \frac{\epsilon}{S}$$

or, if S_0, the *specific surface area*, represents the total surface area of 1 cc. of the particles exclusive of the intergranular free space, $S = S_0(1 - \epsilon)$, and

$$r_h = \frac{\epsilon}{S_0(1 - \epsilon)}$$

The Kozeny Equation. Kozeny (5) assumed that a randomly packed bed can be approximated by a collection of capillaries in which case Poiseuille's equation for a circular capillary of true length L_e can be written

$$\bar{u}_o = \frac{r^2 \Delta p}{8 \eta L} = \frac{r_h{}^2 \Delta p}{2 \eta L_e}$$

For gaseous flow, of course, the velocity should be corrected for compressibility as in equation 5.9, hence the use of $\bar{u}_o = u p_o / \bar{p}_a$. The true length L_e is distinguished from the apparent length L since the actual path through a column or bed is most unlikely to be a straight line. Since, also it is unlikely that the capillaries in a packed column can be considered circular, the equation must be slightly modified, the 2 in the denominator being replaced by a constant k_0. The value of k_0 varies from about 1.5 to 3 for the various capillary shapes that can be imagined, but it is most likely that, in the majority of packed beds, capillaries will be rectangular, elliptical or annular for which shapes k_0 lies between 2 and 2.5.

Substituting for r_h in terms of the porosity and specific surface area

$$\bar{u}_o = \frac{\epsilon^2 \Delta p}{k_0 \eta S_0{}^2 (1 - \epsilon)^2 L_e} \tag{5.11}$$

Carman (6) pointed out that a further correction to the velocity is needed since $\bar{u}_o$ is calculated by dividing the volume flow rate F by the free cross-sectional area O; thus it corresponds to the distance travelled in unit time along the axis of the column. Because of the undulating nature of the path travelled, the actual pore velocity $\bar{u}_t$ must be greater than $\bar{u}_o$ by a factor L_e/L and since it is $\bar{u}_t$ which should have appeared in equation 5.11 we have

$$\bar{u}_o = \left[\frac{L}{L_e}\right]\left[\frac{\epsilon^2 \Delta p}{k_0 \eta S_0{}^2 (1 - \epsilon)^2 L_e}\right]$$

whence, multiplying top and bottom by L, we get

$$\bar{u}_o = \left[\frac{L}{L_e}\right]^2\left[\frac{\epsilon^2 \Delta p}{k_0 \eta S_0{}^2 (1 - \epsilon)^2 L}\right] \tag{5.12}$$

The ratio (L_e/L) is called the tortuosity, and its value is somewhat difficult to estimate. The roughest approximation of the ratio is given by assuming that the gas travels a sinuous path, moving clockwise around half the circumference of one particle and then counter-clockwise around half that of the next particle. Thus, in travelling forward two particle diameters it travels the equivalent of one circumference. On this basis, the tortuosity would be $\pi/2$. The above model assumes a particular form of flow and that the particles are spherical, and so is unrealistic. Consideration of more refined models led Carman (6) to assume a tortuosity of $\sqrt{2}$. Accepting this value, which has some experimental support, and taking $k_0 = 2.5$, we can write equation 5.12 approximately as

$$\bar{u}_o = \frac{\epsilon^2 \Delta p}{5\eta S_0{}^2 (1 - \epsilon)^2 L} \tag{5.13}$$

This equation contains only measurable parameters, unmeasurable ones such as u_t and L_e having been eliminated. However, S_0 is something which may prove extremely difficult to determine, and so it is usual to replace it by an approximation in terms of particle radius or diameter in the following way.

$$S_0 = \frac{\text{surface area of particle}}{\text{volume of particle}}$$

and assuming that the particles are spherical, or almost so, and of diameter d_p,

$$S_0 = \frac{4\pi r^2}{1.33\pi r^3} = \frac{3}{r} = \frac{6}{d_p}$$

Substituting for S_0 in equation 5.13 then gives

$$\bar{u}_o = \frac{d_p{}^2 \epsilon^2 \Delta p}{180\eta L(1 - \epsilon)^2} \tag{5.14}$$

This equation, known as the Kozeny-Carman equation, is identical with the semi-empirical equation of Blake (7) and is a reasonably good approximation to the experimentally found relation of velocity with other parameters. Experiments with packings, ranging in shape and nature from glass spheres to steel wire crimps, yield values for the numerical term in equation 5.13 between 4.7 and 5.2. The adoption of the average value 5.0 is, therefore, reasonable, and should undoubtedly be acceptable for gas chromatographic columns. Confirmatory evidence for this view hardly

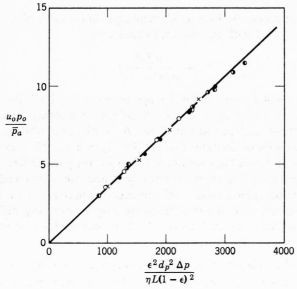

FIG. 3. Diagram illustrating the applicability of the Kozeny-Carman equation to flow of gas through chromatographic columns containing solvent/support in the range 1 to 10 per cent w/w on Sil-O-Cel.

exists, but Figure 3 illustrates data obtained by Bohemen and the author (8) which relate to columns containing various proportions of polyethylene glycol and 100 to 150 mesh Sil-O-Cel firebrick. In this diagram, $u_o p_o / \bar{p}_a$ is plotted against the group

$$\frac{d_p^{\,2} \epsilon^2 \, \Delta p}{\eta L (1 - \epsilon)^2}$$

for the flow of nitrogen at 50°C. According to equation 5.14 all the data should fall on a common line of slope 1/180. A common line is certainly obtained but the slope differs from the expected value by about 50 per cent. Nevertheless, the diagram shows how the flow characteristics of different columns can be correlated. The value of the slope may, of course, be in error, because the particle diameter assumed in the calculation was the average for the mesh range 100–150. If it were assumed that the fraction had been entirely 150 mesh the slope would have been in almost exact agreement with the theory, but this aspect of the problem will be discussed later.

If equation 5.14 is multiplied on both sides by ϵ, the velocity involved becomes $\bar{u}_a$ and we have

$$\bar{u}_a = \frac{d_p{}^2 \epsilon^3 \, \Delta p}{180 \eta L (1 - \epsilon)^2} \tag{5.15}$$

It is in this form that the Kozeny-Carman equation is most often quoted. Comparison of 5.15 with equation 5.5 shows that

$$B_0 = \frac{d_p{}^2 \epsilon^3}{180(1 - \epsilon)^2} \tag{5.16}$$

The dimensions of B_0 are thus cm.^{2} in agreement with 5.2 and its order of magnitude can readily be assessed. A column containing particles of diameter 0.01 cm. and porosity 0.38 has $B_0 \simeq 10^{-7}$ cm.^{2} while a similar column of particles of diameter 0.05 cm. has $B_0 \simeq 2.5 \times 10^{-6}$ cm.^{2}

The values of B_0 cited are minimum values for the particle sizes quoted since porosities lower than 0.38 are unlikely in unconsolidated media such as gas chromatographic columns. If, however, the porosity of a column is directly measured, and this is a relatively easy matter, any differences between calculated and experimental specific permeabilities must be due to one or both of the following:

a. The particle size calculated from sieve mesh sizes may be in error, or a wide range of particle sizes may be contained in a given sample of material.

b. The numerical factor, 180, in equation 5.15 is derived for spherical particles and so may be inappropriate.

c. If differences in B_0 for dry and wetted packings are observed it may be inferred as due to the presence of the liquid.

Studies of permeabilities can obviously provide information about the above possibilities and, in particular, through (*c*) about the location of solvent in packed columns.

THE AVERAGE VELOCITY

The retention volume of a solute in gas chromatography depends upon the nature and amount of the solvent or adsorbent, the temperature, the free gas volume of the column and the carrier gas flow rate. The compressibility of the carrier gas introduces another variable which may be of considerable magnitude. To illustrate this, consider the elution of some solute from two capillary columns of different diameter but containing the same weight of solvent, the same free gas volume and at the same temperature. The pressure drop across the wider tube must be smaller than that over the narrower one for any given flow rate. Thus, the average pressure is higher in the latter and the average velocity is lower. It is, in fact, the velocity which is important and not the volume flow, since the latter is simply the product of velocity and area. Clearly, the time of retention of a solute must be longer in the narrower capillary than in the wider one and so if retention time or volume (p. 205) is to mean anything in chromatography the effect of pressure gradient must be corrected for. This is a relatively simple matter, fortunately, the method having been deduced originally by James and Martin (9).

Again using Boyle's law, we have

$$puO = p_o u_o O$$

and

$$u = \frac{p_o u_o}{p}$$

We also know from Darcy's equation that

$$u = \frac{-B_0}{\epsilon \eta} \frac{dp}{dl}$$

and so

$$u_o = \frac{-B_0}{\epsilon p_o \eta} p \frac{dp}{dl} \tag{5.17}$$

Since flow rates are almost always measured at the outlet end of the column it is convenient to let u_o and p_o represent the velocity and pressure there. We can rewrite 5.17 in the form

$$dl = \frac{-B_0}{\epsilon p_o u_o \eta} \cdot p \, dp \tag{5.18}$$

and multiplying through by p

$$p \, dl = \frac{-B_0}{\epsilon p_o u_o \eta} p^2 \, dp \tag{5.19}$$

The average pressure $\bar{p}$ is given by

$$\bar{p} = \frac{\int p \, dl}{\int dl}$$

which from 5.18 and 5.19 becomes

$$\bar{p} = \frac{\int_{p_o}^{p_i} p^2 \, dp}{\int_{p_o}^{p_i} p \, dp}$$

which gives

$$\bar{p} = \frac{2}{3}\left[\frac{(p_i^3 - p_o^3)}{(p_i^2 - p_o^2)}\right]$$

and, after rearrangement,

$$\frac{\bar{p}}{p_0} = \frac{2[(p_i/p_o)^3 - 1]}{3[(p_i/p_o)^2 - 1]} \tag{5.20}$$

Since $\bar{p}/p_0 = V_0/\bar{V}$ we have

$$\bar{V} = \frac{3V_0[(p_i/p_o)^2 - 1]}{2[(p_i/p_o)^3 - 1]} = fV_0 \tag{5.21}$$

Thus, the true average retention volume can be calculated from that measured at the outlet pressure by use of equation 5.21. The correction involved corresponds to reducing the retention volume to the hypothetical value it would have at zero pressure drop. Table 1 illustrates the difference in the average pressure obtained from equation 5.20 and by simple arithmetic averaging, that is $\bar{p}_a = (p_i + p_o)/2$.

TABLE 1

p_o atm.	p_i atm.	$\bar{p}$ from (5.20)	$\bar{p}_a$ Arithmetic	Approximate Difference in Per Cent
1	1.5	1.264	1.25	1
	2.0	1.556	1.50	4
	4.0	2.80	2.50	12
	10.0	6.67	5.50	20
	100.0	66.70	50.50	33

This table brings out several important points. First, the use of arithmetic mean pressures will lead to errors greater than 1 per cent even when p_i/p_o is as small as 1.5, and in accurate gas chromatographic measurements of retention times it is, therefore, probably only justifiable to use the arithmetic mean when the pressure ratio is 1.1 or less. Secondly, as the pressure ratio increases, the correction factor $\bar{p}/p_o$ tends towards $2p_i/3p_o$. This can be seen from the table by comparison of $\bar{p}$ when p_i is 10 or 100 atmospheres. Summarising these results,

$$\frac{p_i}{p_o} < 1.1 \qquad \bar{p} = \frac{p_i + p_o}{2}$$

$$10 > \frac{p_i}{p_o} > 1.1 \qquad \text{Equation 5.20}$$

$$\frac{p_i}{p_o} > 10 \qquad \bar{p} = \frac{2p_i}{3}$$

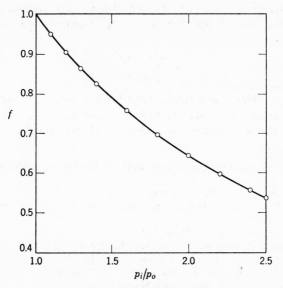

FIG. 4. Gas compressibility correction curve; f is plotted against p_i/p_o.

TABLE 2

TABULATED VALUES OF $f = \dfrac{3}{2}\left[\dfrac{(p_i/p_o)^2 - 1}{(p_i/p_o)^3 - 1}\right]$ FOR VALUES OF

(p_i/p_o) BETWEEN 1 AND 2.6

p_i/p_o	0.0000	0.0100	0.0200	0.0300	0.0400	0.0500	0.0600	0.0700	0.0800	0.0900
1.00	1.0000	0.9950	0.9900	0.9851	0.9803	0.9754	0.9706	0.9658	0.9611	0.9563
1.10	0.9517	0.9470	0.9424	0.9378	0.9333	0.9287	0.9242	0.9198	0.9154	0.9110
1.20	0.9066	0.9023	0.8980	0.8937	0.8895	0.8853	0.8811	0.8769	0.8728	0.8687
1.30	0.8646	0.8606	0.8566	0.8527	0.8487	0.8447	0.8408	0.8371	0.8333	0.8295
1.40	0.8257	0.8219	0.8182	0.8145	0.8109	0.8073	0.8037	0.8001	0.7965	0.7930
1.50	0.7895	0.7860	0.7825	0.7791	0.7757	0.7723	0.7690	0.7657	0.7624	0.7591
1.60	0.7558	0.7526	0.7494	0.7462	0.7430	0.7399	0.7368	0.7337	0.7306	0.7275
1.70	0.7245	0.7215	0.7185	0.7155	0.7126	0.7097	0.7068	0.7039	0.7010	0.6982
1.80	0.6954	0.6926	0.6898	0.6870	0.6843	0.6815	0.6788	0.6762	0.6735	0.6708
1.90	0.6682	0.6656	0.6630	0.6604	0.6579	0.6553	0.6528	0.6503	0.6478	0.6453
2.00	0.6429	0.6404	0.6380	0.6356	0.6332	0.6308	0.6285	0.6261	0.6238	0.6215
2.10	0.6192	0.6169	0.6146	0.6124	0.6101	0.6079	0.6057	0.6035	0.6013	0.5992
2.20	0.5970	0.5949	0.5928	0.5906	0.5885	0.5865	0.5844	0.5823	0.5803	0.5783
2.30	0.5763	0.5742	0.5723	0.5703	0.5683	0.5664	0.5644	0.5625	0.5606	0.5587
2.40	0.5568	0.5549	0.5530	0.5512	0.5493	0.5475	0.5456	0.5438	0.5420	0.5402
2.50	0.5385	0.5367	0.5349	0.5332	0.5314	0.5297	0.5280	0.5263	0.5246	0.5229

The correction equations 5.20 and 5.21 have been verified many times over and there is no doubt of their validity. Figure 4 shows a plot of the function

$$f = \frac{3}{2}\left[\frac{(p_i/p_o)^2 - 1}{(p_i/p_o)^3 - 1}\right]$$

against p_i/p_o. This is accurate enough for many purposes but when the highest accuracy is desired it is best to use tabulated values. A sufficiently comprehensive collection of this nature is included in Table 2.

REFERENCES

1. Golay, M., *Gas Chromatography*, 1958, Butterworths, London (editor, D. H. Desty), p. 67.
2. Bohemen, J. and J. H. Purnell, (see ref. 1), p. 6.
3. Carman, P. C., *Flow of Gases through Porous Media*, 1956, Butterworths, London, p. 8.
4. Alder, B., *J. Chem. Phys.*, 1955, **23**, 263.
5. Kozeny, J., *S. B. Akad. Wiss. Wien.* 1927, **Abt. IIa. 136**, 271.
6. Carman, P. C., *Trans. Inst. Chem. Engnrs.*, 1937, **15**, 150.
7. Blake, F. C., *Trans. Amer. Inst. chem. Engrs.*, 1922, **14**, 415.
8. Bohemen, J., and J. H. Purnell (unpublished work).
9. James, A. T., and A. J. P. Martin, *Biochem. J.*, 1952, **50**, 679.

CHROMATOGRAPHIC
THEORY

Differences in the partition coefficients of mixed substances can be utilised for their separation in any one of three ways. First, in the *elution technique*, a discrete sample of a mixture is introduced into a column, after which it is swept through by an inert, flowing phase. Partition of the mixed substances between the flowing and a fixed phase occurs many times during the period of residence in the column and, in consequence, some separation of components occurs.

In the second possible approach, known as *displacement development*, again a discrete sample of a mixture is introduced into a column, but the flowing phase in this instance contains, or may completely consist of, some gas, vapour or liquid which is very much more strongly sorbed by the fixed phase than any component of the mixture. As a result, there is competition for the fixed phase between the flowing phase and the components of the mixture, which, as a result, are progressively displaced along the column at different rates.

The third method, *frontal development*, employs a continuous stream of the mixture being analysed which may or may not be diluted, at constant initial concentration, in an inert carrier fluid. The components of the mixture are sorbed by the fixed phase until the equilibrium condition for each component is established and so the moving front of mobile phase is depleted of the mixture components in direct proportion to their partition coefficients. The net result is a separation in the moving front and appearance of the components at the column outlet at different times.

6
TECHNIQUES
OF
CHROMATOGRAPHY

73

Both the displacement and frontal techniques either depend upon or may involve sorptive competition, a process which introduces much uncertainty into the theory of the methods and which, in practice, may be expected to act adversely as regards the effectiveness of separations. In principle, the elution method does not suffer this drawback, and so it may be expected to be the most useful and trouble free technique. This view receives so much support in practice that relatively little effort has gone into the study of the other two methods. It is certainly true to say that, at this time, only the elution method is of any practical importance and, in consequence, it will be described first and in greatest detail.

ELUTION CHROMATOGRAPHY

The ultimate unit of an elution system is comparable with the simple extraction system so commonly used in preparative chemistry to transfer materials from one liquid to another, from which they can be recovered with greater ease and a higher degree of purity. In consequence, it is profitable to consider the basis of the partitional extraction method as an introduction to a detailed study of elution chromatography.

Consider the extraction of w gm. of some solute, originally dissolved in Δv_1 ml. of liquid 1, by Δv_2 ml. of solvent 2. The partition coefficient K can be taken, in this instance, to be defined in terms of concentrations such that

$$K = \frac{c_1}{c_2}$$

Hence, if after equilibration of the two phases, w_1 gm. remain in liquid 1 we have,

$$K = \frac{w_1 \, \Delta v_2}{\Delta v_1 (w - w_1)} \tag{6.1}$$

or, on rearrangement,

$$w_1 = w \frac{K \, \Delta v_1}{\Delta v_2 + K \, \Delta v_1} \tag{6.2}$$

Suppose now that the layer of liquid 2 is removed and replaced by a fresh volume of pure liquid 2, and further, that K is independent of concentration, then, on re-equilibrating liquid 1 we have

$$w_2 = \frac{w_1 K \, \Delta v_1}{\Delta v_2 + K \, \Delta v_1} \tag{6.3}$$

or, if we substitute for w_1 from equation 6.2,

$$w_2 = w \left(\frac{K \, \Delta v_1}{\Delta v_2 + K \, \Delta v_1} \right)^2 \tag{6.4}$$

After r identical operations of this sort, we have

$$w_r = w\left(\frac{K\,\Delta v_1}{\Delta v_2 + K\,\Delta v_1}\right)^r \tag{6.5}$$

As is seen later, the bracketed function bears a striking resemblance to quantities of the greatest chromatographic importance.

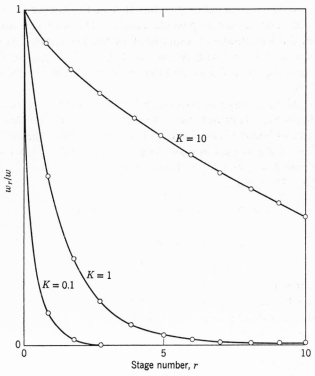

FIG. 1. The variation of concentration in liquid 1 with the number of extractions by liquid 2 for three solutes of $K = 10$, 1 and 0.1, respectively.

Figure 1 illustrates the variation of w_r/w with r in the extraction from liquid 1 of three solutes of $K = c_1/c_2 = 10$, 1 and 0.1, respectively, by liquid 2, the volumes of the two liquids being assumed equal. After only three operations, less than 1 per cent of the solute of $K = 0.1$ remains in the layer 1 while seven operations would be needed to achieve this for the solute of $K = 1$. A very large number of operations would be required to extract any reasonable quantity of the third solute. Evidently, therefore, a few operations would provide a means of separating the solutes of $K = 10$

and $K = 0.1$ although the practical application of the method would undoubtedly be somewhat laborious and more so if the partition coefficients were more nearly comparable.

Ways and means of making the extraction procedure more effective can readily be deduced from equation 6.5. Thus,

a. The most important factor is undoubtedly the magnitude of K, or for separation, the difference in the values of the relevant K's.

b. Δv_1 should be as small as possible, that is, the sample for analysis should be as concentrated as possible initially. This view can readily be substantiated if we consider the example of a single extraction stage ($r = 1$) of a substance of $K = 1$ with $\Delta v_2 = 1$ and $\Delta v_1 = 1$ or 0.1. In the first instance, from equation 6.5 we find that $w_r/w = 0.5$ while in the second, $w_r/w = 0.09$.

c. r should be as large as possible, a fact so evident as to require no further discussion. However, we can consider the situation that only a fixed volume of liquid 2 is available. It is readily seen that the best results are obtained if this is used in many small amounts rather than one large one. Suppose $K = 1$ and $\Delta v_1 = 1$ and a total volume of 10 ml. of liquid 2 is available. Then, when

$$r = 10, \qquad \Delta v_2 = 1, \qquad w_r/w = 0.001$$

while, if

$$r = 1, \qquad \Delta v_2 = 10, \qquad w_r/w = 0.9$$

Obviously, what we may call manual extractive partitional separation could be carried out but consideration shows that the number of operations needed even for simple separations would be enormous. The separation of two substances differing in partition coefficient by a factor as great as a hundred would involve over forty extractions for a recovery of 96 per cent of each component at 99 per cent purity. The process, however, can equally obviously be made automatic if many extraction vessels were linked in series with equilibrated phases moving on at intervals. This approach forms the basis of the elegant work of Craig and his collaborators (1, 2) and such machines are commonly called Craig machines. Basically, such a machine consists of very many separating vessels in series, each roughly half filled at the start of an experiment with one of the chosen immiscible liquids. The first vessel contains a solution of the mixture to be analysed and to this is added a volume of the second liquid phase. The apparatus is rocked until equilibration is achieved and then tilted such that the liquid 2 is transferred from vessel 1 to vessel 2. At the same time, a fresh volume of liquid 2 enters vessel 1. This process is repeated many times and, eventually, liquid 2 flows out of the apparatus. The components of the original mixture move through the apparatus at different rates and so emerge separately.

If we apply the principles of effective operation listed earlier, it is seen that the best results would require extremely small extraction vessels and the more the better. Obviously, there are mechanical limitations to this approach and the Craig machine must be of limited utility. Carrying the argument to its logical conclusion, however, we see that the separating vessels could be replaced by a packed column with continuous flow of phase 2 if the operation could be conducted so slowly that equilibration between phases occurred at all times, and if the phase 1 were unable to leave the column. Evidently, the packed column arrangement bears the same relation to a Craig machine that a packed distillation column does to a bubble-cap plate distillation unit. Presuming that a packed column could be operated, we have a chromatographic system and we see that the analogy with partitional extraction immediately suggests the concept that a column can be regarded as a series of finite and equal volumes, in each of which one equilibration occurs. This is the basis of the application of the theoretical plate concept in chromatography and it is further seen that we can say that the most effective use of a column will be made if the fundamental volume is as small as possible, or, alternatively, if a column contains the maximum number of fundamental volumes. In addition, the effectiveness of the column may be expressed as the number of separating vessels a Craig machine capable of the same separation would contain. Finally, since equilibration between phases is known to be a relatively slow process, we can assume that, in so far as the partitional mechanism is concerned, the column will function best when operated slowly. There is little doubt in view of the foregoing that in principle, if not in time, the Craig machine was the forerunner of chromatography.

As is seen in the succeeding chapter, the sequence of equilibrations leads to binomial, Poisson or Gaussian distributions of the solutes passing through an elution column. The exact form of distribution depends upon the experimental arrangements and procedure and it is normally the case that there is no great error involved if Gaussian distributions are assumed. In consequence of this, the characteristic chromatogram obtained from an elution has the form shown in Figure 2 which illustrates the gas-liquid separation of some *n*-paraffins. This result is, of course, obtained if some system which records instantaneous concentration in the column effluent is employed. Occasionally an integrating system is used when the chromatogram has the appearance of a number of S-shaped steps as shown in Figure 3, which is taken from the work of James (3).

The elution technique, like any other, is equally applicable to gas-liquid as to gas-solid chromatography and both approaches have yielded excellent

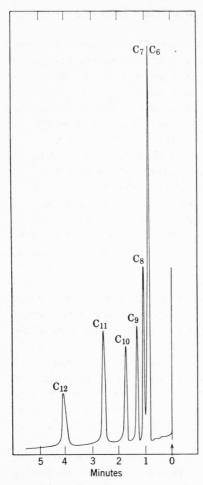

FIG. 2. A typical elution chromatogram: n-paraffins (C_6 to C_{12}) are eluted by H_2 ($p_o = 1$ atm.) at 102°C. from a 7-ft. column containing 2 per cent w/w polyethylene glycol (400) supported on 100 to 120 B.S.S. mesh Sil-O-Cel. Detection by direct flow hot wire katharometer. Sample size ~10 μg.

results. It will be recalled that in the discussion of partitional extraction a partition coefficient independent of concentration was assumed. This type of coefficient is very frequently met with in gas-liquid chromatography, as was pointed out in Chapter 2, whereas, in gas-solid systems, partition coefficients which vary widely with concentration are common. On these grounds it is to be expected that gas-liquid chromatography will be the more useful of the two methods and, hence, that gas-liquid elution chromatography will be the best and most widely applicable of all the possible techniques. It is only in the realm of permanent gas, or low molecular weight material, analysis that gas-solid techniques are likely to compete successfully with gas-liquid methods, although it may be that if eventually adsorbent solids of desirable characteristics can be developed, the former may become more attractive and find wider application.

DISPLACEMENT DEVELOPMENT

This form of chromatography was pioneered by Tiselius (4) and Claesson (5) and although there appears to be no record of its being attempted in gas-liquid systems, it has several times been used with success in gas-solid systems (6, 7, 8, 9, 11).

The competition of solutes or adsorbates with the displacer vapour results in each being pushed along as a plug ahead of the displacer, the width of the plug being determined by the concentration. The rate of forward movement of the plug clearly depends upon the relative partition coefficients of the adsorbate and the displacer. Substances of low partition coefficient move through a column very rapidly while those of higher K move more slowly. Finally, when the column is saturated with displacer, this breaks through. As a result, a concentration sensitive detector would yield a chromatogram showing a series of steps in which, unless a large excess of diluent gas were present, the height of each step would identify the emerging component. This characteristic introduces some difficulties such as that a thermal conductivity cell, for example, might not be able to distinguish between compounds which were displaced one after the other if their conductivities were similar. The chromatogram would then show no

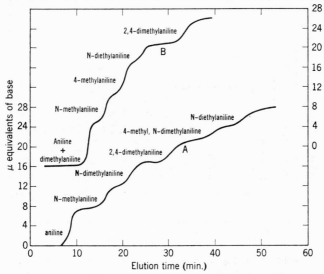

FIG. 3. Illustration of recording of elution chromatograms by automatic titration integral detector. Line A pertains to the left-hand scale, line B to the right-hand scale. *By courtesy of the Society for Analytical Chemistry.*

characteristic breaks to indicate different components although these might have been separated in the column. Phillips and his co-workers (6, 7) have attempted to overcome such difficulties by introducing a "marker substance" which is displaced between two substances which cannot be identified when mixed. Thus a step is artificially introduced and a return to the original value of the step height is clear evidence of the presence of both possible components. Another method which may be used is to remove chemically some of the components of a mixture, for example, olefins in hydrocarbon mixtures may be removed with sulphuric acid or bromine. A comparison of chromatograms of treated and untreated mixture would then help considerably in identification.

Despite these expedients, there is little doubt that displacement techniques are of little value except, perhaps, for the concentration of small component fractions, since there are several other drawbacks. For example, any column can only reasonably be used once since even a back-flushing technique can be of little use since, by definition, the displacer must be very strongly adsorbed. Further, the plugs of adsorbate are never cleanly separated and between each plug there exists a region of "indistinctness" which must lead both to an equivalent indistinctness in the chromatogram and difficulty in any theoretical treatment. In the author's opinion, it is

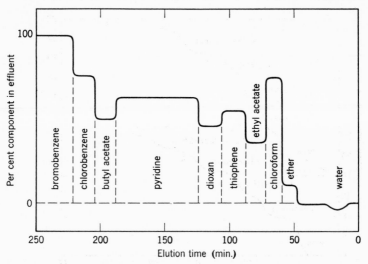

FIG. 4. An example of a displacement development chromatogram. The column contained active charcoal at 100°C., and the displacer vapour was bromobenzene. *By courtesy of the Society for Analytical Chemistry.*

unlikely that the displacement method can be improved beyond the level already achieved by Phillips and his collaborators. Figure 4 shows a typical displacement chromatogram obtained by them (16).

FRONTAL DEVELOPMENT

This technique was first applied in gas-solid systems by Roth, Ohme and Nikish (10) and later by Claesson (8). The only example of its application to gas-liquid systems, until very recently, was in the work of Phillips (6, 7).

The moving phase initially consists of the material under analysis either pure or diluted, and as it moves down the column the components of the mixture are stripped out in order to saturate the packing. In fact, some of all the components appears at the column exit simultaneously with the carrier gas but at such low concentration that their presence cannot be detected. Ultimately, the least strongly retained component saturates the whole column packing and then passes out of the column at the same concentration as it entered. The chromatogram obtained with a concentration sensitive detector then shows a step which is S-shaped. Subsequent components appear in turn, each appearing as a step and each, of course, contaminated by the preceding substances. The last component finally breaks through when the chromatogram is complete, the emerging gas then being identical with the ingoing sample. The time of individual breakthrough characterises the various substances and the heights of the steps

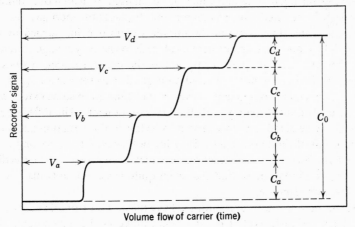

FIG. 5. Idealised frontal analysis chromatogram.

are a measure of their concentration, provided there has been no competition between sorbates.

If a volume V_a of carrier flows between the start of the analysis and the time when a component breaks through then the weight w_a of adsorbed or dissolved material is V_a times the initial concentration c_a, that is,

$$w_a = V_a c_a$$

w_a is, thus, the weight of substance sorbed by the column weight of sorbent and hence, w_a/c_a represents a partition coefficient which is measurable from V_a. Provided the components of a mixture do not compete with each other there should be no complications and an ideal chromatogram should look like that illustrated in Figure 5. If there is competition there is little point in attempting to use the system although Claesson (5) has attempted to develop the theory for such a situation. In the early work, the carrier stream was almost always so rich in the mixture that there was very considerable competition between components. This led to variation in apparent partition coefficients with concentration and as a result, the times of breakthrough and the proportionate step heights were concentration dependent.

Further difficulties which may be encountered are, first, that differential detectors may show marked reduction of sensitivity towards all but the first component to appear from the column, and, secondly, that viscosity changes occur during analysis and cause flow changes. To understand these points let us reconsider events in a frontal analysis in which the sample is undiluted with carrier gas. Initially, the column must contain some gas, presumably nitrogen or helium which has been used to clean it out. Sample stream is then directed into the column and displaces the inert gas, but not at constant rate, since some of the sample stream is being sorbed by the column filling, and the displacement itself leads to viscosity change. Eventually, when the first component appears at the column outlet, it does so mixed with helium or nitrogen, and so a good detector sensitivity is obtained. The second component, however, while mixed to some extent with the carrier, is diluted mainly with the first component. The difference in the property detected is almost certain to be less in this situation and so an apparent fall off in detector sensitivity for both the first and second components is observed. The situation becomes even worse for succeeding substances and may be so bad that even quite large amounts may evoke little detector response.

The formidable drawbacks outlined have meant that frontal analysis has never been seriously exploited. It should, however, be remembered that the method has inherently some attractive features, such as the fact that even if the sample stream were highly diluted, say 100 or 1000 times, the amount of sample present would still be so high that there would be no problem in sensitivity of detection. In addition—and this presupposes that we have some knowledge of the experimental results discussed in later chapters—frontal development involves only what corresponds to the leading edge of an elution peak which we know (p. 104) to be almost always very much sharper than the trailing edge. This is illustrated in Figure 6 which is taken from the work of Glueckauf (15). The diagram shows theoretically calculated frontal and elution chromatograms for an ideal column and a solute having (a) a linear partition isotherm and (b) a non-linear, Langmuir type partition isotherm. The figure shows clearly the adverse result of the non-linear isotherm, while, in addition, it is evident that in either case, but for (b) in particular, the frontal breakthrough curve is very much sharper than is the elution band. The front of the latter is, however, itself very sharp. In elution chromatography bands are never truly symmetrical although, admittedly, rarely as bad as that shown in Figure 6b. Hence, the frontal method is, generally, more effective than the elution technique in terms of band width.

A very considerable advance has recently been made by Boeke (12) who, seeking to exploit the above described situation, has re-explored the possibilities of gas-liquid and to some extent gas-solid frontal analysis. Most of the problems associated with the technique can be overcome by working at high dilution, say 100 or 1000 times. If dilution is made after the column but before the detector, the sensitivity problem no longer enters into the

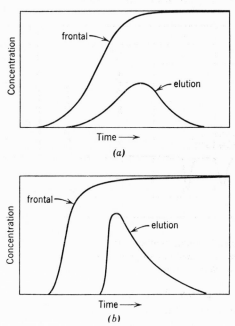

FIG. 6. Illustration of comparable frontal and elution chromatograms for (*a*) a linear partition isotherm and (*b*) a Langmuir type non-linear isotherm. *By courtesy of the Faraday Society.*

reckoning and conventional thermal conductivity cells have more than sufficient sensitivity for the job. However, if there is serious deviation from ideal behaviour in the column it is necessary to dilute the sample stream before the column. Dilution to one-hundredth or one-thousandth the original concentration can be readily brought about for gas or vapour streams and in these conditions the concentrations are comparable to those pertaining in elution columns, and so the method should be as reliable.

Boeke chooses not to work with the integral type curves one would normally obtain, and converts these very simply to differentials. This is done by running the column effluent through two detectors in series, the two being separated by a delay volume of chosen size. If the two detectors form one half of a bridge, the difference signal is a measure of the slope of the integral curve, and the resultant curve recorded is bell shaped, as in elution chromatography. The greatest sensitivity is obtained if the delay line is big, but, in practice, Boeke has found that sensitivity of detection is so far from being a limiting factor that any reasonable delays can be tolerated. Figure 7 illustrates a differential frontal chromatogram of a lower hydrocarbon mixture which shows something of the promise of the

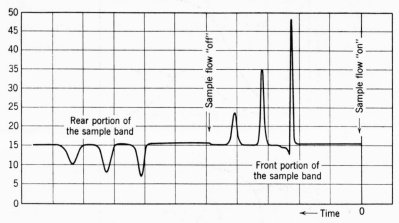

FIG. 7. "Differentiated" frontal analysis chromatogram of isomeric hexanes. Note high efficiency (N per ft. > 2000) of sorption peaks and the much broader desorption peaks. *By courtesy of Butterworths.*

technique. It seems highly likely that, as a result of this recent work and certainly in so far as substances of low to medium boiling point are concerned, there may be some swing back to frontal analysis, particularly in the field of process analysis and control where the large sample size required presents no problem.

One further aspect of frontal development which should be mentioned is the fact that adsorption isotherms can very readily be measured in this way. The method, pioneered by Phillips (13), has recently been used by Bohemen, Langer, Perrett and Purnell (14) with good effect. This aspect of the technique is discussed in greater detail in a later chapter.

EXPERIMENTAL REQUIREMENTS FOR GAS CHROMATOGRAPHY

Irrespective of the particular technique employed, the general structure of gas chromatographic apparatus is the same. The column may be a capillary or may consist of a glass or metal tube packed with granulated adsorbent or, in gas-liquid chromatography, a non-adsorbent granulated solid coated with involatile solvent. The carrier gas supply is almost always taken from a cylinder and metered into the column through a simple valve system. In the elution and displacement techniques, a sample injection system must be incorporated between cylinder and column while, in both the displacement and frontal analysis methods, some form of saturator system is needed. At the outlet end of the column there must be an instrument for detecting and measuring the materials in the column effluent and, for convenience, although not essential, a gas flow measuring device. From what was said in the earlier chapters it is evident that partition coefficients are highly temperature sensitive, and so a good thermostat is essential. This may be of any type, provided it maintains adequate temperature control.

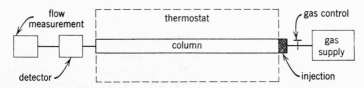

FIG. 8. Block diagram illustrating the apparatus requirements for all forms of gas chromatography.

It is evident that the essential apparatus for gas chromatography, illustrated in block form in Figure 8, is extraordinarily simple and much the same whatever technique is employed, and this, combined with its remarkable power, combines to make it such an effective tool.

REFERENCES

1. Craig, L. C., and O. Post, *Anal. Chem.*, 1949, **21**, 500.
2. Craig, L. C., W. Hausmann, E. H. Ahrens and E. J. Harfenist, *Anal. Chem.*, 1951, **23**, 1236.
3. James, A. T., *Anal. Chem.*, 1956, **28**, 1564.
4. Tiselius, A., *Arkiv. Kemi Mineral. Geol.*, 1943, **16A**, 11.
5. Claesson, S., *Disc. Faraday Soc.*, 1949, **7**, 34.
6. James, D. H., and C. S. G. Phillips, *J. Chem. Soc.*, **1953**, 1600.
7. Griffiths, J. H., and C. S. G. Phillips, *J. Chem. Soc.*, **1954**, 3446.
8. Claesson, S., *Arkiv. Kemi Mineral. Geol.*, 1946, **23A**, 133.
9. Turner, N. C., *Natl. Petrol. News*, 1943, **35**, 234.
10. Roth, F., W. Ohme and A. Nikish, *Oel u. Kohle*, 1942, **37**, 1133.
11. Turkel'taub, N. M., *Zhur. Anal. Khim.*, 1950, **5**, 200.
12. Boeke, J., *Gas Chromatography*, 1960, Butterworths, London (editor, R. P. W. Scott), p. 88.
13. James, D. H., and C. S. G. Phillips, *J. Chem. Soc.*, **1954**, 1066.
14. Bohemen, J., S. H. Langer, R. H. Perrett and J. H. Purnell, *J. Chem. Soc.*, **1960**, 2444.
15. Glueckauf, E., *Trans. Faraday Soc.*, 1955, **51**, 1540.
16. Griffiths, J., D. James and C. S. G. Phillips, *Analyst*, 1952, **77**, 897.

7

THE THEORETICAL PLATE CONCEPT

The concept of the theoretical plate was originally introduced into distillation theory in an attempt to find a quantitative method of expressing the efficiency of a distillation column. It derives from the so-called Konowalew's rule, which connects the relative volatility α with the saturation vapour pressures and concentrations of pairs of components of a mixture. For a two-component mixture we can write,

$$\alpha = \frac{p_1}{p_2} = \frac{f_1 x_1 p_1^{0}}{f_2 x_2 p_2^{0}}$$

p and p^0 representing the partial and saturation vapour pressures, respectively, x the mole fraction and f the activity coefficient. In accord with this equation, a plot of the boiling point of the mixture against composition is as shown in Figure 1, and it is seen that a mixture of composition X_1 when heated is in equilibrium with vapour of composition X_2. If this vapour were removed from the system, cooled down and re-equilibrated, the liquid of composition X_3 would be in equilibrium with vapour of composition X_4. At each step, therefore, the vapour becomes richer in the lower boiling component and after a sufficient number of operations a more or less pure sample of this material would be obtained.

The process described is one of diminishing returns and is much better carried out in a column when it becomes continuous. The efficiency of the column can then be expressed in terms of the number of theoretical equilibrations it achieves. Thus, a column starting with a mixture X_1 and yielding distillate of composition X_2 has achieved a separation equivalent to one theoretical

86

plate, while if the distillate obtained were X_4, the separation would correspond to that over two theoretical plates. To describe a column solely by the number of theoretical plates, N, which it appears to contain, may be very misleading since, for example, a single plate column may be 1 cm. or 1 m. long. A better measure of column efficiency is thus, the height (length) equivalent to a theoretical plate, H, which is the length of the column divided by the number of plates (L/N).

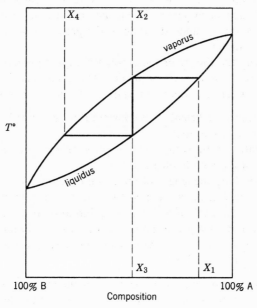

FIG. 1. Vapour-liquid equilibrium diagram for a binary liquid mixture without azeotrope formation.

The similarity between the processes occurring in distillation and chromatography was first realised by Martin and Synge (1) and this paved the way for the introduction of the theoretical plate concept into chromatography. In this approach, a chromatographic column is envisaged as consisting of many identical volume elements in each of which the concentration of solute in the various phases which may be present is both uniform within the phase and corresponds in amount to a fixed equilibrium value.

Before proceeding farther, we would do well to consider the possible shortcomings of the plate concept. From Figure 1 we see that, had the equilibrium loop been narrower, the extent of separation corresponding to one theoretical plate would have been less, and further, the same would be true if the initial composition of the mixture had been X_2 instead of X_1.

Thus, the height equivalent to a theoretical plate depends both upon the nature of the mixture to be separated and its composition. In addition, we know that finite times are required for equilibration between phases and so it must be anticipated that too rapid operation of a distillation column would reduce its efficiency. It is to be expected, therefore, that the theoretical plate concept will no more provide the perfect answer to the problem of describing the efficiency of a chromatographic column than it does for a distillation column. Nevertheless, it is true to say that it represents the most valuable approach yet made and has proved to be of inestimable value in advancing our understanding of the processes occurring in chromatographic columns.

In developing the theory of the chromatographic process a number of simplifying assumptions must be made. Those adopted by Martin and Synge (1) and, later, by James and Martin (2) were as follows:

a. The partition coefficient, K, is constant throughout the column and is independent of concentration.

b. Equilibration of the solute between phases is rapid compared with the rate of travel of the mobile phase.

c. Diffusion along the length of the column in any phase is negligible.

d. The column can be considered to consist of a number of identical volume elements, in each of which one equilibration occurs.

e. The flow of mobile phase can be regarded as discontinuous, that is, it consists of a stepwise addition of volumes of mobile phase, each equal to the free volume per plate.

The first assumption appears to be valid for the majority of systems and is, at worst, a very good approximation. In addition, the relevant partition coefficient appears to be the same as is found in static experiments and is not some "dynamic" one particular to the chromatographic process (p. 419). The second and third assumptions are clearly contradictory since the rapid attainment of equilibrium necessitates rapid diffusion in all phases, no other mechanism for mass transfer being obvious at first sight. The last assumption is now known from the work of Glueckauf (3) to be unsatisfactory in some respects, and a more satisfying approach is to assume continuous addition of mobile phase to the column as, of course, occurs in practice. Although the continuous flow model has superceded the discontinuous one, the latter is mathematically much simpler and, in any case, leads to the same result, and for this reason as well as the historical importance of the work of Martin and Synge, both theories will be outlined here. Since equilibrium at all times, a linear partition isotherm and the absence of diffusional disturbances are assumed, this view of the chromatographic process is known as *linear ideal* chromatography.

THE DISCONTINUOUS MODEL

Figure 2 illustrates our view of the column, each plate consisting of two "volumes." In a gas-liquid column there are the volumes of free gas space ΔV_g and of liquid ΔV_l while in a gas-solid column there would be ΔV_g and ΔV_a. The sum of the volumes in either case is the total plate volume Δx, thus,

$$\Delta V_g + \Delta V_l = \Delta x \qquad (7.1)$$

The volume occupied by the inert solid support in a gas-liquid column need never come into the reckoning, and for theoretical purposes the total

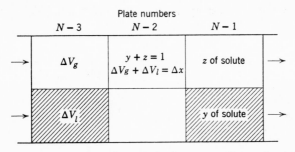

FIG. 2. Diagrammatic view of a packed column according to the plate theory.

column volume is to be regarded as the sum of the volumes of free gas space and involatile solvent and not as the volume of the containing tube.

Consider now the elution of 1 ml. of gaseous solute initially placed in the first plate of a column filled with pure carrier gas. Let the partition co-efficient and the respective volumes of free space and solvent (or adsorbent) be such that, at equilibrium, a fraction z of the solute in the plate exists in the gas phase and a fraction y in solution. The addition now of ΔV_g of carrier gas to the first plate causes an equal movement of carrier through every plate in the column, the z ml. of solute in the gas phase in plate 1 being swept into plate 2 in the process. When the movement of carrier gas ceases, re-equilibration occurs in plates 1 and 2. In plate 1 a volume yz ml. of solute enters the gas phase while y^2 ml. remain in solution. In plate 2, yz ml. goes into solution while z^2 ml. remains in the gas phase. At this point a further volume of carrier gas ΔV_g is added to the column and the whole process repeated, this time with transport of solute into plate 3. The situation after $4.\Delta V_g$ have passed through the column is shown in Figure 3 in which the total volume of solute in each plate is tabulated. The arrows indicate the volume passed on from plate to plate with each addition of carrier gas while the extreme right hand column lists a mathematical description of the distribution of solute throughout the column. Clearly, in each plate, the quantity of solute corresponds to a term in a binomial expansion and so, if r volumes of carrier gas have been added to the column the distribution can be represented by the expansion of $(z + y)^r$. If we designate the number of any plate by N the value of any term in the expansion is given by

$$Q_{N+1} = \frac{r! \, (y)^{r-N}(z)^N}{N! \, (r - N)!} \tag{7.2}$$

If it is desired to know the quantity of solute in the tenth plate we must let $N = 9$ in the calculation.

In order to have some measure of the rate of movement of a solute band through a column we must fix on some reference point. The most obvious

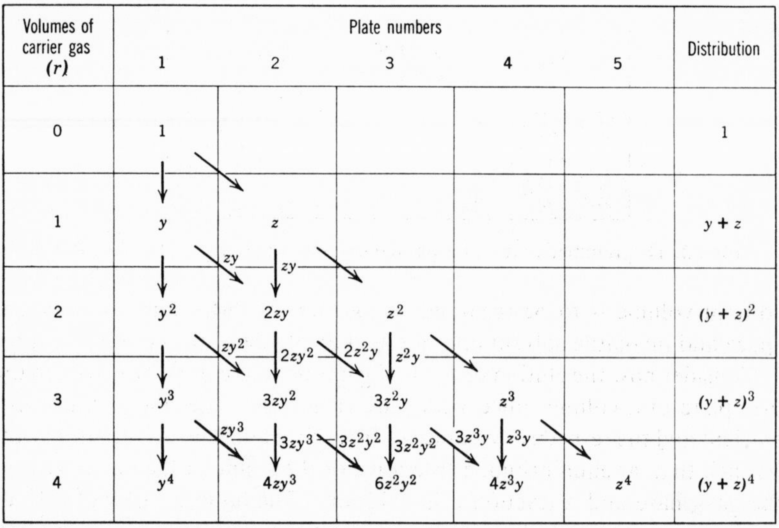

Volumes of carrier gas (r)	Plate numbers					Distribution
	1	2	3	4	5	
0	1					1
1	y	z				$y + z$
2	y^2	$2zy$	z^2			$(y + z)^2$
3	y^3	$3zy^2$	$3z^2y$	z^3		$(y + z)^3$
4	y^4	$4zy^3$	$6z^2y^2$	$4z^3y$	z^4	$(y + z)^4$

FIG. 3. Illustration of the distribution of solute in a column after the passage of four plate free volumes of carrier gas. The initial sample volume injected into plate 1 is taken as 1 ml.

point to choose is the maximum of the solute distribution curve, and the position of this maximum in terms of various experimental parameters can readily be evaluated from equation 7.2.

Assume that the $(N + 1)$th plate contains more solute than any other at a time when r free gas volumes ΔV_g have passed through the column. It then follows that this plate contains more solute than it does when either $(r - 1)$ or $(r + 1)$ volumes have passed. Thus, from equation 7.2 we have

$$\frac{r! \, y^{(r-N)}z^N}{(r - N)!} > \frac{(r - 1)! \, y^{(r-N-1)}z^N}{(r - N - 1)!}$$

and after rearranging and substituting $(1 - z)$ for y

$$r(1 - z) > r - N$$

that is,

$$N < rz$$

Similarly,

$$\frac{r! \, y^{(r-N)} z^N}{(r - N)!} > \frac{(r + 1)! \, y^{(r+1-N)} z^N}{(r + 1 - N)!}$$

which leads to

$$N > (r + 1)z$$

To all intents and purposes, therefore,

$$N = rz \qquad (7.3)$$

and to calculate Q_{max}, N must simply be replaced by rz in equation 7.2, this quantity occurring in the $(rz + 1)$th plate from the injection end of the column.

If r is a large number the following approximations can be made: $y^{(r-N)} \simeq y^r = (1 - z)^r = e^{-rz}$, while $r!/(r - N)! \simeq r^N$. Hence, equation 7.2 can be written

$$Q_{N+1} = \frac{(rz)^N e^{-rz}}{N!} \qquad (7.4)$$

and, further, Stirling's approximation is

$$N! = \frac{(2\pi N)^{\frac{1}{2}} N^N}{e^N}$$

hence,

$$Q_{N+1} = \frac{(rz)^N e^{(N-rz)}}{(2\pi N)^{\frac{1}{2}} N^N} \qquad (7.5)$$

According to equation 7.3, when Q_{N+1} becomes Q_{max}, $N = rz$ and so

$$Q_{max} = (2\pi N)^{-\frac{1}{2}} \qquad (7.6)$$

In more general terms, had we started with m ml. of solute in plate 1 rather than 1 ml.

$$Q_{max} = \frac{m}{(2\pi N)^{\frac{1}{2}}} \qquad (7.7)$$

If the solute band moves through a column of N plates in time t its rate of movement is N/t. The moment during the elution when solute leaves the column at the greatest rate is when the maximum of the elution curve emerges. Thus, the maximum rate of escape of solute, S, is given by

$$S = \frac{N Q_{max}}{t} = \frac{N m}{t(2\pi N)^{\frac{1}{2}}}$$

and so

$$N = \frac{2\pi S^2 t^2}{m^2} \tag{7.8}$$

The term S is related to the maximum height of the elution curve in the same way as the term m is related to its area. Thus, replacing S and m by peak height, h, and area, O, respectively, 7.8 becomes

$$N = \frac{2\pi h^2 t^2}{O^2} \tag{7.9}$$

This equation contains only measurable quantities and so permits the determination of N from experimental data. It must be remembered that the dimensions of the product (ht) must be the same as those of O in order that N may be dimensionless.

The theory of Martin and Synge has been further developed by Mayer and Tompkins (4) particularly in the direction of the prediction of the number of plates needed to obtain a required purity of the products. As will be seen later, however, such calculations may be very considerably in error if either columns of low efficiency or solutes of low partition co-efficient are dealt with and the work of Glueckauf gives more reliable results. Consequently, the problem of the degree of purity of eluted materials will be discussed later in terms of the latter treatment.

The Retention Volume. The time of passage of a solute through any chromatographic column varies inversely as the carrier gas flow rate and so the most suitable way of expressing this time is in terms of the volume flow between injection of the solute into the column and its emergence at the outlet end. This volume, the retention volume V_R', is normally independent of carrier gas flow rate and can readily be related to various measureable quantities as follows.

The fraction z of solute existing in the gas phase in any plate (*cf.* equation 6.5) is given by

$$z = \frac{c_g \Delta V_g}{c_g \Delta V_g + c_l \Delta V_l}$$

c_g and c_l representing the concentration of solute in the gas and liquid phases, respectively. Since $K = c_l/c_g$,

$$z = \frac{c_g \Delta V_g}{c_g \Delta V_g + K c_g \Delta V_l}$$

that is,

$$z = \frac{\Delta V_g}{\Delta V_g + K \Delta V_l}$$

Equation 7.3 states that when the maximum of an elution curve is found in the $(N + 1)$th plate, $N = rz$, hence, if the $(N + 1)$th plate is taken to be the detector system, N is the total number of plates in the column while $r \, \Delta v_g$ is the peak retention volume of the solute.
Thus,

$$V_R' = r \, \Delta V_g = N \, \Delta V_g / z$$

Hence,

$$V_R' = N(\Delta V_g + K \, \Delta V_l)$$

and if we write $N \, \Delta V_g = V_d$, the total gas free, or dead, space in the column and $N \, \Delta V_l = V_l$, the total volume of solvent (or solid adsorbent in gas-solid chromatography), we get the retention volume equation,

$$V_R' = V_d + KV_l = V_d + V_R \tag{7.10}$$

V_R' may be called the apparent retention volume and V_R the true retention volume. This is the basic equation of gas chromatography and is of very considerable theoretical importance, since it connects the thermodynamic quantity K with column parameters.

GRAPHICAL ILLUSTRATION OF THE CHROMATOGRAPHIC PROCESSES

Equation 7.2 can be used to calculate solute distribution curves for small values of r and Figure 4 illustrates such curves for three solutes. The conditions assumed are that $r = 10$, $\Delta V_g = \Delta V_l$ and that K is $\frac{7}{3}$, 1 or $\frac{3}{7}$. The corresponding values of z are, therefore, 0.7, 0.5 and 0.3. The solute of lowest partition coefficient can be seen to have moved most rapidly down the column, its peak maximum being located in, or near, plate 8. The maxima of the other two solutes are in about the sixth and fourth plates. These values accord with those calculated from equation 7.3.

Figure 5 illustrates the principle of the separation process in some detail. It shows the distribution of the solutes of $K = \frac{7}{3}$ and $\frac{3}{7}$ at $r = 5$, 10 and 15. When $r = 5$ the maxima are separated by two plates, but the chromatogram, shown as a broken line, gives no indication of a separation. At $r = 10$ two peaks have appeared in the chromatogram, but the valley between is shallow. At $r = 15$, there is a very reasonable separation of the peaks, and although this is not complete, it is evident that it would require only about fifty theoretical plates to give an adequate result. This example illustrates a number of important points. First, even though the ratio of partition coefficients is over 5, a fair number of theoretical plates is necessary for near complete separation. By comparison, a distillation column of only four or five plates would be adequate. Second, once solute is introduced into any plate it can never thereafter be entirely removed since a quantity y^r must always remain. This is in part an explanation of the

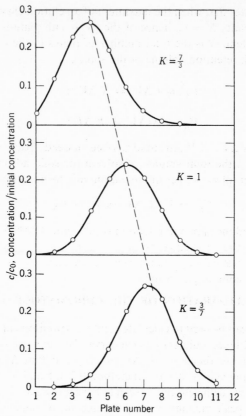

FIG. 4. Binomial distribution of three solutes in a column. Conditions are $\Delta V_g = \Delta V_l$, $r = 10$, $K = 7/3$, 1 and 3/7, respectively.

finding that when a detector of low sensitivity is replaced by one of higher sensitivity much carrier gas must be allowed to flow through the column before a stable base line can be obtained. Finally, if no plate can ever be completely freed of solute it is clearly impossible to prepare absolutely pure materials by gas chromatography, since no two solutes can ever be completely separated. The description "absolutely pure" is a matter of definition, and the choice of an acceptable level of impurity will always be a matter of individual decision.

THE CONTINUOUS FLOW MODEL

The most important work in this direction up to this time is that of Glueckauf (3) whose conclusions have been verified by the more recent studies of van Deemter, Klinkenberg and Zuiderweg (5) and, in part, by Young (6). Apart from the greater sophistication of the continuous flow

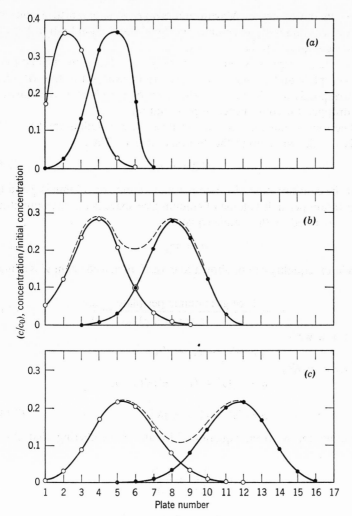

FIG. 5. Illustration of the separation of two solutes of $K = 7/3$ and $3/7$ respectively. The diagram shows how separation increases with travel through the column, i.e. with the sequence (a) $r = 5$, (b) $r = 10$ and (c) $r = 15$.

model, Glueckauf's approach has the advantage over others in that it leads to equations which permit calculation of N, not only from the familiar bell shaped elution curves, but also from the S-shaped breakthrough curves characteristic of frontal analysis and displacement chromatography.

Before proceeding with the derivation of the various equations it is convenient to list some of the assumptions and definitions which are necessary.

a. As in the theory of Martin and Synge, K is assumed a constant, diffusion longitudinally is assumed negligible and equilibration between phases is considered to be instantaneous.

b. A volume of gas V is required to transport solute from the first to the $(N-1)$th plate and a volume $(V+\Delta V)$ to transport it to the Nth plate. ΔV corresponds to ΔV_g in the earlier part of the chapter, the subscript being dropped for convenience in presentation.

c. The total volume of the column up to and including the $(N-1)$th plate is $x - \Delta x$ while up to the Nth plate it is x. Thus,

$$N\,\Delta x = x \tag{7.11}$$

d. If the concentration of solute per unit volume of column is q and the concentration per unit volume of column free space is c_g, these quantities can be connected by the simple equation

$$q = ac_g \tag{7.12}$$

This latter equality can be shown to exist if, first, a constant α' is defined by

$$\alpha' = \frac{\text{Free gas volume per plate}}{\text{Total volume of a plate}} = \frac{\Delta V}{\Delta x} \tag{7.13}$$

We can now write

$$q = \alpha' c_g + (1 - \alpha')c_l$$

and since $c_l = Kc_g$

$$q = c_g[\alpha' + (1 - \alpha')K] = ac_g$$

where

$$a = [\alpha' + (1 - \alpha')K] \tag{7.14a}$$

Substituting for α' from equation 7.13 and remembering that $\Delta x = \Delta V_g + \Delta V_l$,

$$a = \frac{\Delta V_g}{\Delta x} + \frac{K\Delta V_l}{\Delta x}$$

or,

$$a\,\Delta x = \Delta V_g + K\Delta V_l = \Delta V_r'$$

Comparison with equation 7.10 shows that the product of $a\,\Delta x$ is the apparent retention volume per plate, $\Delta V_r'$, sometimes called the effective plate volume, and if we multiply both sides of the above equation by N we get

$$ax = V_R'. \tag{7.14b}$$

From this point the subscript in the term c_g will be dropped in order to simplify the nomenclature and 7.12 will be written

$$q = ac$$

Frontal Development.   Consider now the situation in a column, originally containing pure carrier gas, which has been fed with a mixture of carrier and solute vapour of constant composition. If this mixture has flowed as far as the Nth plate the amount of solute in that plate can be written either as $\Delta V c_{x-\Delta x}$ or as $q_V\,\Delta x$. The amount of solute in the $(N-1)$th plate is either $\Delta V c_x$ or $q_V\,\Delta x$. Now, the next addition of ΔV of the gas mixture into the column will move the solute out of the $(N-1)$th plate and into the Nth plate. The change in amount of solute in that plate is thus $\Delta V(c_{x-\Delta x} - c_x)$ or, alternatively, $\Delta x(q_{V+\Delta V} - q_V)$. These quantities are, of course equal

$$\Delta V(c_{x-\Delta x} - c_x) = \Delta x(q_{V+\Delta V} - q_V)$$

If the differences in parentheses are sufficiently small they can be replaced by differentials according to Taylor's theorem.

$$c_{x-\Delta x} - c_x = -\left(\frac{\partial C}{\partial x}\right)_V \Delta x + \left(\frac{\partial^2 C}{\partial x^2}\right)_V \frac{\Delta x^2}{2} \tag{7.15}$$

$$q_{V+\Delta V} - q_V = \left(\frac{\partial q}{\partial V}\right)_x \Delta V + \left(\frac{\partial^2 q}{\partial V^2}\right)_x \frac{\Delta V^2}{2} \tag{7.16}$$

Terms in powers higher than the square can be neglected, and by substitution we get

$$\left(\frac{\partial C}{\partial x}\right)_V + \left(\frac{\partial q}{\partial V}\right)_x + \left(\frac{\partial^2 q}{\partial V^2}\right)_x \frac{\Delta V}{2} - \left(\frac{\partial^2 C}{\partial x^2}\right)_V \frac{\Delta x}{2} = 0 \tag{7.17}$$

This equation is the material balance equation for discontinuous flow. Continuous flow corresponds to the situation when $\Delta V = 0$, that is, when the volume increment of flowing gas is zero. Thus, the material balance equation for continuous flow is simply

$$\left(\frac{\partial C}{\partial x}\right)_V + \left(\frac{\partial q}{\partial V}\right)_x + \left(\frac{\partial^2 C}{\partial x^2}\right)_V \frac{\Delta x}{2} = 0 \tag{7.18}$$

Differentiating 7.12 with respect to volume gives

$$\left(\frac{\partial q}{\partial V}\right)_x = a\left(\frac{\partial c}{\partial V}\right)_x$$

and substituting this in 7.18

$$\left(\frac{\partial C}{\partial x}\right)_V + a\left(\frac{\partial C}{\partial V}\right)_x + \left(\frac{\partial^2 C}{\partial x^2}\right)_V \frac{\Delta x}{2} = 0 \tag{7.19}$$

In order to solve this equation it is convenient to transform into the dimensionless quantities N and M. N, of course, is defined by equation 7.11,

$$N = \frac{x}{\Delta x} \quad \text{and so,} \quad \left(\frac{\partial N}{\partial x}\right) = \frac{1}{\Delta x} \quad \text{and} \quad \left(\frac{\partial N}{\partial x}\right)^2 = \frac{1}{\Delta x^2}$$

M is defined by the equation

$$M = \frac{V}{a \, \Delta x}$$

V being the volume flow up to any point in the column. Differentiation gives

$$\left(\frac{\partial M}{\partial V}\right) = \frac{1}{a \, \Delta x}$$

The differentials occurring in 7.19 can be written

$$\left(\frac{\partial C}{\partial x}\right) = \left(\frac{\partial C}{\partial N}\right)\left(\frac{\partial N}{\partial x}\right) = \left(\frac{\partial C}{\partial N}\right)\frac{1}{\Delta x}$$

$$\left(\frac{\partial^2 C}{\partial x^2}\right) = \left(\frac{\partial^2 C}{\partial N^2}\right)\left(\frac{\partial N}{\partial x}\right)^2 = \left(\frac{\partial^2 C}{\partial N^2}\right)\frac{1}{\Delta x^2}$$

$$\left(\frac{\partial C}{\partial V}\right) = \left(\frac{\partial C}{\partial M}\right)\left(\frac{\partial M}{\partial V}\right) = \left(\frac{\partial C}{\partial M}\right)\frac{1}{a \, \Delta x}$$

Substituting these values in 7.19 gives

$$\left(\frac{\partial C}{\partial N}\right)_M + \left(\frac{\partial C}{\partial M}\right)_N - \tfrac{1}{2}\left(\frac{\partial^2 C}{\partial N^2}\right)_M = 0 \tag{7.20}$$

According to equation 7.14b, the product $a \, \Delta x$ is the apparent retention volume per plate, hence, M represents the number of theoretical plate retention volumes in the volume V. Clearly, when $V = V_R'$, $M = N$.

The boundary conditions applicable to 7.20 are that for a column of N plates at a time when no carrier gas has entered the column,

$$M = 0, \qquad N > 0, \qquad c = 0$$

while, when carrier containing solute at concentration c^o enters the column

$$M > 0, \qquad N = 0, \qquad c = c^o$$

The solution of this problem is

$$\frac{c}{c^o} = \tfrac{1}{2} - A_\epsilon\left(\frac{N - M}{\sqrt{M}}\right) \tag{7.21}$$

for values of N greater than 3. No one, of course, would be interested in a column of so few plates, and so the solution is effectively exact.

$A_\epsilon(t)$ is the area of the normal curve of error defined by

$$A_\epsilon(t) = \frac{1}{\sqrt{2\pi}} \int_0^t e^{-t^2/2} \, dt$$

which is tabulated in many places. M can be eliminated from 7.21 since

$$N = \frac{V_R'}{a\,\Delta x} \quad \text{and} \quad M = \frac{V}{a\,\Delta x}$$

In consequence,

$$\frac{N - M}{\sqrt{M}} = \sqrt{N}\left[\frac{V_R' - V}{(VV_R')^{1/2}}\right]$$

and 7.21 becomes

$$\frac{c}{c^o} = \frac{1}{2} - A_\epsilon\left[\sqrt{N}\,\frac{V_R' - V}{\sqrt{VV_R'}}\right] \tag{7.22}$$

This equation is clearly of the right form, since the limiting value of $A_\epsilon(t)$ is $\frac{1}{2}$ and so, when $V_R' \gg V$, that is, when no solute has reached the outlet end of a column, $c/c^o = 0$. When $V_R' = V$, $c/c^o = \frac{1}{2}$ and, finally, when $V \gg V_R$, the area of the error curve is $-\frac{1}{2}$ and $c/c^o = 1$. When the term in brackets is unity, the area of the error curve is 0.3413, hence $c/c^o = 0.1587$. Thus, if we measure V from injection to the point on the break-through curve where $c/c^o = 0.1587$, calling it V', we get

$$N = \frac{V'V_R'}{(V_R' - V')^2} \tag{7.23}$$

This equation offers the only method of determining the efficiency of a chromatographic system which gives S-shaped break-through curves.

The Experimental Measurement of N in Frontal Analysis. Figure 6 illustrates three break-through curves calculated with the aid of equation 7.22. An apparent retention volume of 500 ml. has been assumed and curves are shown for $N = 50$, 200 and 800. The increasing steepness of the curves with increasing N is evident, and it follows also that V' and V_R' become more nearly identical. This suggests that equation 7.23 might be even further simplified to

$$N = \left(\frac{V_R'}{V_R' - V'}\right)^2 \tag{7.24}$$

The approximation involved can readily be calculated, some values are listed in Table 1.

TABLE 1
COMPARISON OF N CALCULATED FROM 7.23 AND 7.24

N (7.23)	N (7.24)	Approximate Error, %
800	817	2
200	216	8
50	57	14

It appears that the approximation equation 7.24 is adequate if column efficiencies are greater than about a thousand theoretical plates. This view is given even more point if the accuracy with which it is necessary to measure V_R' and V' is estimated. Table 2 gives some indication of this.

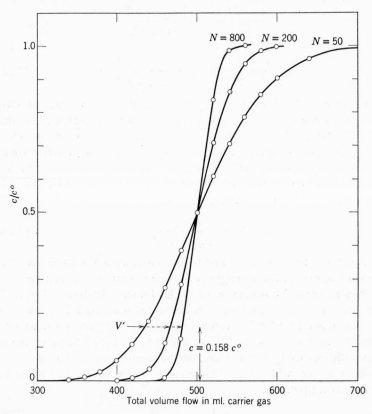

FIG. 6. Calculated frontal analysis break through curves for three ideal columns of $N = 50$, 200 and 800, respectively.

There is no doubt that V' and equally, V_R', have to be located very precisely and more so with increasing column efficiency. Thus, for the 800-plate column V' or V_R' must be measured within 0.1 ml. if the calculated number of plates is to be within 1 per cent of the true value. It is, unfortunately, the case that the location of V' within these limits is extremely difficult and so, since few workers would employ columns of less than about a thousand plates, the error involved in the use of equation 7.24 is, in comparison, relatively slight. It must be remembered, however, that if V_R' is smaller than the value assumed in the example all of the errors are greater, and in these circumstances it may be essential to use the exact equation 7.23.

Elution Curves. The theory of the elution of a band of finite width rather than one of infinite width is identical with that developed up to this point, except that the boundary conditions relevant to the solution of equation 7.20 are different. The initial width of the solute band can be described in several ways, for example, in terms of the length or volume of column over which the solute is spread. The most suitable description is, however, in terms of the number of theoretical plates N_0 over which it is introduced, and the boundary conditions can then be evaluated as follows. If the

TABLE 2

VALUES OF N FOR VARIOUS VALUES OF $V'(V_R' = 500$ ml.$)$

True V' (ml.)	True N	V' (ml.)	N	Approximate Error Plates per ml.	Approximate Error % per ml.
482.6	800	482	744 ⎤	100	12
		483	835 ⎥		
		484	940 ⎦		
466	200	460	143 ⎤	12	6
		465	190 ⎥		
		470	260 ⎦		
434	50	430	44 ⎤	1.5	3
		435	52 ⎥		
		440	60 ⎦		

sample has been introduced but no carrier gas has entered the column, the situation in some early plate N is that solute extends farther down the column while the concentration in each plate where solute occurs is c^o. Before solute is introduced $c = 0$ and N is greater than N_0 while, after solute has moved well down the column the conditions at the front of the column are that $N = 0$ and $c = 0$. Thus,

$$M = 0, \quad N > N_0 = 0, \quad c = 0$$
$$M = 0, \quad N_0 > N > 0, \quad c = c^o$$
$$M > 0, \quad N = 0, \quad c = 0$$

The solution of equation 7.20 is then

$$\frac{c}{c^o} = A_\epsilon\left(\frac{N - M}{\sqrt{M}}\right) - A_\epsilon\left(\frac{N - N_0 - M}{\sqrt{M}}\right) \tag{7.25}$$

The two terms in equation 7.25 differ only by N_0 and so, if this is small compared to N, Taylor's theorem can again be used to replace the difference by differentials, as with equations 7.15 and 7.16. Thus,

$$\frac{c}{c^o} = N_0 \left\{ \frac{\partial}{\partial N} \left[A_\epsilon \left(\frac{N - M}{\sqrt{M}} \right) \right] \right\} - \left(\frac{N_0{}^2}{2} \left\{ \frac{\partial^2}{\partial N^2} \left[A_\epsilon \left(\frac{N - M}{\sqrt{M}} \right) \right] \right\} \right)$$

(7.26)

further terms being neglected. From our earlier definition of $A_\epsilon(t)$

$$\frac{\partial}{\partial N} \left[A_\epsilon \left(\frac{N - M}{\sqrt{M}} \right) \right] = \frac{1}{\sqrt{2\pi M}} \exp \left[- \frac{(N - M)^2}{2M} \right]$$

and

$$\frac{\partial^2}{\partial N^2} \left[A_\epsilon \left(\frac{N - M}{\sqrt{M}} \right) \right] = \frac{M - N}{M\sqrt{2\pi M}} \exp \left[- \frac{(N - M)^2}{2M} \right]$$

Substitution of these in equation 7.26 gives

$$\frac{c}{c^o} = \left\{ \frac{N_0}{\sqrt{2\pi M}} \exp \left[- \frac{(N - M)^2}{2M} \right] \right\} - \left\{ \frac{N_0{}^2 (M - N)}{2M\sqrt{2\pi M}} \exp \left[- \frac{(N - M)^2}{2M} \right] \right\}$$

or, when terms are collected, and numerator and denominator are multiplied by $N^{1/2}$

$$\frac{c}{c^o} = \frac{N_0}{\sqrt{2\pi M}} \left\{ \left(\frac{N}{M} \right)^{1/2} \left[1 + \frac{N_0(N - M)}{2M} \right] \right\} \exp \left[- \frac{(N - M)^2}{2M} \right]$$

Provided that N is reasonably large, as it will almost always be in gas chromatography, elution peaks are narrow and $M \gg (N - M)$. Hence we can make the approximations

$$1 + N_0 \frac{(N - M)}{2M} = \exp \left[N_0 \frac{(N - M)}{2M} \right]$$

and

$$\left(\frac{N}{M} \right)^{1/2} = \exp \left[\frac{N - M}{2M} \right]$$

which lead to

$$\frac{c}{c^o} = \frac{N_0}{\sqrt{2\pi N}} \exp \left[- \frac{(N - M)}{2M} (N - M - N_0 - 1) \right]$$

To a very close approximation this can be written

$$\frac{c}{c^o} = \left(\frac{N_0}{\sqrt{2\pi N}} \right) \exp \left\{ - \left[\frac{(N - N_0/2 - M)^2}{2M} \right] \right\}$$

an equation which would be exact if $N_0{}^2 = 4(M - N)$. If now, the effective number of plates N' is defined by

$$N' = N - \frac{N_0}{2}$$

that is, the true number of plates minus half the original band width, then we have

$$\frac{c}{c^o} = \frac{N_0}{\sqrt{2\pi N}} \exp\left[-\frac{(N'-M)^2}{2M}\right] \qquad (7.27)$$

In order to eliminate N_0, which could be very difficult to measure experimentally, we can express the initial solute band width in a different way, that is, in terms of the volume of column $N_0 \Delta x$. The total quantity of solute m injected into the column is then $q N_0 \Delta x$ or, alternatively, $ac^o N_0 \Delta x$, hence

$$N_0 = \frac{m}{ac^o \Delta x}$$

and equation 7.27 becomes

$$\frac{c}{c^o} = \frac{m}{ac^o \Delta x \sqrt{2\pi N}} \exp\left[-\frac{(N'-M)^2}{2M}\right]$$

but according to equation 7.14b, $a \Delta x = V_R'/N'$ which leads to

$$c = \frac{m\sqrt{N'}}{V_R'\sqrt{2\pi}} \exp\left[-\frac{(N'-M)^2}{2M}\right] \qquad (7.28)$$

The maximum value of c is clearly that when the exponential term is unity since the exponent is negative and so

$$c_{\max} = \frac{m\sqrt{N'}}{\sqrt{2\pi}V_R'} \qquad (7.29)$$

whence,

$$N' = 2\pi\left(\frac{V_R' c_{\max}}{m}\right)^2 \qquad (7.30)$$

which is identical with equation 7.8, as derived from the theory of James and Martin, when the feed band width N_0 is so small that $N' = N$. When N_0 is not small, equation 7.30 supercedes 7.8.

An alternative approach which leads to an equation from which N' can be experimentally calculated more easily is as follows. Remembering our definition of M and N we can write

$$\frac{(N'-M)^2}{2M} = \frac{\left(\dfrac{V_R'}{a \Delta x} - \dfrac{V}{a \Delta x}\right)^2}{\dfrac{2V}{a \Delta x}} = \frac{1}{a \Delta x}\frac{(V_R'-V)^2}{2V}$$

Substituting for $a \Delta x$ from equation 7.14b again and combining equations 7.28 and 7.29 gives

$$c = c_{\max} \exp\left[-\frac{N(V_R'-V)^2}{2VV_R'}\right]$$

Considering now the point on the elution curve where $c = c_{\max}/e$ and $V = V_e'$ we see that since $c/c_{\max} = e^{-1}$

$$N' = \frac{2V_e'V_R'}{(V_R' - V_e')^2}$$

V_e' is the apparent retention volume of the point on an elution curve where the height is $1/e$ of the peak height, while $(V_R' - V_e')$ is the half width of the peak at this point. If the width $2(V_R' - V_e')$ is called β then

$$N' = \frac{8V_e'V_R'}{\beta^2} \tag{7.31}$$

and if N' is big enough, V_R' and V_e' are sufficiently close that

$$N = 8\left(\frac{V_R'}{\beta}\right)^2 \tag{7.32}$$

If the feed volume is sufficiently small $N' = N$ and since, in any case, it is N' which is experimentally measured, there is little point in continuing to distinguish between the two, which is why N has been used in equation 7.32. It must be remembered that, ideally, N should always be measured as near zero feed volume as possible if it is to be used for theoretical purposes.

Other Theoretical Plate Equations.   There are several possible variants of equation 7.32. One which was first suggested by van Deemter and his associates (5) has become widely known and is the method recommended by several international committees for evaluating N from elution curves. In order to deduce this it is simplest to refer to Figure 7 which illustrates the relationship between width and height at various points on a Gaussian curve. The width at the point of inflexion corresponds to two standard deviations, 2σ; at the half height it is $2\sigma\sqrt{2\ln 2}$, while $\beta = 2\sigma\sqrt{2}$. The distance between the points of intersection of the tangents to the inflexion point and the base of the elution curve is $4\sigma = \beta\sqrt{2} = w$. Hence,

$$\beta^2 = \frac{w^2}{2}$$

and, from equation 7.32,

$$N = \left(\frac{4V_R'}{w}\right)^2 = 16\left(\frac{V_R'}{w}\right)^2 \tag{7.33}$$

Many gas chromatographic peaks are unsymmetrical and V_R' may vary considerably with the amount of solute eluted. In addition V_R' diminishes progressively as the feed volume increases. However, the retention volume of the rear of the elution curve, and sometimes of the front, may be constant for reasons which are discussed elsewhere. In consequence, it is useful to

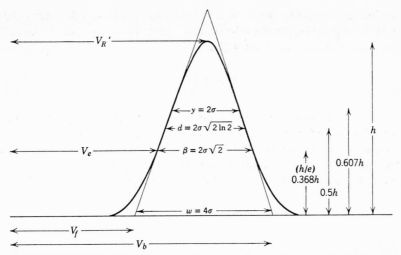

FIG. 7. Illustration of the relationship between width and height on a Gaussian curve.

cast equation 7.33 into a form which contains not V_R' but the retention volume corresponding to the intercept of the front or rear tangent to the inflexion point on the base of the elution curve. These volumes may be called V_f and V_b respectively. From Figure 7 we see that

$$V_R' = V_f + \tfrac{1}{2}w = V_b - \tfrac{1}{2}w$$

hence,

$$N = \left[\frac{4V_f}{w} + 2\right]^2 \tag{7.34a}$$

and similarly,

$$N = \left[\frac{4V_b}{w} - 2\right]^2 \tag{7.34b}$$

A further alternative is to replace β by the width, d, of the elution curve at the half height. From Figure 7 it is clear that

$$d^2 = \beta^2(\ln 2) = 0.693\beta^2$$

and substituting this in equation 7.32 leads to

$$N = 5.545\left(\frac{V_R'}{d}\right)^2 \tag{7.35}$$

Finally, since the width between inflexion points, y, corresponds to two standard deviations

$$N = 4\left(\frac{V_R'}{y}\right)^2 \tag{7.36}$$

An interesting relationship which follows from equation 7.36 relates the theoretical plate height H to the standard deviation expressed in terms of distance. Substituting 2σ for y gives

$$N = \left(\frac{V_R'}{\sigma}\right)^2$$

and if the standard deviation is expressed as a distance, l, V_R' can be replaced by the column length L. This follows since $V_R' = Ft_r$, where F is the gas flow rate and t_r is the time of retention; equally, $l = F\tau$ where τ is the standard deviation in units of time. Hence, $(V_R'/l)^2 = (t_r/\tau)^2$ and multiplying top and bottom by the band velocity gives $(V_R'/\sigma)^2 = (L/l)^2$. Thus,

$$N = \frac{L}{H} = \frac{L^2}{l^2}$$

and

$$H = \frac{l^2}{L} \tag{7.37}$$

We can thus redefine the theoretical plate height very succinctly as "the variance per unit length of column." This view of H is much the simplest and, indeed, the most important, since, as is seen in Chapter 8, equation 7.37 can be used to simplify considerably the theory of non-ideal chromatography.

The Experimental Determination of N for Elution Curves.   It is apparent that any one of eight equations may be employed as the basis of the measurement of N from experimental elution curves. Of these, equations 7.8 and 7.30 are virtually identical, and the use of either involves measurement of the area under the curves, a procedure which is certainly laborious and which becomes increasingly inaccurate with diminishing area. For these reasons these equations need not be too seriously considered and it is to be hoped that equations 7.31 through 7.36 will present a better approach.

The comparison of the suitability of the remaining equations is most conveniently carried out by reference to Figure 8. In this, three fairly typical elution curves are shown. Curve A is not very commonly met with in practice, having an extended front and a sharp, near Gaussian tail. Curve B is truly Gaussian while curve C, the mirror image of A, has a sharp front and a long tail and is the type of elution curve most often encountered. All the data necessary to the calculation of N from each equation is contained in the diagrams, the measurements being relative to an assumed V_R' of 10 units. In order also to get some idea of the situation at high values of N it is worthwhile calculating N for a value of $V_R' = 100$ units at the same peak widths as shown. The representation of this situation in a diagram of

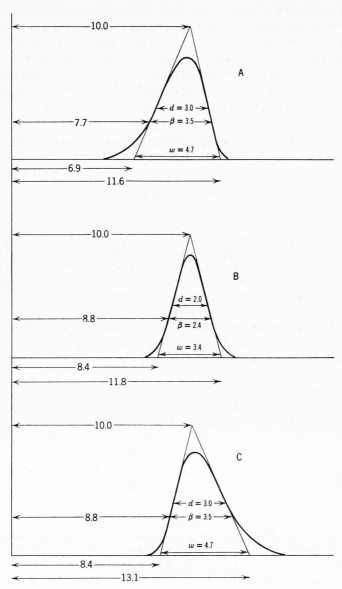

FIG. 8. Elution curves used for the comparison of the theoretical plate equations. Calculated data are listed in Table 3.

reasonable scale would be somewhat difficult and so this has not been done. For the calculations, however, it is only necessary to add 90 units to each retention volume leaving β, d and w unchanged. The data calculated from the diagram are listed in Table 3. For the symmetrical curve B all the equations give the same result. Such curves are rarely met with in practice and so it is the data for the asymmetric curves which merits most attention.

In the first instance we may consider the data in the table in terms of the two groups of equations, those of Glueckauf (7.31, 7.32, 7.35 and 7.36) and

TABLE 3

VALUES OF N CALCULATED FROM FIGURE 8. FEED VOLUME ASSUMED NEGLIGIBLE

	Curve A		Curve B		Curve C	
Equation	$V_R' = 10$	$V_R' = 100$	$V_R' = 10$	$V_R' = 100$	$V_R' = 10$	$V_R' = 100$
7.31	50.5	6370	122	13700	57.5	6430
7.32	65	6500	139	13900	65	6500
7.35	63	6300	138	13800	63	6300
7.33	72	7200	139	13900	72	7200
7.34a	62	7100	140	13900	84	7350
7.34b	62	7100	141	13900	84	7350

those suggested by van Deemter (7.33, 7.34a and 7.34b). At the higher values of V_R' and N there is reasonably close agreement within each group but the Glueckauf equations yield consistently lower values of N. As Glueckauf has shown, approximations in the theory always lead to exaggerated values of N and so, if we assume that the equations giving the lowest values are most nearly correct it would appear that the Glueckauf equations are preferable to the van Deemter.

At the lower values of V_R' and N it is clear that the equations of the van Deemter group are not self consistent, thus, for curves of type A equations 7.34 yield lower values of N than does equation 7.33 while for type C the reverse is true. This is a consequence of the fact that equations 7.34 automatically make allowance for asymmetry and so tend, effectively, to eliminate it. They, therefore, indicate what a column may do rather than what it has done. It is the latter, of course, in which one is primarily interested and so equations 7.34 would have to be used with considerable caution. On these grounds it would probably be better, generally, to use equation 7.33, but since again this gives a value of N about 12 per cent higher than that derived from the approximate Glueckauf equations it would seem certain that the latter are to be preferred.

It should be pointed out that this view, which was put forward some time ago by the Purnell (7) and Littlewood (8) conflicts with the recommendations of several international committees (9). Nevertheless, the data listed in the table cannot be ignored, and there is the further point that the procedures based on the Glueckauf equations involve only direct measurements on the experimental curves, unlike the van Deemter equations, the use of which necessitates the drawing of tangents to the inflexion points. There is undoubtedly considerable room for error in this process and, in the author's experience, it usually leads to a considerable exaggeration of the column efficiency, which is normally of the order of 15 per cent and may even be as great as 50 per cent.

Accepting that the Glueckauf equations are probably the most reliable basis for the procedure of determining N from experimental curves the question of which to use arises. The choice between equations 7.32 and 7.35 is difficult, but since 7.35 involves measuring the peak width at the half height rather than the $(1/e)$th height it is slightly more convenient. On the other hand, it is probably wisest to measure the peak width as low as possible on the curve. At high values of N there is relatively little difference between the more correct equation 7.31 and 7.35, but when N is small the discrepancy may be great. The percentage error involved in the use of 7.35 is $100(V_R' - V_e')/V_e'$ and so, if the calculated value of N is to be within 2 per cent of the true value N must be about five thousand plates. For highly accurate work, therefore, it would appear essential to determine N either from 7.31 or from the equations

$$N = 5.545\left(\frac{V_R' V_e'}{d^2}\right) \tag{7.38a}$$

or

$$N = 8\left(\frac{V_R' V_e'}{\beta^2}\right) \tag{7.38b}$$

THE FEED VOLUME

According to equation 7.28 the only effect of the finite width of the feed band is to shorten the column by half the width of the band, that is, $N_0/2$. This, however, is only true if the various approximations made in the theory are justifiable. The greatest approximation involved is that whereby the difference in equation 7.25 is replaced by the differentials of equation 7.26. For this to be valid the original feed band width must be less than one quarter of the average band width when the solute leaves the column. If this is not so, differentials of order higher than the second should be introduced. The average band width leaving the column corresponds to two standard deviations, that is, $\beta/\sqrt{2}$, as can be seen from Figure 7. From equation 7.32

$$\beta = \frac{\sqrt{8}(V_R')}{\sqrt{N}}$$

thus the maximum permissible feed volume V_F is given by

$$V_F < \frac{\beta}{4\sqrt{2}} = \frac{V_R'}{2\sqrt{N}} \qquad (7.39)$$

This equation, which has also been deduced by van Deemter et al. (5) in a somewhat different way, indicates two important practical points. First, the more efficient a column becomes the smaller is the permissible feed volume and, secondly, for a given column the permissible feed volume increases with increasing retention volume. These views are illustrated by the data in Table 4 which indicates the order of magnitude of V_F for various values of N and V_R'.

TABLE 4

FEED VOLUMES CALCULATED FROM EQUATION 7.39

N	V_R' (ml.)	V_F (ml.)
1000	10	0.16
	100	1.60
	1000	16.00
10000	10	0.05
	100	0.50
	1000	5.00

Although V_F increases with V_R' it is not always possible to take advantage of this in practice. If, for example, it is desired that the feed volume should not affect the efficiency of a column for any solute in a mixture to be analysed then that feed volume cannot be bigger than the permissible value for the least strongly retained solute. If the analysis is to be carried out in a reasonable time it is commonly the case that the first component to emerge from the column will have a retention volume of, at most, 100 ml., in which case the feed volume must not exceed 1.60 ml. for a 1000-plate column. If now the average molecular weight of the solutes in the mixture is assumed to be 100, 1 mg. would occupy 0.224 ml. at N.T.P. or about 0.3 ml. at atmospheric pressure and 100°C. The maximum permissible total sample size of all components of a mixture is, thus, about 5 mg. If a 10,000-plate column were used the sample would have to be less than about 1.5 mg., while if the average molecular weight were less than 100 the sample size would have to be proportionately reduced. These values assume that the sample is undiluted by carrier gas, a most unlikely state of affairs, and so it is clear that even with quite inefficient columns the maximum sample size cannot be much greater than 1 mg. and, depending on the extent of dilution by carrier gas, is likely to be considerably less than this.

Finally, the theory up to this point has assumed that the sample, whether it enters the column pure or diluted does so in a plug. If this is not so, and several factors, for example, slow volatilisation of a liquid sample, or the fact that the velocity profile in a flowing gas is parabolic (p. 59) could contribute to this, the situation becomes complex. The detailed treatment of this form of sample introduction has been presented by Porter, Deal and Stross (12) but will not be treated here since it is of academic interest only and in practice, the best approach is to avoid such a situation. This can to a large extent be brought about by ensuring rapid vaporisation of samples and, where sample introduction is by means of some sort of gas burette, by

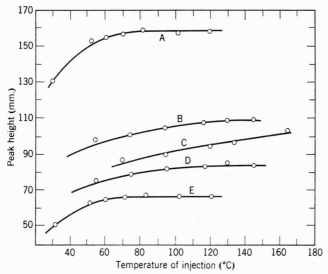

FIG. 9. The effect of injection temperature on apparent column efficiency: A, acetone; B, chloroform; C, carbon tetrachloride. *By courtesy of Chemistry and Industry.*

keeping this volume as small as possible and the diameter of any pipe or tube to a minimum. Thus, for any given volume it is better to use a long narrow injection chamber rather than a short wider one (p. 134).

Figure 9 illustrates the effect of insufficiently rapid vaporisation of liquid samples on the apparent efficiency of a column. The diagram, taken from the work of Pollard and Hardy (10) shows a plot of N against the temperature of the volatilisation chamber immediately before the column. In general it is found that the temperature of vaporisation of the sample must be at least 50°C. above the boiling point of the highest boiling component of the mixture analysed. This undoubtedly introduces difficulties in the separation of high boiling mixtures and suggests that ultimately it may be best to deal only with vapour samples. In order to be certain that column pre-heater deficiencies contribute nothing to band broadening in a column it is safest always to check band widths for standard sized samples at a number of injection temperatures and then to work well above the minimum value corresponding to an adequate rate of volatilisation.

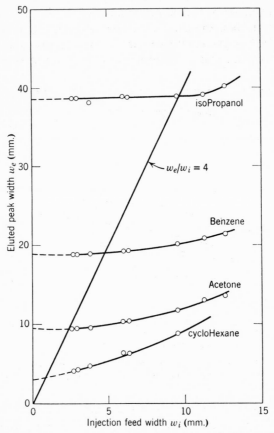

FIG. 10. Experimental data (15) showing dependence of H upon feed volume V_F. Results are plotted as emergent band width (w_e) against injection band width (w_i). The line of theoretical slope $w_e/w_i = 4$ is shown. The data relate to elution from a 5 ft. column of 20 per cent w/w polyethylene glycol on 100–150 mesh Sil-O-Cel at 50°C. *By courtesy of the Chemical Society.*

Returning to equation 7.39, Figure 10 shows a plot of band width against feed volume for several solutes eluted from the same column. It is clearly difficult to decide exactly at what point on the curves the feed volume ceases to have any appreciable effect upon the band width, but generally it is found that for various solutes V_F lies within ± 20 per cent of the value predicted by 7.39. Both theory and experiment indicate only too clearly that sample introduction must be made in as compact a form as possible if the maximum column performance is to be realised.

SEPARATING POWER AND EFFICIENCY OF COLUMNS

As pointed out by Glueckauf (3) the number of plates a column contains only provides a measure of the separation it can achieve if the true retention due to solution or adsorption is very considerably greater than the column free space, that is, that in effect $V_R' = V_R$. In practice, of course, this situation cannot often be achieved since, if it is true for the first substance eluted, the last components of a mixture would take an excessive time to emerge from a column. In consequence, most practical work is conducted with V_R, for at least the early peaks, being comparable to V_d.

The author (11) has discussed this situation and proposed that a separation factor S be defined in a way analogous to equation 7.33. Thus,

$$S = 16\left(\frac{V_R}{w}\right)^2 \tag{7.40}$$

If now it is accepted that two substances can be regarded as exactly separated (for practical purposes) when their peak maxima are separated by six standard deviations, (see Figure 7), we can write for the two substances

$$V_{R_2} - V_{R_1} = 1.5\left[\frac{w_1 + w_2}{2}\right]$$

and if it is assumed, as is reasonable, that $w_1 \simeq w_2$, then

$$V_{R_2} - V_{R_1} = 1.5\, w_2$$

Substituting for w_2 in equation 7.40 leads to

$$S = 36\left[\frac{V_{R_2}}{V_{R_2} - V_{R_1}}\right]^2 \tag{7.41}$$

The relative *true* retention volumes of the two substances can be called α and defined by

$$\alpha = V_{R_2}/V_{R_1} \gg 1$$

and so equation 7.41 becomes

$$S = 36\left[\frac{\alpha}{\alpha - 1}\right]^2 \tag{7.42}$$

α, as defined, is always greater than unity and although the inverse of the distillational quantity, the relative volatility, it is so similar that we can consider it to be the gas chromatographic relative volatility.

If now equation 7.33 is divided by 7.42

$$\frac{N}{S} = \left(\frac{V_d + V_R}{V_R}\right)^2$$

which, on rearrangement, gives

$$N = S\left[1 + 2\left(\frac{V_d}{V_R}\right) + \left(\frac{V_d}{V_R}\right)^2\right] \qquad (7.43)$$

or, when 7.42 is invoked

$$N = 36\left(\frac{\alpha}{\alpha - 1}\right)^2\left[1 + 2\left(\frac{V_d}{V_R}\right) + \left(\frac{V_d}{V_R}\right)^2\right] \qquad (7.44)$$

The separation factor S as given by equation 7.42 clearly defines the separation and is a theoretical value independent of column parameters. The actual value of S for any column and solute must be evaluated by application of equation 7.40 to experimental data.

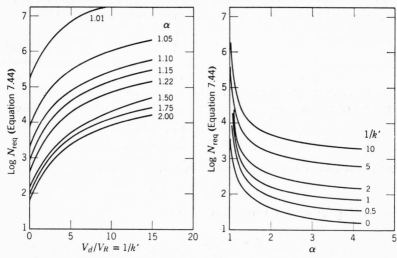

FIG. 11. Plot of N_{req} against V_d/ V_{R_2} $(= 1/k'_2)$ for the "exact" (6σ) separation of pairs of substances of different values of α. *By courtesy of the Chemical Society.*

FIG. 12. Data of Figure 11 plotted in the form of N_{req} against α for a range of values of V_d/V_{R_2} $(= 1/k'_2)$.

A simple example illustrates the profound effect of the use of excessive values of V_d/V_R. Consider the case of the separation of a pair of substances for which $\alpha = 2$; S, from equation 7.42 is then 144. We see from equation 7.43 that, as expected, when $V_R \gg V_d$, $N = S$; hence the number of plates required to separate the substances in the example is also 144. On the other hand, if the column were constructed in such a way that $V_d = 10V_R$, while again $S = 144$, the necessary number of plates would be 17,400.

Figure 11 illustrates plots of N against (V_d/V_R) for various values of α while Figure 12 shows a similar diagram for graphs of N against α for various values of (V_d/V_R). N, it must be remembered, is the number of theoretical plates required to perform exactly a given separation defined by α or, of course, S. Provided that the true retention volume is large enough N can be calculated directly from equation 7.42, otherwise, the use of 7.44 is essential and in these conditions it should always be borne in mind that a highly efficient column may have little separating power. An interesting consequence of equation 7.44 is that when $V_R \gg V_d$ and $\alpha \to \infty$, $N = 36$, in other words, the effective zero in gas chromatography corresponds to a column efficiency of 36 theoretical plates.

RESOLUTION

In consequence of the widely voiced need for some function which expresses the power of a column to separate compounds an International Committee (9) has recently suggested that the resolution, R, of a column should be defined by

$$R = \frac{2(V_{R_2} - V_{R_1})}{w_1 + w_2}$$

Exact separation as defined previously, that is, when back and front of adjacent peaks reach the base line at the same point, corresponds to $R = 1.5$, values less than this implying incomplete separation. The treatment of separation factors presented earlier was based on a value of $R = 1.5$.

THE COMPARISON OF DISTILLATION AND CHROMATOGRAPHIC COLUMN EFFICIENCIES

It is of interest to ascertain the relationship, if any, of the theoretical plate efficiency of chromatographic and distillation columns. Obviously, the only direct comparison that can be made involves the assumption that, in the chromatographic column $V_R \gg V_d$, when the number of plates required for given values of α can be calculated from 7.42. These results can be compared to those determined for a distillation column from the approximate fractionation equation

$$\alpha^N = 850$$

Some results obtained in this way are listed in Table 5.

It is clear that very many more theoretical plates are required in gas chromatography than in distillation and as seen from a comparison of the final two columns, the discrepancy is approximately as the square of the number of plates required in distillation. Although there is such a difference in the requirements of the two methods it is certain that the greater number of plates demanded by the chromatographic technique is very considerably more easily realised and utilised in practice.

TABLE 5

COMPARISON OF THEORETICAL PLATE REQUIREMENTS FOR
GAS CHROMATOGRAPHY AND DISTILLATION

α	N_{dist}	N_{GC}	N_{dist}^2	$N_{\text{GC}} - 36$
1.015	460	162,000	200,000	
1.075	93	7,100	8,700	
1.157	46	1,940	2,100	
1.245	31	940	960	
1.375	21	485	440	449
2.000	10	144	100	108
2.830	7	87	49	51

REFERENCES

1. Martin, A. J. P., and R. L. M. Synge, *Biochem. J.*, 1941, **35**, 1358.
2. James, A. T., and A. J. P. Martin, *Biochem. J.*, 1952, **50**, 679.
3. Glueckauf, E., *Trans. Faraday Soc.*, 1955, **51**, 34.
4. Mayer, S. W., and E. R. Tompkins, *J. Amer. Chem. Soc.*, 1947, **69**, 2866.
5. van Deemter, J. J., F. J. Zuiderweg and A. Klinkenberg, *Chem. Eng. Sci.*, 1956, **5**, 271.
6. Young, J. F., *Gas Chromatography*, 1958, Academic Press, New York (editors, V. J. Coates et al.), p. 15.
7. Bohemen, J., and J. H. Purnell, *Gas Chromatography*, 1958, Butterworths, London (editor, D. H. Desty), p. 6.
8. Littlewood, A. B. (see ref. 7) p. 23.
9. See *Gas Chromatography*, 1958, Butterworths, London (editor, D. H. Desty), p. xi.
10. Pollard, F. H., and C. J. Hardy (see ref. 9) p. 115.
11. Purnell, J. H., *J. Chem. Soc.*, 1960, 1268.
12. Porter, P. E., C. H. Deal and F. H. Stross, *J. Amer. Chem. Soc.*, 1956, **78**, 2999.
13. Bohemen, J., and J. H. Purnell, *J. Chem. Soc.*, 1961, 2630.

The theoretical plate theory as outlined in the previous chapter was applied to the simple model of a linear ideal process. That is, a linear partition isotherm was assumed and equilibration of phases at all points in a column was considered not only to be instantaneous but to correspond to the thermodynamic value. Linear ideal chromatography is, of course, unattainable in practice, and the closest approach we can hope for is probably linear non-ideal chromatography. In this case, the partition isotherm may still be linear but equilibration between phases is not immediate. In addition, various diffusional processes contribute to band spreading.

Liquid-solid or liquid-liquid chromatography is almost certainly of the non-linear ideal type, since partition isotherms are likely to be curved while mass transfer may be rapid in consequence of the small size of adsorbent particles or the thinness of liquid films. In liquids, of course, longitudinal diffusional effects should be negligible. The theory of this process has been developed in some detail by De Vault (1). A significant aspect of this form of chromatography is that solute bands, as they move along, generally develop sharp fronts and diffuse tails, a situation not uncommon in gas chromatography. Where curved partition isotherms prevail it is to be expected that mixed substances will, under certain conditions, compete for adsorbent or solvent. In such circumstances, retention volumes will be highly concentration dependent and this, as well as the shape of the bands, may help to identify the type of system under study. From a practical point of view, it is

8
RATE
THEORIES
OF
CHROMATOGRAPHY

probable that linear non-ideal chromatography is to be preferred to non-linear ideal.

The last possibility is that a system may be both non-linear and non-ideal. The theory accompanying such a state of affairs is highly involved and cannot be said to be understood to any extent.

In the simple theoretical plate theory presented earlier the important quantities were, so to speak, static. In the more realistic rate theories certain kinetic processes which contribute to the diffuseness of bands, that is, the non-ideality, are taken into account, and since these processes are more or less rate determining, theories which account for them are known by that name. Of the three possibilities, only the linear non-ideal type of system is readily accessible to theoretical treatment and since, in any case, it is most likely to be the one applicable to gas-liquid chromatography, if not to gas-solid chromatography, it has received the most attention.

Significant advance dates from the work of Lapidus and Amundsen (2) who discussed the band broadening resulting from both a finite rate of mass transfer and longitudinal diffusion. They deduced a general equation from which particular solutions can be derived. This was followed by Tunitskii (3) who introduced the further possibility of eddy diffusion and diffusion within a solid particle, but it was Glueckauf and his associates (4, 5) who first showed how such factors as particle size, particle diffusion and diffusion in the film around the particle could be related to the height equivalent to a theoretical plate. Even so, their results were not obviously applicable and it was left to Klinkenberg and Sjenitzer (6) and more specifically, van Deemter, Zuiderweg and Klinkenberg (7) to develop a more general approach.

There is no doubt that the work of these authors and its application to experiment by Keulemans and Kwantes (8) has had an enormous influence on the course of development of gas-liquid chromatography. The theory of van Deemter et al. takes into account the fact that a solute in the gas phase must spread longitudinally while diffusion into a solvent will be sufficiently slow that equilibrium will not quite be achieved. Further, it is supposed that the inhomogeneity of the packing will cause the flowing gas phase to split up and recombine, the spreading of solute being due to the resulting spread in gas (solute) velocities. This effect is termed eddy diffusion, a name which is not particularly appropriate, as has been pointed out by Golay (9).

The basic approach to the theory is statistical and makes use of the theorem that for a group of independent statistical processes occurring simultaneously the total variance is the sum of the individual variances while the mean is the sum of the individual means. The variance is the square of the standard deviation, which in turn is the deviation from the mean of an average particle or molecule. In terms of the Einstein equation, 4.16

$$l^2 = 2Dt$$

l is the standard deviation, while l^2 is the variance. In gas chromatographic terms, the retention volume, expressed in the same units as l would be the mean. In order to simplify the problem, the theory, which is only outlined here, is taken in separate sections, and the theoretical plate height deduced in terms of the various contributory factors. Since we see from Glueckauf's equation, 7.31, that H is proportional to l^2 it will be valid simply to add the independent contributions to H of the various mechanisms.

DIFFUSIONAL SPREADING

Although solutes pass through a column in times which depend largely upon their partition coefficients, each spends on average the same time in the gas phase. The difference in retention time arises because they do not all spend the same time in solution (or adsorbed). The time which they spend in the gas phase will be determined by the total column free volume and the average gas velocity and, thus, corresponds to the time taken for a solute of $K = 0$ to pass through a column.

The extent of diffusional spreading with time was illustrated in Chapter 4, and the general equation, 4.20, was derived. The solution to that equation for the condition that the concentration was $1/e$ of the maximum yielded the result

$$l_e^2 = 4\bar{D}_g t$$

or, in terms of the standard deviation, l,

$$l^2 = 2\bar{D}_g t$$

According to equation 7.37, $\bar{D}_g$ corresponding to the average column pressure,

$$H = \frac{l^2}{L} = \frac{2\bar{D}_g t}{L} = \frac{2\bar{D}_g}{\bar{u}} \tag{8.1}$$

since t is the time spent in the moving gas phase in the column, $L/t = \bar{u}$, the average linear gas velocity.

van Deemter et al. suggest that in view of the tortuous path pursued within the column a labyrinth factor γ should be introduced. That is,

$$H = \frac{2\gamma \bar{D}_g}{\bar{u}} \tag{8.1a}$$

The value $\gamma = 0.5$ to 1.0 suggested by van Deemter et al. has been interpreted by some workers as an indication that γ is to be identified with the tortuosity constant of the Kozeny-Carman equation. That this is incorrect is evident since, in evaluating the effect of diffusion on H, $\bar{u}$ was only introduced by substitution for the time t. The time taken to move a distance L at velocity $\bar{u}$ is exactly the same as the time taken to travel a distance L_e at a velocity $\bar{u}L_e/L$. Most, but by no means all, of the experimental evidence to date suggests that some factor is required, but it seems unlikely to be the tortuosity factor of the Kozeny-Carman equation.

One possibility which has recently been discussed by Barrer (10) is that the factor γ results from sideways diffusion into regions which are out of equilibrium as a result of the non-isotropic fibrilar nature of the column (anastomosis). One point which is clear is that the presence of packing cannot increase the diffusion rate and so $\gamma < 1$. A further possibility lies in the fact that the tortuous nature of the flow path in a packed column means that diffusion along the axis of the column may be prevented because of the presence of particles. This would mean that longitudinal diffusion would only be possible during part of the time of residence of molecules in the gas phase. It is not clear whether this is, in fact, the case, or whether the column is sufficiently non-isotropic to obliterate the effect.

EDDY DIFFUSION

In the region of viscous fluid flow, very much below the point where turbulence sets in, the pattern of streamlines remains the same if all dimensions or velocities are multiplied by a constant amount. If the column packing in chromatography is not isotropic, then across any plane at right angles to the direction of flow the channels may be of varying size. Thus, since the pressure drop is the same, some longitudinal spreading of a plug of solute molecules should occur since the time taken to pass through narrow channels will be greater than that for passage through wider ones. In view of the similarity of flow patterns, however, the amount of spreading of the molecules must be a constant fraction of the time itself, provided the molecules stay with the carrier fluid and do not diffuse away. Thus, if the time is doubled, so must the spreading and so, since the time taken to pass a particle of diameter d_p at velocity $\bar{u}$ is $(d_p/\bar{u})$, the spread in times of passage, τ, that is the standard time deviation, is

$$\tau = \text{constant}\left(\frac{d_p}{\bar{u}}\right) = \sqrt{2\lambda}\left(\frac{d_p}{\bar{u}}\right)$$

whence,

$$\tau^2 = 2\lambda\left(\frac{d_p}{\bar{u}}\right)^2$$

If now it is assumed that the irregularities are statistically distributed, and remembering that $\bar{u}\tau$ is the distance spreading, l, we have

$$l^2 = 2\lambda d_p^2$$

If the column length is L then the number of times the maldistribution occurs during passage through the column is L/d_p and, since values of l^2 can be added, the total spread during passage over the column length is

$$l^2 = 2\lambda \, d_p L$$

Thus, from equation 7.37,

$$H = \frac{2\lambda \, d_p L}{L} = 2\lambda \, d_p \tag{8.2}$$

If this result is compared with 8.1 it is seen why the process is called a diffusion and also why a constant $\sqrt{2\lambda}$ rather than λ was introduced. From the comparison it follows that here we have an effective diffusion coefficient E given by

$$E = \lambda \, d_p \bar{u}$$

or, on substitution from 8.2

$$E = \bar{u}L/2N$$

This result, first deduced by Kramers and Alberda (11), shows that if the eddy process is operative, the plate height must decrease with decreasing d_p. What the value of λ will be can only be guessed, but for gas chromatographic systems, Klinkenberg and Sjenitzer (6) have cited values of 1 to 4 while Keulemans and Kwantes (8) record values as high as 8. In only one instance does a value less than 1 seem to have been suggested, although Klinkenberg and Sjenitzer were careful to point out that as a consequence of the ease of radial diffusion of gases in packed beds very small values of λ might be observed experimentally. Recent work (12, 13, 14) has been interpreted as meaning that in properly prepared columns λ may be so small as to be negligible. This result is open to criticism, Glueckauf (15), for example, considers that λ must always be at least 0.5. The whole question of the magnitude of λ is controversial and is discussed in greater detail in the succeeding chapter. It is pertinent, however, to point out that if a column is badly prepared such that channelling occurs the effect of this will be so great as to exaggerate very considerably the true eddy effect.

RESISTANCE TO MASS TRANSFER

A mass transfer operation can be identified by the fact that it involves two phases in contact, material flowing between these two phases and doing so, in part at least, by diffusion. Since this is so, resistance to mass transfer in the gas phase is likely to be very considerably less than in liquids, although this can often be offset by making the liquid a very thin film in which the distances to be traversed are much smaller than in the gas phase.

If two phases are in contact then there will be a movement towards equilibrium, the rate of this movement being determined by the displacement from equilibrium. Thus, the closer a system gets to equilibrium, the more slowly it moves. At equilibrium, of course, no further change is apparent. In going from one phase to another, molecules must pass through an interface of some kind. It is generally assumed that there is no hindrance to passage through this interface although this is not always true. Thus, resistance to mass transfer is usually taken to be located in one or both of the phases in contact. On this hypothesis then, there must be a sharp concentration change where the phases meet and there is no way of knowing whether this transitional region extends over the first or the first hundred molecular layers. It is generally assumed that in the first layers the concentration is the thermodynamic equilibrium concentration and so we are able to write an equation for the rate at which molecules are transferred since it is assumed that the rate of transfer through a phase is proportional to the prevailing concentration gradient. Thus, if the concentration at the interface is c_i while the average bulk concentration is c then by analogy with Fick's law of diffusion,

$$\frac{dc}{dt} \propto c_i - c$$

or,

$$\frac{dc}{dt} = \bar{\alpha}(c_i - c)O$$

where $\bar{\alpha}$ is the mass transfer coefficient and O is the area of the interface.

If a linear partition coefficient is assumed ($K = c_l/c_g$) and if we consider first the transport of solute from the gas phase into the solvent, then

$$\frac{dc}{dt} = \bar{\alpha}(Kc_g - c_l')O$$

c_i is, by hypothesis, the equilibrium value of c_l, that is, Kc_g. Thus, c_l' as it occurs in the equation is the out of equilibrium value.

Looked at from the point of view of emergence of solute molecules from the liquid phase

$$\frac{dc}{dt} = \bar{\alpha}(c_l' - Kc_g)O$$

We can now apply these equations to the solution of the problem of the effect of the finite rate of mass transfer on the efficiency of gas chromatographic columns. In the derivation of van Deemter et al. the effect of longitudinal diffusional spreading of solute in the gas phase was considered simultaneously but since this has already been considered it will be omitted here. Further, van Deemter et al. were able to substantiate the view that the contributions of each spreading mechanism to the theoretical plate height could be added, a result which justifies the present simplified approach.

Figure 1 illustrates the processes occurring in one plate of a column. There is transfer of solute into and out of the solvent while, simultaneously, the carrier gas flow moves solute along at some velocity $\bar{u}$. Then, if the fractional volume of the plate occupied by gas is F_g while that taken up by solvent is F_l, this is true also of the cross-sectional area. Thus, the material balances per unit cross-sectional area are

$$F_g\left(\frac{dc_g}{dt}\right) = -F_g\bar{u}\left(\frac{dc_g}{dl}\right) + \bar{\alpha}(c_l' - Kc_g) \qquad (8.3)$$

Gain of   Lost to plate   Gain of solute
solute in plate   by convection   in gas phase
gas phase   from gas phase   from liquid

and in terms of the liquid phase

$$F_l\frac{dc_l}{dt} = \bar{\alpha}(Kc_g - c_l') \qquad (8.4)$$

Gain in solute   Same
in liquid phase
of plate

Lapidus and Amundsen (2) have obtained a general solution for these equations for the case when the sample was originally introduced into the

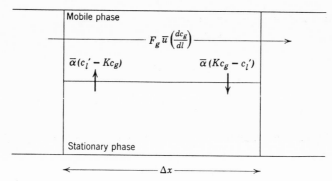

FIG. 1. Diagrammatic view of the sorption processes occurring in a single theoretical plate according to rate theory.

column as a sharp pulse or plug of length t_0 seconds (N_0 plates) at concentration c^o. Their equation is fairly complicated and van Deemter et al. have shown that provided the column contains a sufficient number of plates many approximations are valid, and the result simplifies to

$$\frac{c}{c^o} = \frac{\beta t_0}{\sqrt{2\pi\sigma^2}} \exp\left[-\frac{(L/\bar{u} - \beta t)^2}{2\sigma^2}\right] \qquad (8.5)$$

wherein,

$$\beta = \frac{F_g}{F_g + KF_l}$$

and

$$\sigma^2 = \frac{2\beta^2 F_i^2 LK^2}{\bar{\alpha} F_g \bar{u}}$$

L is the column length, σ is the equivalent of the standard deviation in units of time, and t is the total elution time up to the point under consideration.

The resemblance of this equation to 7.27 of Chapter 7 is evident, and through a comparison we can obtain a value for the theoretical plate height H. Equating exponents and making the slight approximation that $N = M$, which will be valid if N is very big (narrow peaks), an assumption already made in any case, gives

$$\frac{(N - M)^2}{2M} = \frac{(L/\bar{u} - \beta t)^2}{2\sigma^2} \tag{8.6}$$

M, it will be remembered, corresponded to the number of elution volumes contained within the plates up to the point on the elution curve in question (p. 98), that is,

$$M = \frac{V}{\Delta V_r'}$$

and if the cross-sectional area is O

$$\Delta V_R' = HO(F_g + KF_i)$$

while

$$V = F_g \bar{u} t O$$

whence

$$M = \frac{\beta \bar{u} t}{H}$$

Finally, the column length $L = NH$ and making the appropriate substitutions leads to

$$\frac{(NH - \beta \bar{u} t)^2}{NH^2} = \frac{(NH - \beta \bar{u} t)^2 \bar{\alpha} F_g \bar{u}}{2\beta^2 \bar{u}^2 F_i^2 K^2 NH} \tag{8.7}$$

which gives

$$H = \frac{2\bar{u}}{\bar{\alpha}} \left[\frac{\beta^2 F_i^2 K^2}{F_g} \right]$$

which, on rearrangement and substitution for β gives

$$H = \frac{2\bar{u}F_g}{\bar{\alpha}} \cdot \frac{1}{[(F_g/KF_i) + 1]^2} \tag{8.8}$$

If now we define

$$k = F_g/KF_i$$

$$H = \frac{2\bar{u}F_g}{\bar{\alpha}(1 + k)^2}$$

The function k was symbolised k' in the original van Deemter paper but the latter has been used widely for the inverse, that is,

$$k' = \frac{KF_l}{F_g}$$

As is seen later, the distinction is important.

The only unknown quantity remaining now is $\bar{\alpha}$. The overall mass transfer resistance $1/\bar{\alpha}$ may be written as the sum of the resistances in all phases, that is,

$$\frac{1}{\bar{\alpha}} = \frac{1}{\bar{\alpha}_g} + \frac{1}{K\bar{\alpha}_l}$$

If it is assumed that resistance in the gas phase is negligible, which will be the case if the liquid phase is very viscous or thick, $1/\bar{\alpha}_g$ can be neglected and then, following van Deemter et al., the following simplified solution of the general equation for diffusion into a layer can be used

$$\bar{\alpha}_l = \frac{\pi^2 D_l a_p}{4 d_f}$$

where D_l is the diffusion coefficient of the solute in the liquid phase, d_f the effective thickness of the layer of liquid, and a_p is the specific surface area of the film. The specific surface area can be eliminated since, by definition,

$$a_p d_f = F_l$$

which leads to

$$\bar{\alpha}_l = \frac{\pi^2 D_l F_l}{4 d_f{}^2}$$

Substituting this value in the expression for $1/\bar{\alpha}$ gives

$$\frac{1}{\bar{\alpha}} = \frac{4 d_f{}^2}{\pi^2 D_l K F_l}$$

which on insertion in equation 8.8 gives

$$H = \frac{8 d_f{}^2 F_g \bar{u}}{\pi^2 D_l (1 + k)^2 K F_l} \tag{8.9}$$

which simplifies to

$$H = \frac{8 k d_f{}^2 \bar{u}}{\pi^2 (1 + k)^2 D_l} \tag{8.10a}$$

Recently, van Deemter (16) has modified this slightly to

$$H = \frac{2}{3} \frac{k}{(1 + k)^2} \frac{d_f{}^2}{D_l} \cdot \bar{u} \tag{8.10b}$$

SIMPLIFIED VAN DEEMTER EQUATION

By combination of equations 8.1a, 8.2 and 8.10b we arrive at the celebrated equation of van Deemter, Zuiderweg and Klinkenberg,

$$H = 2\lambda d_p + \frac{2\gamma \bar{D}_g}{\bar{u}} + \frac{2k d_f{}^2 \bar{u}}{3(1 + k)^2 D_l} \tag{8.11}$$

which is commonly written, for simplicity, as

$$H = A + \frac{\bar{B}}{\bar{u}} + C_l \bar{u} \tag{8.12}$$

from which it is seen that H, plotted against $\bar{u}$, should yield a hyperbola with a minimum value of H at some velocity $\bar{u}_{min}$. The values of these quantities can readily be derived by setting $dH/d\bar{u} = 0$, when

$$\frac{dH}{d\bar{u}} = 0 = -\frac{\bar{B}}{\bar{u}^2} + C_l$$

which gives

$$\bar{u}_{min} = (\bar{B}/C_l)^{\frac{1}{2}} \tag{8.13}$$

which on substitution in equation 8.12 gives

$$H_{min} = A + 2(\bar{B}C_l)^{\frac{1}{2}} \tag{8.14}$$

The appropriate value of the gas velocity is apparently the compressibility averaged value. The compressibility correction factor f is given by equation 5.21 and so

$$\bar{u} = u_o f = \frac{3}{2} u_o \left[\frac{(p_i/p_o)^2 - 1}{(p_i/p_o)^3 - 1} \right]$$

where u_o is the gas velocity at the outlet pressure p_o. If, however, we look again at equation 8.11 it is seen that the term $\bar{B}$ may not be a constant since D_g is inversely pressure dependent and every velocity corresponds to a different average pressure. Since

$$D_g = \frac{D_g{}^o p_o}{p}$$

it follows that while the velocity at the column inlet is reduced due to the high pressure, so also is the rate of diffusion in the same proportion. For example, suppose a column operates from three atmospheres to one, then in the first plate the velocity is x cm. per sec. and the diffusion coefficient is y cm.^{2} per sec. while in the last plate the velocity is $3x$ cm. per sec. and the diffusion coefficient is $3y$ cm.^{2} per sec. Thus, the ratio D_g/u is independent of pressure. In consequence of this the van Deemter equation is more conveniently written

$$H = A + B_o/u_o + C_l \bar{u} \tag{8.15}$$

where B_o is the diffusion term at the outlet pressure of the column. The appropriate value of D_g over the whole length of the column is then that corresponding to the outlet pressure, $D_g{}^o$. Alternatively, of course we might write B_i/u_i in equation 8.15 but this is clearly much less convenient. It can be seen from equation 8.15 that there is no simple graphical way of illustrating the dependence of H upon the velocity except when the pressure drop across the column is so small that in effect $u_o = \bar{u}$.

MASS TRANSFER RESISTANCE TERM FOR FILM DISTRIBUTION OF SOLVENT

The contribution of mass transfer resistance in solution to H as given in equation 8.10b was derived without special regard to the actual mode of distribution of the solvent. One very special mode which may occur in packed columns and which is generally assumed for all capillaries, is that of a true, continuous film. In this situation the ambiguous quantity d_f can be eliminated and replaced by the measurable parameter d_p, the particle diameter or by r_0, the capillary radius. The procedure is as follows. If we liken a packed column to a series of parallel capillaries as is done in flow studies (p. 63), we can say that the liquid film is so thin that to all intents and purposes the volume of liquid in a column of length L is given by

$$V_l = \pi \, d_p \, d_f L$$

if we make the reasonable assumption that the radius of a capillary is comparable to $d_p/2$.

The volume of gas space in the column is, similarly,

$$V_d = \frac{\pi d_p{}^2 L}{4}$$

if d_f is small compared with d_p. Hence,

$$\frac{V_l}{V_d} = \frac{F_l}{F_g} = \frac{4d_f}{d_p}$$

and

$$k' = \frac{KF_l}{F_g} = \frac{4Kd_f}{d_p} \tag{8.16}$$

a result comparable to that first deduced by Desty, Goldup and Whyman (17) in slightly different fashion in connection with their studies of capillary column performance.

If we now consider k and k', as defined earlier, it is a simple matter to show that

$$\frac{k'}{(1 + k')^2} = \frac{k}{(1 + k)^2}$$

which explains why the misinterpretation of k', so common in the literature, has not affected the evaluation of experimental data. We can thus write equation 8.10b as

$$H = \frac{2}{3}\left[\frac{k'}{(1 + k')^2}\right]\left(\frac{d_f{}^2}{D_l}\right)\bar{u} \qquad (8.17)$$

Rearranging equation 8.16 to

$$d_f{}^2 = \frac{d_p{}^2(k')^2}{16K^2}$$

and substituting this value in equation 8.17 gives

$$C_l = \frac{(k')^3 d_p{}^2}{24K^2 D_l(1 + k')^2} \qquad (8.18)$$

This expression for C_l is identical with that deduced in different fashion for capillary columns by Golay (18).

THE EXTENDED VAN DEEMTER EQUATION

In the simplified treatment, resistance to mass transfer in the gas phase was neglected on the basis that it would be small in comparison to that in the liquid phase. Recently, van Deemter has discussed this (16) and suggested an extended equation for H in which a gas resistance term was included. The value of this term may be derived if we once more consider equation 8.8, that is,

$$H = \frac{2\bar{u}F_g}{\bar{\alpha}(1 + k)^2}$$

and substitute for $\bar{\alpha}$ in this case, the value of $\bar{\alpha}_g$ from the correlation formula of Ergun (19), as suggested by van Deemter et al. (7). This may be written

$$\alpha_g = \frac{25\bar{D}_g a_p{}^2}{6F_g}$$

which, when substituted into equation 8.8, gives

$$H = \frac{12F_g{}^2\bar{u}}{25\bar{D}_g a_p{}^2(1 + k)^2}$$

To proceed farther, certain assumptions are necessary in order to eliminate the specific surface area of the solvent, a_p. van Deemter et al. assume that the support can be regarded as spherical with solvent distributed as a surface film, when, as seen on p. 64,

$$a_p = 6\left[\frac{1 - F_g}{d_p}\right]$$

Substitution then gives

$$H = \left[\frac{F_g{}^2}{(1 - F_g)^2}\right]\left[\frac{d_p{}^2\bar{u}}{75\bar{D}_g(1 + k)^2}\right] \qquad (8.19)$$

We can now convert this to a form containing the more familiar function k'. Since $k' = 1/k$,

$$\frac{1}{(1 + k)^2} = \frac{(k')^2}{(1 + k')^2}$$

In this instance it is to be noted that the distinction between k and k' is important. We thus have

$$H = \frac{F_g^2}{(1 - F_g)^2} \cdot \frac{d_p^2 \bar{u}}{75 \bar{D}_g} \cdot \frac{(k')^2}{(1 + k')^2} \qquad (8.20a)$$

Two avenues of approach are now open. van Deemter et al. apparently assume that F_g is comparable to the porosity ϵ of the column, that is, the inter-particle gas space. This approach is consistent with the identification of a_p given above and with the assumption that the liquid film can be regarded as a layer of $a_p = F_l/d_f$ (p. 127) and not as a collection of drop-lets. On the other hand, in the original paper, a diagrammatic illustration of the basic assumptions indicated that the intra-particle gas space should be included in F_g. Proceeding on the basis that $F_g = \epsilon$ and assuming a reasonable value, say $\epsilon = 0.45$, $F_g^2/(1 - F_g)^2 \simeq 2/3$ and then with only slight approximation, equation 8.20 becomes

$$H = \frac{0.01(k')^2 d_p^2 \bar{u}}{(1 + k')^2 \bar{D}_g} \qquad (8.20b)$$

the result quoted by van Deemter.

The alternative view that the intra-particle gas space contributes to F_g still permits the earlier substitution for a_p but leads to the result

$$H = \frac{K^2 d_p^2 \bar{u}}{75 D_g (1 + k')^2} \qquad (8.20c)$$

In the single situation that $F_l = F_g$, equations 8.20b and 8.20c are identi-cal, since the numerical factors are clearly very approximate. One signifi-cant aspect of either van Deemter form of the gas phase mass transfer term is that when K, that is, also k', tends to zero so, too, does the contribution of the process to H. This result is a consequence of the fact that the non-uniform velocity profile consequent on streamline gas flow is not taken into account, the van Deemter terms relating only to processes at right angles to a flow which was assumed to be uniform. However, Taylor (20) has shown that, in a capillary tube, in the complete absence of partition, the velocity profile in combination with the slowness of radial diffusion leads to considerable material spreading of a diffusional character along the column length with an effective diffusion coefficient D^* defined by

$$D^* = \frac{r_0^2 \bar{u}^2}{48 \bar{D}_g}$$

where r_0 is the radius of the capillary. From this, by analogy with the derivation of equation 8.1, we would expect that, for a substance of $K = 0$, the contribution of the process to H would be

$$H = \frac{r_0^2 \bar{u}}{24 \bar{D}_g}$$

or, if it is assumed for the moment that $r_0 = d_p/2$ for a packed column, then

$$H = \frac{d_p^2 \bar{u}}{96 \bar{D}_g} \tag{8.21a}$$

As seen later, this result is deducible from the more recent chromatographic theory of Golay (18). Again, Westhaver (21) has shown that when K is effectively infinite, as in a wetted wall distillation column, the velocity profile effect contributes to H according to the equation

$$H = \frac{11 r_0^2 \bar{u}}{24 \bar{D}_g} = \frac{11 d_p^2 \bar{u}}{96 \bar{D}_g} \tag{8.21b}$$

If these results are compared with 8.20b it is seen that while the latter gives $H = 0$ at $K = 0$, 8.21a gives a value of H virtually identical with the maximum of 8.20b, that is, at $K \to \infty$. In this condition 8.21b predicts that the radial diffusion process must contribute more than ten times as much to H as does simple axial diffusion. A further point is that, of course, equations such as 8.21a and 8.21b take in the latter process in any case.

While these considerations indicate clearly that the van Deemter gas resistance term is of little consequence, they show also that a C_g term must be included in the general rate equation in addition to C_l. Verification of this view comes from a simple calculation using 8.21b. Suppose $d_p = 0.03$ cm., $\bar{u} = 10$ cm. per sec. and $\bar{D}_g = 0.05$ cm.^{2} per sec., then $H \simeq 0.02$ cm. This is between 5 and 10 per cent of commonly observed theoretical plate heights.

We may thus extend the general form of the rate equation to

$$H = A + \frac{B_o}{u_o} + C_l \bar{u} + C_g^{\,o} u_o \tag{8.22}$$

wherein $C_g^{\,o}$ represents the radial (gas resistance) diffusion term. The appropriate velocity for use with $C_g^{\,o}$ is, by analogy with equation 8.15, that calculated for the outlet column pressure. As given by van Deemter (16), the extended rate equation is,

$$H = 2\lambda d_p + \frac{2\gamma D_g^{\,o}}{u_o} + \frac{2}{3} \frac{k'}{(1 + k')^2} \frac{d_f^2 \bar{u}}{D_l} + \frac{(k')^2 d_p^2 u_o}{100 D_g^{\,o}(1 + k')^2} \tag{8.23}$$

it being borne in mind that the last term is almost certainly of negligible proportions.

GOLAY THEORY OF CAPILLARY COLUMN ACTION

Almost all theories of packed column performance make use of the approximation that the many channels through the packing can be regarded as a bundle of parallel capillaries, more or less identical and of about the same diameter as the particles themselves. If the theoretical plate height of a packed column is constant from one capillary channel to another it is evident that if instead of using them in parallel they were used in series, a very large number of theoretical plates would be available. This simple idea was first put forward in discussion by Martin (22) but was realised only when Golay (9, 18), independently, studied the theoretical basis of capillary operation and carried out the first rudimentary experiments.

One serious problem associated with a single capillary is, of course, that it can accommodate only a very small amount of material both as solvent and sample. In a packed column these quantities are larger in proportion to the greater number of capillaries. In the author's view, therefore, capillary columns are to be regarded as elementary packed columns, and it would be surprising if the theory of the operation of such columns turned out to be very different from that of packed columns. One great advantage that capillaries hold is, of course, that they are much more uniform than packed columns in which the capillaries are of variable shape and dimensions, and further, solute spreading in consequence of eddy diffusion cannot occur in a true capillary since there is no packing. The theory is, thus, liable to be simpler and to represent more closely the actual performance of the columns.

Golay's theoretical approach, therefore, was simplified considerably by the fact that eddy diffusion and packing tortuosity are absent in a cylindrical capillary system. Further, one can put precise values into expressions for gas mass transfer effects at right angles to the direction of flow. This latter problem, which was briefly discussed in connection with the extended van Deemter equation, is one of sufficient importance, as Golay showed, to be worth attempting to deal with.

Golay's approach is to consider the general diffusion law as written in equation 4.2. If now, a superimposed carrier gas flow in the x direction occurs we have

$$D_g\left(\frac{\partial^2 c}{\partial x^2} + \frac{\partial^2 c}{\partial y^2} + \frac{\partial^2 c}{\partial z^2}\right) = \frac{\partial c}{\partial t} + u\frac{\partial c}{\partial x}$$

and since the y and z co-ordinates relate to a cylindrical cross section the above can be written as

$$D_g\left(\frac{\partial^2 c}{\partial r^2} + \frac{1}{r}\frac{\partial c}{\partial r} + \frac{\partial^2 c}{\partial x^2}\right) = \frac{\partial c}{\partial t} + u\frac{\partial c}{\partial x} \qquad (8.24)$$

In order to take into account the parabolic velocity profile of the flowing gas the expression derived for the velocity on p. 58 can be introduced, thus

$$u = u_{\max}\left(1 - \frac{r^2}{r_0^2}\right) = 2\bar{u}\left(1 - \frac{r^2}{r_0^2}\right) \tag{8.25}$$

where r_0 is the capillary radius, r is any distance from the tube centre, u is the gas velocity at the point r and $\bar{u}$ is the average gas velocity. We now have

$$\bar{D}_g\left(\frac{\partial^2 c}{\partial r^2} + \frac{1}{r}\frac{\partial c}{\partial r} + \frac{\partial^2 c}{\partial x^2}\right) = \frac{\partial c}{\partial t} + 2\bar{u}\left(1 - \frac{r^2}{r_0^2}\right)\frac{\partial c}{\partial x} \tag{8.26}$$

and also the boundary condition at the wall ($r = r_0$), that,

$$\frac{2\bar{D}_g}{r_0}\left(\frac{\partial c}{\partial r}\right)_{r=r_0} = -k'\left(\frac{\partial c}{\partial t}\right)_{r=r_0} \tag{8.27}$$

k' being the ratio of the total amount of solute in the immobile phase to that in the gas phase. It is thus the k' of the van Deemter treatment.

The rate of movement of the solute band along the x axis, that is, down the column, is $[1/(1 + k')]$ times the velocity of the carrier gas. In order to relate the diffusional spreading directly to the mass centre of the band it is, therefore, convenient to convert to a co-ordinate x_1 which is related to x through

$$x_1 = x - \frac{\bar{u}t}{1 + k'} \tag{8.28}$$

x_1 is thus the difference between the distance moved by the carrier gas front and that moved by the band. In other words, the x co-ordinate now moves at the speed of the band. Differentiating, it is seen that

$$(\partial x_1)_{k't} = (\partial x)_{k't} \quad \text{and} \quad (\partial^2 x_1)_{k't} = (\partial^2 x)_{k't}$$

hence

$$\bar{D}_g\left[\frac{\partial^2 c}{\partial r^2} + \left(\frac{1}{r}\right)\left(\frac{\partial c}{\partial r}\right) + \frac{\partial^2 c}{\partial x_1^2}\right] = \frac{\partial c}{\partial t} + 2\bar{u}\left(1 - \frac{r^2}{r_0^2}\right)\frac{\partial c}{\partial x_1} \tag{8.29}$$

It is now necessary to modify the time co-ordinate in the term $(\partial c/\partial t)$. This can be done by the usual means for change of variables. If a new set of co-ordinates r_1, x_1 and t_1 is taken

$$\frac{\partial c}{\partial t} = \left(\frac{\partial c}{\partial r_1}\right)\left(\frac{\partial r_1}{\partial t}\right) + \left(\frac{\partial c}{\partial x_1}\right)\left(\frac{\partial x_1}{\partial t}\right) + \left(\frac{\partial c}{\partial t_1}\right)\left(\frac{\partial t_1}{\partial t}\right)$$

but $\partial r_1/\partial t = 0$ and, further, $\partial t_1/\partial t = 1$. This leaves

$$\frac{\partial c}{\partial t} = \left(\frac{\partial c}{\partial x_1}\right)\left(\frac{\partial x_1}{\partial t}\right) + \frac{\partial c}{\partial t_1}$$

From equation 8.28 we have

$$\frac{\partial x_1}{\partial t} = -\frac{\bar{u}}{1 + k'}$$

and so

$$\frac{\partial c}{\partial t} = \left(-\frac{\partial c}{\partial x_1}\right)\left(\frac{\bar{u}}{1 + k'}\right) + \frac{\partial c}{\partial t_1} \tag{8.30}$$

Hence the general equation 8.29 becomes

$$\bar{D}_g\left[\frac{\partial^2 c}{\partial r^2} + \left(\frac{1}{r}\right)\left(\frac{\partial c}{\partial r}\right) + \frac{\partial^2 c}{\partial x_1^2}\right] = \frac{\partial c}{\partial t_1} + \bar{u}\left(\frac{1 + 2k'}{1 + k'} - \frac{2r^2}{r_0^2}\right)\frac{\partial c}{\partial x_1} \tag{8.31}$$

Substitution in equation 8.27 from equation 8.30 yields the new boundary conditions

$$\frac{2\bar{D}_g}{r_0}\left(\frac{\partial c}{\partial r}\right)_{r=r_0} = -k'\left(\frac{\partial c}{\partial t_1}\right)_{r=r_0} + \frac{k'\bar{u}}{1 + k}\left(\frac{\partial c}{\partial x_1}\right)_{r=r_0} \tag{8.32}$$

If now it is accepted that c never differs greatly from the average radial concentration $\bar{c}$, we can write

$$c = \bar{c} + \Delta c$$

and then substitute appropriately for $\partial c/\partial r$ and $\partial c/\partial x_1$ in equation 8.31 and for all terms in c in equation 8.32. Then, multiplying the modified equation 8.31 by the operator

$$\frac{2}{r_0^2}\int_0^{r_0} r\, dr$$

we convert, by an alternative technique, all remaining terms in c to terms in $\bar{c}$. Now, after integration of remaining terms in $\bar{c}$ and elimination of differentials of $\bar{c}$ as a function of r since they are zero, the modified form of the boundary equation 8.32 can be subtracted to give the important general equation

$$\bar{D}_g\frac{\partial^2 \bar{c}}{\partial x_1^2} = (1 + k')\frac{\partial \bar{c}}{\partial t_1}$$
$$+ \left\{\frac{2\bar{u}}{r_0^2}\int_0^{r_0}\left(\frac{1 + 2k'}{1 + k'} - \frac{2r^2}{r_0^2}\right)r\, dr\, \frac{\partial \Delta c}{\partial x_1}\right\} - \frac{k'\bar{u}}{1 + k'}\left(\frac{\partial \Delta c}{\partial x_1}\right)_{r=r_0} \tag{8.33}$$

A term in $\partial \Delta c/\partial t$ disappears because of the presence of a comparable one in $\bar{c}$. On the other hand, terms in $\partial \Delta c/\partial x$, are not negligible in comparison with those in $\partial^2 \bar{c}/\partial x_1^2$ and so must remain.

To solve equation 8.33, Δc must be expressed as a function of $\bar{c}$ differentials. This can be done by replacing c in equation 8.31 by $\bar{c} + \Delta c$ and again dropping differentials of $\bar{c}$ with respect to r and terms in Δc when they occur with terms in $\bar{c}$. From this equation, equation 8.33 is subtracted, the resultant expression being integrated to give

$$\Delta c = \Delta c_0 + \frac{1}{4\bar{D}_g}\left\{-k'r^2\left(\frac{\partial \bar{c}}{\partial t_1}\right) + \bar{u}\left[\frac{(1+2k')r^2}{1+k'} - \frac{r^4}{2r_0^2}\right]\left(\frac{\partial c_1}{\partial x_1}\right)\right\}$$

(8.34)

Differentiation of this, when Δc_0 vanishes, followed by substitution in equation 8.33 gives

$$\left\{\bar{D}_g + \left[\frac{1+6k'+11(k')^2}{48(1+k')^2}\right]\frac{\bar{u}^2 r_0^2}{\bar{D}_g}\right\}\left(\frac{\partial^2 \bar{c}}{\partial x_1^2}\right) = (1+k')\left(\frac{\partial \bar{c}}{\partial t_1}\right) \quad (8.35)$$

Differentials in $\partial x_1/\partial t_1$ are neglected since the rate of change of the concentration gradient with time must be negligible. Equation 8.35 is obviously formally similar to Fick's diffusion equation (4.2) with an effective diffusion coefficient D_e given by

$$D_e = \left[\bar{D}_g + \frac{[1+6k'+11(k')^2]\bar{u}^2 r_0^2}{48(1+k')^2\bar{D}_g}\right]$$

Following the derivation on p.119 the theoretical plate height is then given by

$$H = \frac{2\bar{D}_e}{\bar{u}} = \frac{2D_e^o}{u_o}$$

that is,

$$H = \frac{2D_g^o}{u_o} + \frac{[1+6k'+11(k')^2]r_0^2}{24(1+k')^2 D_g^o}u_o \quad (8.36)$$

The longitudinal diffusion term is clearly the same as that derived earlier and so the contribution of the radial diffusion/velocity profile band spreading mechanism to the theoretical plate height is

$$H = C_g^o u_o = \frac{[1+6k'+11(k')^2]r_o^2 u_o}{24(1+k')^2 D_g^2} \quad (8.37)$$

This result agrees entirely with expectation since, when $k'=0$,

$$H = \frac{r_0^2 u_o}{24D_g^o}$$

as predicted by the Taylor equation (8.21a), whereas, when k' is very great

$$H = \frac{11r_0^2 u_o}{24D_g^o}$$

as predicted by Westhaver's equation (8.21b).

It was shown earlier that if a packed column was approximated by a bundle of parallel capillaries the van Deemter C_l term for mass transfer resistance in the liquid phase could be written

$$C_l = \frac{(k')^3 \cdot r_0^2}{6K^2 D_l (1 + k')^2}$$

where r_0 was the radius of the equivalent capillary. This value of C_l is identical with that derived by Golay for the same term and there is, therefore, little point in detailing the laborious mathematics of the Golay treatment, particularly since it is shown later that the simple stochastic picture gives essentially the same result. Accepting this view we may immediately write the Golay equation for circular capillaries

$$H = \frac{2D_g^{\,o}}{u_o} + \left(\frac{[1 + 6k' + 11(k')^2}{24(1 + k')^2}\right)\left(\frac{r_0^2 u_o}{D_g^{\,o}}\right) + \frac{(k')^3 r_0^2 \bar{u}}{6K^2 D_l (1 + k')^2} \quad (8.38)$$

or, more simply

$$H = \frac{B_o}{u_o} + C_g^{\,o} u_o + C_l \bar{u} \quad (8.39)$$

These equations can, for convenience, be called the extended rate equations for capillaries.

RADIAL DIFFUSION IN, AND AN EXTENDED RATE EQUATION FOR PACKED COLUMNS

Golay has suggested (18) that the radial diffusion term is likely to be even more significant in packed columns than in capillaries, in consequence of the distorted nature of the cross-section of the tubes of flow. If this is the case, both the simplified and extended forms of the van Deemter equation are obviously inadequate.

We can estimate roughly what the ratio $C_g^{\,o}/C_l$ is likely to be under various conditions in a capillary and so determine the validity of Golay's view. If we assume $k' = 1$, $K = 10$, $D_g^{\,o} = 3.3 \times 10^{-2}$ cm.^{2} sec.$^{-1}$ and $D_l = 10^{-6}$ cm.^{2} sec.$^{-1}$ it turns out that $C_l/C_g^{\,o} = 80$. This value appears high but it must be remembered that the value taken for D_l is probably high while that for $D_g^{\,o}$ is relatively low. Thus, the ratio represents a likely maximum. Again, with the same diffusion coefficients at $k' = 0.1$ and $K = 10$, $C_l/C_g^{\,o}$ is only about 1.8, while at $K = 50$, $C_l/C_g^{\,o} \simeq 0.1$. Thus, in fact, there is every reason to accept the view that $C_g^{\,o}$ must often compare with, and perhaps exceed C_l. On the other hand, it is equally reasonable to suppose that C_l is always likely to compare with $C_g^{\,o}$ and so cannot be ignored.

It thus appears that the van Deemter expressions derived earlier must be modified and, since knowledge of velocity profiles in packed beds is lacking, the following formal equivalent to the capillary equation must be temporarily suggested:

$$H = 2\lambda\, d_p + \frac{2\gamma D_g^{\,o}}{u_o} + \frac{2}{3}\left[\frac{k'\, d_f^{\,2}}{(1+k')^2 D_l}\right]\bar{u} + \left[\frac{1 + 6k' + 11(k')^2}{24(1+k')^2}\right]\left(\frac{d_p^{\,2}\chi}{D_g^{\,o}}\right)u_o$$

$$(8.40)$$

If solvent distribution were of a true film type the third term would be replaced by equation 8.18 and 8.40 would differ from 8.38 only in the eddy diffusion term and the χ of the last term. Substitution for r_0 from the equations for hydraulic radius and specific surface area (pp. 63–64) suggests a value of about 0.05 for χ.

THE STOCHASTIC APPROACH TO THE RATE THEORY

The method employed by van Deemter, Zuiderweg and Klinkenberg (7) may be called the conservation of material approach. Recently, several authors have attempted to employ a stochastic theory based on the classic random walk problem (23, 24, 25). It should be emphasised that the only real difference in approach lies in the evaluation of the liquid mass transfer term. The most detailed mathematical treatment, in so far as gas chromatography is concerned, is that due to Beynon, Clough, Crooks and Lester (25) although the basis of their treatment lies in the earlier work of Giddings and Eyring (23). Since Giddings (24) has described a very much simpler approach which yields much the same result, it is not proposed to give details of the rather complex mathematics of Beynon et al. whose final equation is

$$H = \frac{1}{2\beta} + \frac{\bar{D}_g}{\bar{u}} + \frac{2\bar{u}}{k''}$$

β is a figure of merit for a column and is clearly comparable to the A term of van Deemter while k_2'' represents the rate constant for solute condensation. The β term is not specifically related to any column parameter while k'' is not identified in detail since this would involve the van Deemter assumption that solute condensation is kinetically a first order process. A somewhat surprising feature of the equation is the absence of the factor 2 in the second term since this occurs in all equations of this type, irrespective of the particular approach adopted in the derivation.

Giddings (24) has developed a simple approach which he takes so far as to evaluate the standard deviations resulting from various processes. From this point it is a simple matter to deduce the value of H and, as is shown in the present treatment, the simple form of the van Deemter equation can in fact be deduced. Consider first the fate of two solute molecules initially together in a column. After some time, as a consequence of random movements, they will be separated. These random movements may be transfers from one phase to another, or from a fast moving part of the gas stream to a slower one, or merely the result of molecular collisions. Assuming that steps either forward or back are possible, after N steps of length Δl, the displacement, that is, the standard deviation of a particle from the origin is given by

$$\sigma = \Delta l \sqrt{N} \qquad (8.41)$$

where σ may be expressed in terms of time (τ) or distance (l). It must be assumed that the theorem of the additivity of separate variances is applicable. The step processes involved are likened to coin tossing, successive tosses leading to more or less separation of molecules but, on the whole, causing separation to increase. The coin tossing analogy implies a symmetrical distribution around a mean, since "heads" and "tails" are equally likely. A Gaussian distribution is evidently, therefore, also to be assumed.

If the average carrier gas speed is $\bar{u}$ then molecules in the gas phase move with this velocity. The overall velocity, however, is much less, since molecules spend time in solution. If we take t_g to be the mean time spent in the gas phase, t_l the mean time spent in solution (or adsorbed) and the mean solute band velocity to be $\bar{u}_r$ we can say that

$$\bar{u}_r = \bar{u}\left(\frac{t_g}{t_g + t_l}\right) \qquad (8.42)$$

Consider first the problem of transfer between phases, every such transfer being considered a random incident. It must be assumed that equilibrium is approached. If there are G sorptions during an elution then there must also be G desorptions, and so the total number of incidents (equilibrations) is $2G$. $2G$ must, obviously, equal the number of steps N occurring in a column and by definition, N is the number of theoretical plates. Substituting τ for σ, Δt for Δl and $2G$ for N in equation 8.41 gives

$$\tau = \Delta t \sqrt{2G} \qquad (8.43)$$

The average time of elution $\bar{t}$ is the sum of the average times spent in the two phases, thus,

$$\bar{t} = t_g + t_l$$

Suppose now that the transition rate from the gas to the liquid phase is r_{gl} and the rate for the reverse process is r_{lg}, then if all molecules spend a time t_g in the gas phase they must undergo $t_g r_{gl}$ sorptions per elution, and hence,

$$G = t_g r_{gl} = t_l r_{lg} \qquad (8.44)$$

and since Δt is to be regarded as the average time required for desorption it is equal to $1/r_{lg}$, that is, seconds per molecule. Eliminating G and Δt from equation 8.43 gives

$$\tau = \frac{(2t_g r_{gl})^{\frac{1}{2}}}{r_{lg}}$$

This result is identical to that derived by the more rigorous methods of Giddings and Eyring (22) and relates the spreading mechanism directly to the rates of the kinetic processes involved. Squaring τ we obtain the time variance

$$\tau^2 = \frac{2t_g r_{gl}}{r_{lg}^{2}}$$

which can be converted to a distance variance by multiplying by the square of the appropriate velocity which, in this case, is $\bar{u}_r$. Thus,

$$l^2 = \frac{2Lr_{gl}\bar{u}}{r_{lg}^{2}}\left(\frac{t_g}{t_g + t_l}\right)$$

t_g having been replaced by the ratio of column length to average gas phase velocity, $L/\bar{u}$ and $\bar{u}_r$ by the appropriate value from equation 8.42.

It can readily be shown from equation 8.44 that

$$\frac{t_g}{t_g + t_l} = \frac{r_{lg}}{r_{lg} + r_{gl}}$$

hence

$$l^2 = \frac{2Lr_{gl}\bar{u}}{(r_{lg} + r_{gl})^2} \tag{8.45}$$

These quantities can now be related to H, the theoretical plate height through equation 7.37

$$H = \frac{l^2}{L}$$

hence

$$H = \frac{2r_{gl}\bar{u}}{(r_{lg} + r_{gl})^2} \tag{8.46}$$

The evaluation of the longitudinal diffusion term is identical with that outlined earlier (p. 119) since the Einstein treatment is equivalent to a random walk approach as evidenced by his studies of Brownian motion. Thus,

$$l^2 = 2\bar{D}_g t_g$$

on substituting for $t_g = L/\bar{u}$, since $\bar{u}$ is the appropriate velocity,

$$l^2 = \frac{2\bar{D}_g L}{\bar{u}}$$

and

$$H = \frac{l^2}{L} = \frac{2\bar{D}_g}{\bar{u}} \qquad (8.47)$$

The contribution of the eddy diffusion to the plate height again is determined in a way that follows closely on that given earlier. Since the streamlines continually bend, molecules must spend some of their time moving at an angle to the apparent direction of flow, that is, along the axis of the column. This lateral movement may also take molecules from a path of one velocity to one of another. If we again consider two molecules approaching a particle, one may flow directly past it, while another may move sideways. The separation at the time when the first molecule just passes the particle is then one particle diameter. Considering this one operation as a random step, we can say that $\Delta l = d_p/\bar{u}$ and $N = L/d_p$, hence, from equation 8.41,

$$\tau^2 = \frac{L d_p}{\bar{u}^2}$$

and so

$$l^2 = L d_p$$

whence

$$H = d_p \qquad (8.48)$$

This value of the contribution of eddy diffusion to the plate height is quoted as the minimum to be expected by Glueckauf (15), that is, by analogy with the van Deemter equation, $\lambda = 0.5$.

Adding now the three equations 8.46, 8.47 and 8.48 for H gives

$$H = d_p + \frac{2\bar{D}_g}{\bar{u}} + \frac{2r_{gl}\bar{u}}{(r_{lg} + r_{gl})^2} \qquad (8.49)$$

This equation is clearly identical in form with the simplified van Deemter equation, differing only in details. Thus, the labyrinth factors 2λ and γ of the van Deemter equation are missing; evidently, if desired they could be included. The form of the third term is, at first sight, somewhat simpler but less instructive than that of $C_l\bar{u}$ in the van Deemter equation. However, from equation 8.44

$$r_{gl} = \frac{r_{lg} t_l}{t_g}$$

and substituting this in equation 8.46 gives

$$H = \frac{2\bar{u}(t_l/t_g)}{r_{lg}(1 + t_l/t_g)^2}$$

and since $(t_l/t_g) = (KV_l/V_d) = k'$, of the van Deemter treatment, Giddings' third term can be written

$$H = \frac{2k'\bar{u}}{(1 + k')^2 r_{lg}} \tag{8.50}$$

In this form the resemblance to the van Deemter mass transfer term is even more evident.

It was pointed out earlier that $1/r_{lg} = \Delta t$, the average time required for desorption of a dissolved molecule. To a reasonable degree of approximation this is the time taken for the solute molecule to traverse half the solvent film thickness in both directions, that is, a distance d_f. Hence, using again the Einstein equation (4.20)

$$l^2 = d_f{}^2 = 2D_l \Delta t$$

and

$$\Delta t = \frac{1}{r_{lg}} = \frac{d_f{}^2}{2D_l}$$

Substitution of this result in equation 8.50 gives

$$H = \frac{k' \cdot d_f{}^2}{(1 + k')^2 D_l} \tag{8.51}$$

The difference between this result and the simplified form of that of van Deemter et al. lies only in the numerical term, $2/3$ (or $8/\pi^2$), of the latter and is negligible in comparison to the several approximations involved. We may thus write equation 8.49 as

$$H = d_p + \frac{2D_g{}^o}{u_o} + \left[\frac{k'}{(1 + k')^2}\right]\frac{d_f{}^2}{D_l}\bar{u} \tag{8.52}$$

introducing again the pressure dependence of D_g.

THE GENERALISED DIFFUSION APPROACH TO RATE THEORY

Giddings (33–35) has recently laid great emphasis on the diffusional character of band spreading processes by attacking the theory through an initial derivation of a basic equation describing local non-equilibrium effects in terms of an effective diffusion coefficient; somewhat in the manner adopted by Taylor (20). If the material balance equation, comparable with equation 8.3, for a given phase is set up, Giddings (34) has shown rigorously that, when kinetic systems do not deviate far from true equilibrium, the equation simplifies considerably and states that the rate of accumulation of solute per unit volume of phase due to the local non-equilibrium, s, is

$$s = (u - \bar{u})\frac{\partial c_e}{\partial l} \tag{8.53}$$

u is the solute velocity at the point in question in the particular phase, $\bar{u}$ is the average downstream velocity in that phase, c_e is the equilibrium concentration of solute and l is the distance coordinate along the column. This equation is formally similar to Fick's first law and so we can write also

$$s = D_e \nabla^2 c_e \tag{8.54}$$

in analogy with the second law. D_e is the effective diffusion coefficient for the spreading process. We can also say that the true concentration c (non-equilibrium) at any point is related to c_e through

$$c = c_e(1 + \epsilon) \tag{8.55}$$

where ϵ is an equilibrium departure term. Since c_e is locally invariant we have

$$s = c_e D_e \nabla^2 \epsilon \tag{8.56}$$

and elimination of s between equations 8.53 and 8.56 gives

$$\nabla^2 \epsilon = \frac{(u - \bar{u})}{D_e}\left(\frac{\partial \ln \bar{c}}{\partial t}\right) \tag{8.57}$$

Here $\bar{c}$ represents the concentration of solute in terms of volume of packing rather than a given phase; $\bar{c}$ and c_e must obviously be related in a simple and constant manner in any locality.

We can now specify the flux of solute through unit area (O) normal to flow as

$$q = \sum \int cu \, dO = \sum \int c_e u \, dO + \sum \int c_e u\epsilon \, dO$$

The last term is responsible for all non-equilibrium effects and, being equal to a non-equilibrium flux can, by analogy with Fick's law be written equal to $D^*(\partial c/\partial l)$, whence

$$D^* = -\frac{\sum \int c_e \epsilon u \, dO}{\partial c/\partial l} \tag{8.58}$$

D^* is thus the effective diffusion coefficient for the non-equilibrium band spreading and is seen to be independent of position and concentration because these quantities are cancelled out of equation 8.58 when the integrated form of equation 8.57 is introduced. It is, however, proportional to the square of the velocity.

The problem of evaluating the contribution of any non-equilibrium process to the theoretical plate height is now reduced to that of solving equation 8.57 appropriately and then applying the familiar relationship $H = 2D/u$.

Giddings has carried out this procedure for the solution of the problems of (a) resistance to mass transfer through a uniform film of liquid and finds the same result for C_l as was found earlier by other methods and, (b) resistance to mass transfer through a static gas layer (*cf.* p. 128). For the latter he found the contribution to H to be

$$H = \left(\frac{k'}{1 + k'}\right)^2 \left(\frac{d^2 \bar{u}}{6 \bar{D}_g}\right)$$

where d is the distance to be travelled by the solute molecules, that is, roughly one pore depth. Thus, if $d \simeq d_p/4$, this result is again more or less identical with that of the van Deemter equation 8.20*b*.

An interesting simplification introduced in Gidding's approach is that it readily permits rather detailed study of the effect of the shape of the column and its packing particles on the magnitude of the C_l term. Thus, if we define the effective pore cross-sectional area O_e by

$$O_e = (d - x')^{n'}$$

where x' is distance into the pore and $n' > 0$, it is relatively easy to show (36) that

$$C_l = \frac{2k'd}{(n' + 1)(n' + 3)(1 + k')^2 D_l}$$

For a uniform film $n' = 0$ and the numerical coefficient is $\frac{2}{3}$ as before. For cylindrical rods (paper chromatography), $n' = 1$ and the coefficient is $\frac{1}{4}$, while for spheres, $n' = 2$ and the coefficient is $\frac{2}{15}$. Interestingly, according to this approach a collection of randomly sized pores behaves as though it were a continuous film.

Finally, Giddings has dealt with the problem introduced by the parabolic velocity gradient of flow and confirms the result of Golay for both cylindrical and square section capillaries. The complete agreement of the results obtained by the various theoretical approaches is clearly of significance since it offers a reasonably reassuring basis for future study.

Non-additive Variances. It was emphasised earlier that the whole of the rate theory as developed here depends upon the validity of the theorem of additive variances, that is, that all chromatographic band spreading processes can be regarded as independent. Giddings has made the point that this is likely to be true only if a single rate process can be regarded as rate controlling. Thus, if processes occurring in different phases are each slow enough to be considered rate controlling, the additivity of variances is unlikely to be correct. Clearly, this view strikes at the root of the theory as it is now accepted and implies that this aspect of the problem demands urgent study. One consequence of this belief which has been developed (35) is that eddy diffusion and gas mass transfer effects cannot be taken to operate separately since they may act individually so as to reduce the effects of the other. If they are, thus, considered as acting in parallel it has been shown that the extended rate equation takes the form

$$H = \frac{1}{1/A + 1/\bar{C}_g \bar{u}} + \frac{\bar{B}}{\bar{u}} + C_l \bar{u}$$

The complications arising when other processes are taken into account have only been partially worked out (34).

THEORETICAL DEPENDENCE OF H
UPON EXPERIMENTAL PARAMETERS

Before going on to discuss in the next chapter the experimental findings in relation to the effect of experimental variables on the theoretical plate height it is convenient to outline what may be expected.

Eddy Diffusion. In packed columns, if an eddy diffusion effect operates, the lowest attainable value of H irrespective of other variables is determined by d_p and λ. The theoretical premises suggest that the minimum value of H should be d_p, but it is probable that channelling of packing would increase this. Since the latter is almost certain to occur to some extent in even the best packed column, values of A in excess of d_p are likely and, indeed, experimentally determined values of A may arise entirely from packing-irregularities.

Longitudinal Gas Diffusion. This must occur in both packed and capillary columns although, if $\gamma < 1$ it should be less significant in the former. Obviously, the contribution of this process to H diminishes with increasing gas velocity and, through reduction of $D_g{}^o$, with increasing carrier gas molecular weight. Similarly, although it should be unaffected by pressure gradient the contribution to H should diminish proportionately with increasing column outlet pressure.

Gas Phase Mass Transfer. The radial diffusion contribution to H may be expected to decrease with decreasing carrier gas molecular weight but to increase with increasing column outlet pressure, since $C_g{}^o \propto 1/D_g{}^o$. This behaviour is, of course, the converse of that expected of B_o, and so the interplay of this term and $C_g{}^o$ will determine the precise effect of carrier gas and pressure. As is shown later, for any type of column the terms are, in fact, exactly mutually opposed, and their combined contribution to H_{min}, although at no other velocity, is then independent of carrier gas identity and pressure. For either packed or capillary columns, $C_g{}^o$ should diminish rapidly with reduced particle size or tube radius.

The dependence of $C_g{}^o$ on k' for a given solute at constant temperature is illustrated in Figure 2, in which $[1 + 6k' + 11(k')^2]/24(1 + k')^2$ is plotted against k'. The function rises rapidly from $1/24$ to $11/24$ and at values of k' greater than about 10 is effectively constant. $C_g{}^o$ is then equal to $(11r_0{}^2/24D_g{}^o)$ for a capillary and $(11\chi\, d_p{}^2/24D_g{}^o)$ for a packed column. Thus, $C_g{}^o$ is then independent of k'. This behaviour is that to be expected when

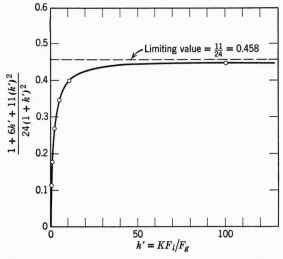

FIG. 2. Illustration of the theoretical dependence of $C_g{}^o$ on k' at constant d_p (or r_0) nd $D_g{}^o$.

solvent/support ratio is changed at constant temperature. An alternative way of changing k' for a given solute/solvent system is, of course, to change the temperature at constant solvent/support ratio. The consequences of this for the function $[1 + 6k' + 11(k')^2]/24(1 + k')^2$ should be again as shown in Figure 2, but the dependence of $C_g{}^o$ on temperature is not accurately reflected by the curve since reduction of k' (higher temperature) would concurrently lead to an increase in $D_g{}^o$. Thus, unless allowance were made for the temperature dependence of $D_g{}^o$, while the shape of a plot of $C_g{}^o$ against k' would be the same, the curve would lie lower than that in Figure 2. Further, since increasing k' corresponds in this case to reduced temperatures and diffusion coefficients, the curve would not reach a maximum.

A further alternative way of changing k' with a given column at constant temperature is to change the solute. Since for every solute $D_g{}^o$ is likely to be different, the effect of this on a plot of $C_g{}^o$ against k' for several solutes would be similar to that described for temperature change. Clearly, the only reliable way to study the inter-relation of $C_g{}^o$ and k' is with one solute and several solvent/support (solvent/free space) ratios at fixed temperature.

One of the considerable advantages claimed for capillary columns (18) has been that C_l is likely to be negligible, in which case the extended rate equation becomes effectively

$$H = \frac{B_o}{u_o} + C_g{}^o u_o$$

While this view is probably an oversimplification (17, 27), we can explore the consequences of this situation. Differentiating as before (p. 126) to find the minimum, we get

$$(u_o)_{\min} = \left(\frac{B_o}{C_g{}^o}\right)^{\frac{1}{2}} \quad \text{and} \quad H_{\min} = 2(B_o C_g{}^o)^{\frac{1}{2}}$$

On inserting the appropriate values of B_o and $C_g{}^o$ we have, when

$$k' = 0; \qquad (u_o)_{\min} = 6.9 D_g{}^o/r_0, \qquad H_{\min} = 0.58 r_0$$
$$k' = \infty; \qquad (u_o)_{\min} = 2.1 D_g{}^o/r_0, \qquad H_{\min} = 1.91 r_0$$

We thus see that in a capillary column wherein resistance to mass transfer in the liquid phase were of no consequence, the contribution of $C_g{}^o$ to $H_{\min}$ would not be likely to exceed the tube diameter. The detailed dependence of $(u_o)_{\min}$ on k' is shown in Figure 3, $(u_o)_{\min}$ being plotted in units of $D_g{}^o/r_0$. It is seen that at $k' = 10$, $(u_o)_{\min}$ corresponds closely to the value for $k' = \infty$. Figure 4 shows the dependence of $H_{\min}$ on k'; $H_{\min}$ is plotted in units of r_0. An interesting deduction which follows from this discussion is that in the absence of mass transfer in solution, substances of the lowest solubility appear to be eluted most efficiently and most swiftly. This is an important point, since it shows that for fastest analysis reduction of C_l is the really pressing problem. One further point to be made is that we can now predict fairly certainly the effect of elution temperature on the contribution of $C_g{}^o$ to H. Increasing the temperature over a range such that k' falls from about 10 to some value close to 0 should diminish the contribution to H by about a factor of 4. The same, of course, would be true of reduction of solvent/support (solvent/free space) ratio.

Minimization of the contribution of B_o and $C_g{}^o$ to H is thus brought about by working with columns of the smallest possible diameter (particle size), with poor solvents in small amount, and at high temperature. The contribution to $H_{\min}$ of $D_g{}^o$ is cancelled between the two terms and so the identity of the carrier gas and its pressure are irrelevant, although both go far in determining $(u_o)_{\min}$ and, hence, analysis speed.

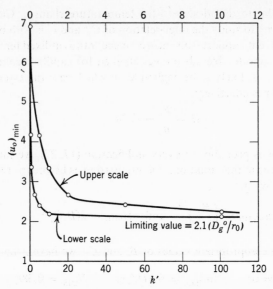

FIG. 3. The theoretical variation of $(u_o)_{\min}$ with k' for a circular capillary column having $C_l \rightarrow 0$. $(u_o)_{\min}$ is plotted in units of $(D_g{}^o/r_0)$.

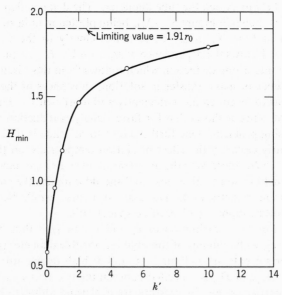

FIG. 4. Theoretical variation of $H_{\min}$ with k' for a circular capillary column having $C_l \rightarrow 0$. $H_{\min}$ is plotted in units of r_0.

Resistance to Mass Transfer in the Liquid Phase. The problem in anticipating the way in which experimental variables determine the contribution of C_l to H is that of knowing the precise mode of liquid distribution in a column. We can consider first the possibility of true film distribution in either a capillary or a packed column. From equation 8.18 we see that C_l diminishes very rapidly with reduced tube diameter or particle size and inversely as the interdiffusion coefficient. Little can be done in the way of controlling the latter but, in principle, high temperatures and solvents of

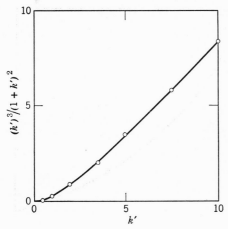

FIG. 5. Expected dependence of the function $(k')^3/(1 + k')^2$ on k'. This plot represents the theoretical variation of C_l with k' at constant K, d_p (r_0) and $\bar{D}_l$ for a column having solvent distributed as a film.

low viscosity should be favourable. The dependence of the function $(k')^3/(1 + k')^2$ on k' is illustrated in Figure 5 and it is seen to rise continuously. Thus, for a given solute/solvent system at constant temperature (constant K, d_f, D_l), Figure 5 represents the variation of C_l with solvent/support ratio. As was pointed out in the previous section, k' can be altered in other ways, but not independently of other variables. A comparison of C_l for a series of solutes with a given column at constant temperature should, however, lead to a result comparable with that shown in Figure 5. On the other hand, variation of k' by changing temperature for a given solute and column could lead to a quite different result. Apart from the fact that d_f^2/D_l is likely to decrease considerably with increasing temperature, we now have also a decreasing K. We can rewrite equation 8.18 in the form

$$C_l = \frac{k'(V_l/V_d)^2 d_p^2}{24(1 + k')^2 \cdot D_l}$$

and so we see that for a given column at varying temperature the dependence of C_l upon k' is virtually identical with that in the situation of droplet distribution of solvent (equation 8.10b). This is discussed in the next section.

From the liquid mass transfer term as originally deduced by van Deemter et al. (equation 8.10b) we see that C_l depends upon d_f^2/D_l. If there is a droplet distribution d_f is unlikely to depend upon solvent/support ratio and will primarily be determined by such things as the extent of wetting of the

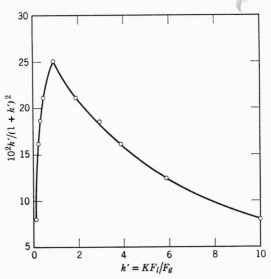

FIG. 6. Theoretically anticipated dependence of the function $k'/(1 + k')^2$ on k'. This plot represents the expected variation of C_l with k' at constant d_f and D_l for a column containing solvent distributed as droplets.

support, the temperature and surface tension of solvent and the pore size of the solid. The dependence of C_l for droplet distribution on k' is shown in Figure 6 where $k'/(1 + k')^2$ is plotted against k'. As k' increases from zero, C_l rises, passes through a maximum and then falls continuously. The position of this maximum can readily be predicted since

$$\frac{dC_l}{dk'} = \frac{2d_f^2}{D_l}\left[\frac{1}{(1 + k')^2}\left(1 - \frac{2k'}{(1 + k')}\right)\right] = 0$$

whence $1 + k' = 2k'$ and $k' = 1$. At this point, $k'/(1 + k')^2 = 0.25$. Figure 6 corresponds to the result to be expected for the effect of change of solvent/support ratio on C_l for a given solute at constant temperature. The curves resulting from change of k' by the other methods available should also show maxima but the curves are likely to be displaced somewhat.

In practice, it is unlikely that solvent distribution will be either exclusively of the droplet or film types, and it is not unreasonable to suppose that at low solvent/support ratios, the former will predominate while, when all pores are occupied, a film can then develop. Thus, a transition from behaviour such as is shown in Figure 6 to that in Figure 5 might occur with increasing solvent/support ratio. Obviously, the precise effects cannot be predicted, but the transition could well lead to an experimental observation of a curve for C_l versus k' of the form shown by the broken line in Figure 7.

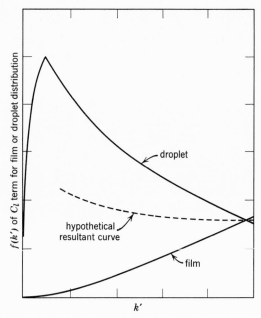

FIG. 7. Illustration of one hypothetical type of dependence of C_l upon k'. The plot is effectively a composite of Figures 5 and 6 and might represent the state of affairs resulting from a change in the mode of solvent distribution with increasing solvent/support ratio.

This diagram can only be taken as illustrative and we can have no real idea of the depth or width of any likely minimum. The possible existence of a minimum, however, is in itself interesting, since it is conceivable that in consequence, experiments conducted over a limited range of values of k' might indicate that C_l was independent of k'.

A further complication is introduced by the fact that if the simplified van Deemter equation were used to evaluate C_l any results obtained would not only be confused by the different forms of the dependence of C_l upon k', but also by any contribution from $C_g{}^o$. The possible combinations of Figures 4, 5 and 6 are many, and almost any apparent dependence of C_l

upon k' might be deduced. From this and the earlier discussion it is evident that the means to reduce C_l are not at all clear cut, and the question must await experimental clarification.

THE APPROACH TO FASTER ANALYSIS

Undoubtedly, every effort should be made to obtain the maximum efficiency from any column, but it is also important that this efficiency be utilised in the minimum time. In other words, large numbers of theoretical plates alone are not the whole aim, but low values of the ratio $H/\bar{u}$. This aspect was discussed originally by the author (28), who showed that since, on the basis of the simplified van Deemter equation, the minimum values of H and $\bar{u}$ for any column and solute are given by

$$H_{\min} = A + 2\sqrt{BC_l}$$

and

$$\bar{u}_{\min} = \sqrt{B/C_l}$$

$$H/_{\min}\bar{u}_{\min} = A\sqrt{C_l/B} + 2C_l$$

On the other hand, writing the simplified van Deemter equation as

$$\frac{H}{\bar{u}} = \frac{A}{\bar{u}} + \frac{\bar{B}}{\bar{u}^2} + C_l$$

we see that

$$\left(\frac{H}{\bar{u}}\right)_{\min} \simeq C_l$$

It was pointed out that in consequence of this the fastest operation of a column does not correspond to working at the velocity corresponding to minimum H. The situation is illustrated in Figure 8, the lines corresponding to $(H_{\min}/\bar{u}_{\min})$ and $(H/\bar{u})_{\min}$ being shown. From the slopes we see that, as predicted above, the latter is less than half the former. If, thus, one used a column of the characteristics shown in the Figure 8, it could be operated for a given value of N, with a length L cm. at 7 cm. sec.$^{-1}$ $(H_{\min}/\bar{u}_{\min})$ or better, with a length $1.7L$ cm. at 30 cm. sec.$^{-1}$. Obviously the latter offers much faster analysis.

We can now go on to establish what further points are of importance in determining the speed of analysis. The approach is based on that of Purnell and Quinn (29), who start with the separation equation (7.44) developed earlier.

$$N_{\text{req}} = 36\left[\frac{\alpha}{\alpha - 1}\right]^2\left[1 + 2\left(\frac{V_d}{V_{R_2}}\right) + \left(\frac{V_d}{V_{R^2}}\right)^2\right]$$

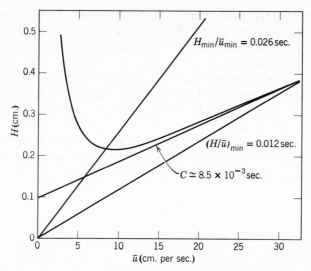

FIG. 8. Plot illustrating the difference between $(H/\bar{u})_{\min}$ and $(H_{\min}/\bar{u}_{\min})$.

The ratio V_d/V_{R_2} is, of course, $1/k'$ in the nomenclature of the rate equation, hence

$$N_{\text{req}} = 36\left(\frac{\alpha}{\alpha - 1}\right)^2\left(\frac{1 + k'}{k'}\right)^2 \tag{8.59}$$

k' being the value appropriate to the second eluted component of an exactly (6σ) separated pair of substances. The elution time t of this component is, by definition,

$$t = \frac{L}{\bar{u}}(1 + k') = \frac{NH}{\bar{u}}(1 + k')$$

hence

$$t = 36\left(\frac{\alpha}{\alpha - 1}\right)^2\left(\frac{H}{\bar{u}}\right)\left[\frac{(1 + k')^3}{(k')^2}\right] \tag{8.60}$$

For fast analysis, as we have seen, we are interested only in the situation that $H/\bar{u} \simeq C = C_l + C_g^\circ/f$, and so

$$t = 36\left(\frac{\alpha}{\alpha - 1}\right)^2 C\left[\frac{(1 + k')^3}{(k')^2}\right] \tag{8.61}$$

This is the basic time equation, from which it is immediately apparent that the fastest analysis is consistent with the use of solvents offering large values of α, that is, selective solvents. In addition, since most often, α increases with reduced temperature, this too appears to be advantageous. As seen later, both these generalisations may need modification.

The Solvent-Free Gas Space Ratio. For a given solute/solvent system k' may be changed in several ways. The most important for the present is by change of solvent/support ratio. It is not immediately possible to deduce the exact dependence of t upon k' since C also depends on k'. Assume, however, in the first instance, that C is independent of k'. Experimental studies (p. 175) suggest that this may often be the case (see also Figure 7). Equation 8.61 may now be differentiated immediately and this process shows t to be a minimum at $k' = 2$. In this situation, therefore, the solvent/support ratio and temperature should be chosen such that $k' = 2$ for the second eluted component of the pair of components in a mixture which are the most difficult to separate. Putting this value in 8.61, gives

$$t_{\min} = 243 \left(\frac{\alpha}{\alpha - 1} \right)^2 C \tag{8.62}$$

while its insertion in 8.59 gives the number of theoretical plates which would be needed for the separation as

$$N_{\text{req}} = 81 \left(\frac{\alpha}{\alpha - 1} \right)^2 \tag{8.63}$$

If we know even roughly the values of α, k', K and also C from a plot of H against $\bar{u}$, we can, obviously, calculate the composition and length of column and the operating velocity after only rudimentary experiments. A point of significance is that when choosing a solvent, that of the largest value of α may not be the best since, if partition coefficients are low it may not be practically possible to achieve the condition $k' = 2$ without seriously overloading the column with solvent.

If C is not independent of k' various possibilities arise and the situation becomes rather complicated. Consider first the case of solvent distribution either as a film or as droplets whose size depends on the amount of solvent present. Then we can write, ignoring for simplicity the compressibility correction factor f,

$$C \simeq C_g{}^o + C_l = \frac{[1 + 6k' + 11(k')^2] r_0{}^2}{24(1 + k)^2 D_g{}^o} + \frac{(k')^3 r_0{}^2}{6(1 + k')^2 K^2 D_l}$$

where r_0 may be either a capillary or a particle radius. The basic time equation becomes

$$t = 36 \left(\frac{\alpha}{\alpha - 1} \right)^2 r_0{}^2 \left\{ \frac{(1 + k')[1 + 6k' + 11(k')^2]}{24(k')^2 D_g{}^o} + \frac{k'(1 + k')}{6K^2 D_l} \right\} \tag{8.64}$$

The time of analysis would evidently be very markedly reduced as r_0 diminished. In order to evaluate the role of the bracketted function it is necessary to make certain assumptions about $D_g{}^o$, D_l and K.

It is generally agreed that the ratio $D_g{}^o/D_l$ must approximate 10^5. However, absolute values must be taken if we are to get a real idea of t. We can assume, therefore, that $D_g{}^o = 10^{-1}$ cm.^{2} sec.$^{-1}$ and $D_l = 10^{-6}$ cm.^{2} sec.$^{-1}$. It can readily be calculated now that $C_g{}^o$ is equal to C_l when $k'/K \simeq 0.01$,

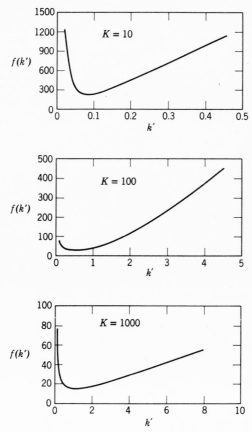

FIG. 9. Plots of $f(k')$ versus k' for values of $K = 10$, 100 and 1000. $f(k')$ calculated from equation 8.64. The diagram shows the occurrence and position of a minimum in analysis time as a function of k'. *By courtesy of Butterworths.*

which corresponds roughly to a 1 per cent w/w packing. Thus, both terms contribute to C in the normal working region. In any circumstances, the bracketted function shows a minimum, and hence the analysis time does also. Figure 9 shows plots of the bracketted function $f(k')$ against k' for various values of K. It is seen that the minimum occurs at low values of k' when K is low, but that the corresponding value of t_{min} is high. As K increases, k'_{min} does also, and t_{min} decreases. Thus, we see that to achieve the fastest analyses with columns in which $d_f \propto k'$, every effort is necessary to work with high partition coefficients. This is illustrated in Figure 10 in which $f(k')_{\min}$, which is a measure of $t_{\min}$, is plotted against K. Very roughly, the lowest acceptable value of K is about 20. The limiting high speed is that corresponding to $C_l = 0$ when $k' \simeq 1$. However, as seen from Figure 9, there is little loss in speed if one works at $k' = 2$, but we see from equation 8.53 that the value of N, and so, the column length, is halved.

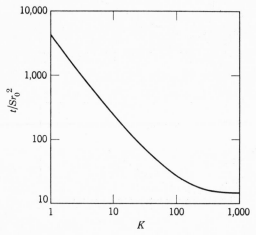

FIG. 10. Variation of minimum value of $f(k')$ and hence, analysis time, with K. *By courtesy of Butterworths.*

Thus, again, $k' = 2$ seems a reasonable generalisation provided partition coefficients are not too low. It is likely that it represents a maximum value. The effect of making wrong assumptions as to the magnitude of $D_g{}^o$ and D_l is predictable. If the diffusion coefficient ratio is less than was assumed, the value of $k'_{\min}$ moves closer to $k' = 1$, but if, as is more likely, the ratio is greater, slightly smaller values of $k'_{\min}$ are found. However, it should be remembered that the discussion has ignored the fact that in reality $C_g{}^o$ is a function of u_o and not $\bar{u}$. The effect of correcting for this is to increase $C_g{}^o$ relative to C_l and thus to make k' tend again to unity. Precise evaluation is, of course, impossible, but as a basis for further development the present approach must be of value, especially since the conclusions apply equally to capillary and to packed columns.

The third possible type of dependence of C upon k' is that in which d_f is independent of k'. Then, the time equation becomes

$$t = 36\left(\frac{\alpha}{\alpha - 1}\right)^2 \left\{ \frac{(1 + k')[1 + 6k' + 11(k')^2]r_0^2}{24(k')^2 D_g{}^o} + \frac{2}{3}\frac{(1 + k')}{k'}\frac{d_f^2}{D_l} \right\} \quad (8.65)$$

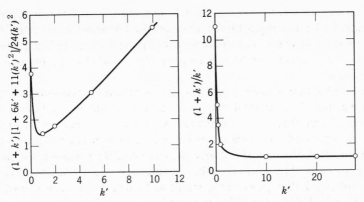

FIG. 11. Plot of the component terms of $f(k')$ of equation 8.65 against k'. The diagram shows minima arising from each, the net position being determined by the ratio C_g^o/C_l.

Figure 11 shows plots of the first bracketted function in units of r_0^2/D_g^o, against k' and also of $(1 + k')/k'$ against k'. The former shows the expected minimum near $k' = 1$ while the latter shows that, above $k' = 4$, the function and hence the time of analysis is independent of k'. The value of the function at $k' = 2$ is about 60 per cent greater than at the minimum. Bohemen (30) has found $d_f^2/D_l = 0.06$ for acetone eluted from a 20 per cent w/w polyethylene glycol/firebrick ($d_p = 0.01$ cm.) column at 50°C. Assuming $D_g^o \simeq 10^{-1}$ cm.^{2} sec.$^{-1}$ we can use these values to plot a graph of analysis time in units of $t(\alpha - 1)^2/36\alpha^2$. This is, effectively, a combination of the plots in Figure 11, and is shown in Figure 12. It is seen that a

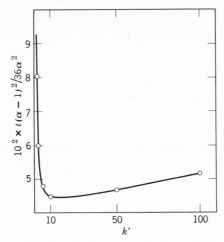

FIG. 12. Composite plot of analysis time as a function of k' for droplet distribution of solvent.

minimum analysis time occurs near $k' = 6$ but at $k' = 2$ the time is only greater in the ratio $6/4.5$, that is, a loss of speed of about 33 per cent. This discrepancy is slight in comparison with the advantages of being able to make the generalisation that, practically, a value of $k' = 2$ represents the optimum.

Consideration of each of the situations which may arise indicates that, irrespective of the dependence of C upon k', columns constructed and operated such that $k' = 2$ for the second eluted component of the pair of solutes which offer the greatest difficulty in their separation of all possible pairs, will usually be within about 50 per cent of the maximum for speed. The situation which arises if all the possible mass transfer mechanisms and solvent distribution processes operate simultaneously, as seems likely to be the case (p. 198) is little different, since the time minima all occur near the same value of k'; the most significant effect would be a modification of the value of the minimum time and the number of theoretical plates needed to effect separation. When detailed experimental studies elucidate the quantitative contributions of all the factors involved a reassessment of the column conditions corresponding to fastest analysis will be needed. In the meantime, the present suggestions seem reasonable.

The Carrier Gas and Operating Pressure. The previous section dealt only with the role of solvent support (or gas free space) ratio and of α in fixing the conditions for fastest analysis. Clearly, the choice of carrier and its pressure is also highly important.

It has already been shown that the extended rate equation leads to a situation wherein the attainable minimum H is hardly dependent on the identity of the carrier gas while the velocity at $H_{\min}$ increases more or less in proportion to $D_g{}^o$. Thus, for a given length of column at the same p_o, hydrogen as carrier offers the possibility of about four times faster analysis than does nitrogen or argon. Thus, hydrogen is, ultimately, the ideal carrier gas for gas chromatography.

The situation, in respect of the optimum outlet column pressure and pressure gradient is interesting. From equation 8.62 we see that, to all intents and purposes,

$$t_{\min} \propto C = C_g{}^o/f + C_l$$

Since $C_g{}^o$ is inversely proportional to $D_g{}^o$ it would appear that a near vacuum at the column outlet would speed analysis greatly provided $C_g{}^o$ were large in comparison with C_l. This situation would be most commonly encountered in columns containing little solvent distributed on coarse support (or lean capillaries) and operated in nitrogen or some other heavy carrier gas. If, on the other hand, the column were highly efficient and operated in hydrogen C_l would, most likely, be greater than $C_g{}^o$ and so any reduction in time as a consequence of reducing p_o to vacuum would not be very great. It must be borne in mind that particularly small values of f, that is, high ratios of p_i to p_o, could be obtained when working near $p_o \simeq 0$ and this would increase the contribution of C_g^o to C very greatly. In addition, of course, it would increase H and, in consequence, the length of column required. This obviously complicates the situation and could mean a loss of speed at low p_o in some cases even where $C_g^o > C_l$.

It would thus appear that what gains in speed through operation at low pressure may be observed will be with relatively inefficient columns operated with dense carrier gases.

Optimum Conditions for Fast Analysis. We can tentatively make the following recommendations.

(a) The choice of solvent (or adsorbent) yielding the largest values of α and of K.

(b) Correct selection of the most difficult separation and choice of solvent/support ratio for this such that $k' = 1$ to 2.

(c) The use of hydrogen as carrier gas.

(d) Probably the use of low column outlet pressures and gas velocities as high as may be compatible with reasonable values of N_{req}, which of course will increase with velocity.

We can speculate briefly on the analysis times which may be attainable. From equation 8.62 we see that, for a column constructed to have $k' = 2$ for the separation contemplated,

$$t_{min} = 243 \left(\frac{\alpha}{\alpha - 1} \right)^2 \left(\frac{C_g^o}{f} + C_l \right)$$

An infinitely easy separation, for example $\alpha > 20$ would then give

$$t_{min} = 243(C_g^o/f + C_l)$$

We know that values of C_g^o and C_l in the neighbourhood of 10^{-4} sec. are attainable, hence, t_{min} becomes about 50 milliseconds. However, at $p_o = 0$, $C_g^o = 0$ and, if as is believed, C_l may be made as small as 10^{-5} sec., simple analysis in the order of a millisecond may be envisaged. More difficult analyses would, of course, require times greater in proportion to $(\alpha/\alpha - 1)^2$ and overall multicomponent analyses would be slower in proportion to $(V_R)_\omega/(V_R)_2$ where ω designates the last eluted component. Even so, it would appear that very complex mixtures may eventually be dealt with in a second or two.

THE EXPERIMENTAL EVALUATION OF k'

While k' can be calculated theoretically from the relationship $k' = KV_l/V_d$ if K, for example, is known, it is virtually always the case that it has to be evaluated chromatographically. V_d represents the elution volume of a non-sorbed gas such as air and so, provided it also represents the total free gas volume of the column (inter + intra particle) we can write

$$k' = (V_R' - V_d)/V_d$$
$$= V_R'/V_d - 1 = t'/t_a - 1 \qquad (8.66)$$

where t denotes retention times, or, for that matter, distances on a recorder chart. However, it is necessary to show that V_d is a measure of total column free volume. That this is the case in capillaries or columns of non-porous support is evident, but it has also been shown to be true for columns of porous support (31). The argument is as follows.

If a gaseous substance is introduced into the first theoretical plate of a column, the carrier gas being, for example, hydrogen, it must be uniformly distributed throughout the gas space very rapidly if there is to be any prospect of the desired equilibration with the stationary phase. That the latter is itself normally rapid and closely attained is proved by the constancy of retention volume over wide ranges of carrier gas flow. Thus, if the substance introduced were air, it must, equally, be rapidly and uniformly distributed throughout the free gas space. Now, when one inter particle volume (V_i) of carrier gas moves into the column, the air contained in the V_i of the first plate must move into the second. There is no doubt whatsoever that carrier flow is between particles and not through them as well, the relevant permeabilities alone would show this to be the case (31). Hence the air in the intra-particle gas space (V_p) of the first plate is left behind to re-equilibrate with the new volume, V_i, of carrier. If continued, the process is clearly identical with stepwise ideal chromatography (p. 89), the necessary immiscibility of phases deriving from the relative motion of the parts of the gas. Hence, using the conventional retention volume equation

$$V_d = V_i + K V_p$$

K, however, since all gases are completely miscible, is unity for all things under all conditions. Hence,

$$V_d = V_i + V_p$$

and V_d, which is often known as the air peak retention volume, is equal to the total free space in a column. This conclusion has several times been proved experimentally (30, 31, 32).

Thus, equation 8.66 can be confidently used to measure k' from experimental data for all kinds of columns. It must be pointed out that if V_d is used to measure porosity, a compressibility correction is necessary.

CALCULATION OF GAS VELOCITY

The extended rate equation contains two velocities, u_o and $\bar{u}$. They are related by the pressure correction factor f as in equation 5.21; that is, $\bar{u} = u_o f$. If, therefore, inlet and outlet pressures are known, the conversion of u_o to $\bar{u}$, and vice versa, presents no problem. However, the calculation of u_o does, and several methods have been employed.

The most common method is to use the air peak retention time and divide this into the column length. For a capillary or non-porous support column this procedure yields $\bar{u}$. This is self-evident since all workers accept the need to modify retention volumes, through the compressibility correction equation 5.21. The conversion to u_o is then straightforward. From what was said in the previous section, however, it is equally obvious that, since the only significant gas velocity is that between particles, for columns of porous support, the procedure gives $V_i\bar{u}/(V_i + V_p)$ which is commonly about $\bar{u}/2$. Whatever method is to be used with columns of porous support, therefore, independent measurement of V_i and V_p is necessary if any velocity is to be correctly evaluated. This is, of course, possible through density measurements, especially those made under mercury.

THE EXPERIMENTAL EVALUATION OF RATE EQUATION CONSTANTS

Studies of the applicability of rate theory have, with one exception, been made in terms of the simplified van Deemter equation. Thus, no widespread attempts have been made to evaluate C_l and $C_g{}^o$ separately and the mass transfer coefficients determined have been a block term which we may designate C. If this C is identified for the moment with C_l of the rate theory, it should clearly be possible, on the basis of the simplified van Deemter equation, to evaluate C graphically by location and measurement of the slope of the asymptote to the high velocity end of the plot of H versus $\bar{u}$. Its intercept at $\bar{u} = 0$ would be A, and a simple calculation would then give an apparent B_o. In the same way a plot of H against $1/u_o$ would permit an asymptotic evaluation of B_o. This technique is obviously restricted to data obtained with columns having large values of C ($\sim 10^{-2}$ sec.) or of B_o, but even then precise location of the asymptotes is difficult, and almost any desired value of A, in particular, can be obtained. If C is small, that is, there is no perceptible rise of the hyperbola at the high velocity end, the graphical method is useless and, in fact, all workers are now agreed that it is generally unsatisfactory. On the other hand, if several well separated sets of experimental values of H, u_o and $\bar{u}$ are used in simultaneous equations, A, B and C may be evaluated by calculation. This approach is tedious, but more reliable, and has been, in the main, the method used by most workers. However, when applied to the extended rate equation, which contains four constants and three variables, the method, in the absence of a computer, becomes virtually impossible.

At this time, the only published evidence on this point derives from the work of Bohemen and the author (30, 31). These workers, however, found several ways of evaluating the four coefficients of the extended rate equation which were both simple and reasonably reliable. The basis of these involved considerable extension of the usual working range of carrier gas velocities and measurements were conducted to as low as $u_o = 0.5$ cm. sec.$^{-1}$ and as high as $u_o = 100$ cm. sec.$^{-1}$. At the low velocity end, plots of H versus $1/u_o$ gave fairly accurate values of A and B_o and these were then used

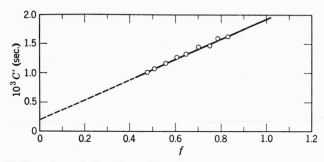

FIG. 13. Experimental data illustrating the predicted linearity of a plot of $C' = C_g{}^o + C_l f$ against f. The data relate to the elution of acetone by nitrogen at 50°C. from a 5-ft. column of 20 per cent w/w polyethylene glycol distributed on 120 to 140 mesh (A.S.T.M.) Sil-O-Cel. *By courtesy of the Chemical Society.*

to evaluate C_l and $C_g{}^o$ in the following way. The mass transfer terms contribute to H as shown below

$$H_{MT} = (C_g{}^o + C_l f)u_o = C' u_o$$

Thus, for every value of u_o and the corresponding H, a value of C' can be deduced, knowing A and B_o. Then, a plot of values of C' for various values of u_o against the corresponding compressibility correction factors f should give a straight line of slope C_l and intercept $C_g{}^o$. Figure 13 illustrates data (30) which substantiate this, but, in practice, it was found that with $p_o \simeq 1$ atm. f could not be varied sufficiently widely with a given column to allow great accuracy, except with support of the very finest mesh. Thus, while a 5-foot column of 120–140 A.S.T.M. Sil-O-Cel yielded the data shown in the figure, at least thirty feet long columns of 30–40 mesh support would be needed to give the same range of f values, which even so is not really great enough to allow very certain extrapolation to the intercept at $f = 0$.

A better method was found to be that of making measurements for a given solute/column system either with two carrier gases or with a given gas at two, fairly widely separated, outlet pressures. Then we have, since A and

C_l should be the same in each case,

Gas 1: $\quad H_1 = A + \left(\dfrac{B_o}{u_o}\right)_1 + (C_g{}^o u_o)_1 + C_l \bar{u}_1$

Gas 2: $\quad H_2 = A + \left(\dfrac{B_o}{u_o}\right)_2 + (C_g{}^o u_o)_2 + C_l \bar{u}_2$

Hence,

$$H_1 - H_2 = \left(\frac{B_o}{u_o}\right)_1 - \left(\frac{B_o}{u_o}\right)_2 + (C_g{}^o u_o)_1 - (C_g{}^o u_o)_2 + C_l(\bar{u}_1 - \bar{u}_2)$$

Re-writing this equation for convenience,

$$\Delta H + C_l \Delta \bar{u} = \left[\left(\frac{B_o}{u_o}\right)_1 - \left(\frac{B_o}{u_o}\right)_2\right] + \left[(C_g{}^o u_o)_1 - (C_g{}^o u_o)_2\right] \quad (8.67)$$

we see that, since by definition, $B_1/B_2 = C_{g_2}/C_{g_1}$, the first bracketed term on the right hand side is large at low velocities and positive, while the second is large at high velocities and is negative. The left hand side of the equation must thus pass through zero and, obviously, at some point therefore, $\Delta H = 0$ when $\Delta \bar{u} = 0$, since $C_l \neq 0$. The best way to use equation 8.67 was found to be by plotting graphs of H_1 and H_2 versus $\bar{u}$ and locating the crossing point of the two curves. Then

$$\left(\frac{B_o}{u_o}\right)_1 - \left(\frac{B_o}{u_o}\right)_2 = (C_g{}^o \bar{u}_o)_2 - (C_g{}^o \bar{u}_o)_1$$

and knowing reasonable values of B_0 and the ratio $(C_g{}^o)_2/(C_g{}^o)_1$, the latter could be evaluated individually with the same degree of approximation as that of the original estimates of $(B_o)_1$ and $(B_o)_2$. Figure 14 illustrates plots of data (31) for the elution of acetone from a 20 per cent polyethylene glycol/Sil-O-Cel (100–150 mesh) column at 51°C. In (a) the data relate to elution in hydrogen with $p_o = 1$, 2 and 3 atm. and H is plotted against u_o recalculated to the value it would have at 1 atm. (u'). The curves come together at low velocities, a feature which substantiates the extended rate equation as written in equation 8.40. In (b), H is plotted against $\bar{u}$ and data for elution in nitrogen with $p_o = 1$ and 3 atm. are included. A number of the expected crossings of the curves are seen and from these $C_g{}^o$ was calculated through the procedure outlined above.

Having once got reasonable, although approximate, values for all four coefficients, a series of successive refinements eventually gave data which reproduced the H/u_o data over the whole velocity range to within ± 1 per cent. A slight complication was introduced by the finding that A was not, apparently, entirely carrier gas independent and a ΔA term had, occasionally, to be used in 8.67. However, this could always be computed from the original A and B estimates.

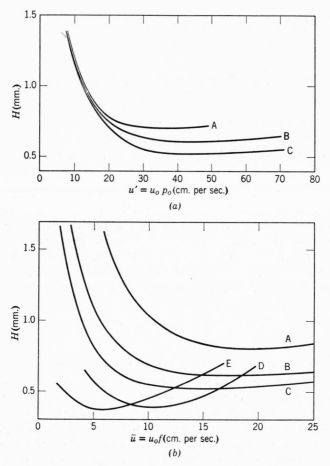

FIG. 14. Data for acetone elution from column described in Figure 13. (*a*) Plots of H against $u_o p_o \, (= u')$ for elution by H_2 with $p_o =$ A, 1 atm.; B, 2 atm.; C, 3 atm. (*b*) Plots of H against $u_o f \, (= \bar{u})$ for elution by H_2 with $p_o =$ A, 1 atm.; B, 2 atm.; C, 3 atm.; and for elution by N_2 with $p_o =$ D, 1 atm.; E, 3 atm. *By courtesy of the Chemical Society.*

A similar, but independent, method of evaluating C_l and $C_g{}^o$ which does not involve initial estimation of A and B_o, has also been used with success by Perrett and the author. Again it is accepted that $(B_o)_1/(B_o)_2 = (C_g{}^o)_2/(C_g{}^o)_1 = (D_g{}^o)_1/(D_g{}^o)_2$, where the subscripts denote data relating either to elution by different carrier gases or by the same gas at different values of p_o. If now, values of H, corresponding to outlet velocities in the same ratio as the appropriate gaseous interdiffusion coefficients, are subtracted the result is that

$$\Delta H = C_l(\bar{u}_1 - \bar{u}_2)$$

since the contributions of A, B_o and $C_g{}^o$ terms are the same in each case. Thus, C_l can be calculated at any velocity, the most consistent results being obtained at high u_o. Following this, a value of C', which is adequate, may be obtained by measuring the slope of the asymptote on a plot of H against u_o, and $C_g{}^o$ evaluated from the relationship

$$C' = C_g{}^o + C_l f$$

A and B_o can then be calculated very quickly through the use of simultaneous equations.

REFERENCES

1. De Vault, D., *J. Amer. Chem. Soc.*, 1943, **65**, 532.
2. Lapidus, L., and N. R. Amundson, *J. Phys. Chem.*, 1952, **56**, 984.
3. Tunitskii, N. N., *Doklady Akad. Nauk.*, *U.S.S.R.*, 1954, **99**, 577.
4. Glueckauf, E., *Disc. Faraday Soc.*, 1949, **7**, 12; 202.
5. Glueckauf, E., *Analyst*, 1952, **77**, 903; *Trans. Faraday Soc.*, 1955, **51**, 1540.
6. Klinkenberg, A., and F. Sjenitzer, *Chem. Eng. Sci.*, 1956, **5**, 258.
7. van Deemter, J. J., F. J. Zuiderweg, and A. Klinkenberg, *Chem. Eng. Sci.*, 1956, **5**, 271.
8. Keulemans, A. I. M., and A. Kwantes, *Vapour Phase Chromatography*, 1956, Butterworths, London (editor, D. H. Desty), p. 15.
9. Golay, M., *Gas Chromatography*, 1958, Butterworths, London (editor, D. H. Desty), p. 15.
10. Barrer, R. M., *Gas Chromatography*, 1958, Butterworths, London (editor, D. H. Desty), p. 35.
11. Kramers, H., and G. Alberda, *Chem. Eng. Sci.*, 1953, **2**, 173.
12. Brennan, D., and C. Kemball, *J. Inst. Petrol.*, 1958, **44**, 14.
13. Littlewood, A. B., *Gas Chromatography*, 1958, Butterworths, London (editor, D. H. Desty), p. 35.
14. Bohemen, J., and J. H. Purnell *Gas Chromatography*, 1958, Butterworths, London (editor, D. H. Desty), p. 6.
15. Glueckauf, E. *Gas Chromatography*, 1958, Butterworths, London (editor, D. H. Desty), p. 33.
16. van Deemter, J. J., *2nd Informal Symp. G. C. Disc. Group*, Cambridge, Sept. 1957.
17. Desty, D. H., A. Goldup and B. H. F. Whyman, *J. Inst. Petrol.*, 1959, **45**, 287.
18. Golay, M., *Gas Chromatography*, 1959, Butterworths, London (editor, D. H. Desty), p. 36.
19. Ergun, S., *Chem. Eng. Progr.*, 1952, **48**, 227.
20. Taylor, G. I., *Proc. Roy. Soc.*, 1954, **A223**, 446; **A225**, 473.
21. Westhaver, J. W., *Ind. Eng. Chem.*, 1942, **34**, 126.
22. Martin, A. J. P., *Vapour Phase Chromatography*, 1957, Butterworths, London (editor, D. H. Desty), p. 2.
23. Giddings, J. C., and H. Eyring, *J. Phys. Chem.*, 1955, **59**, 416.

24. Giddings, J. C., *J. Chem. Phys.*, 1957, **26**, 169.
25. Beynon, J. H., S. Clough, D. A. Crooks, and G. R. Lester, *Trans. Faraday Soc.*, 1958, **54**, 705.
26. Giddings, J. C., *J. Chromatog.*, 1959, **2**, 44.
27. Scott, R. P. W., *5th Informal Symp. G. C. Disc. Group, London*, April 1959.
28. Purnell, J. H., *Ann N. Y. Acad. Sci.*, 1959, **72**, 592.
29. Purnell, J. H., and C. P. Quinn, *Gas Chromatography*, 1960, Butterworths, London (editor, R. P. W. Scott), p. 184.
30. Bohemen, J., and J. H. Purnell, *J. Chem. Soc.*, **1961**, 360.
31. Bohemen, J., and J. H. Purnell, *J. Chem. Soc.*, **1961**, 2630.
32. Primavesi, G. R., *5th Informal Symp. G. C. Disc. Group, Bristol*, Sept. 1959.
33. Giddings, J. C., *J. Chromatog.*, 1960, **3**, 443.
34. Giddings, J. C., *J. Chromatog.*, 1961, **5**, 46.
35. Giddings, J. C., *J. Chromatog.*, 1961, **5**, 61.
36. Giddings, J. C., *Anal. Chem.*, 1961, **33**, 962.

Contributions to the theoretical plate height of a column may come either from sources outside the column such as the use of excessive sample sizes and feed band widths, or from the column itself as a result of the operation of processes associated with the constituent materials, the method of construction and the operating conditions employed. A detailed study of the role of each of the many contributing factors is desirable both in order to test the theory outlined in Chapter 8 and, perhaps more important, in order that columns may be put to the best possible practical use.

A great deal of such work has already been carried out although in almost no case can it be said to be complete or that the results are capable of unequivocal interpretation. This is a consequence of the very complexity of the chromatographic process which makes it difficult to devise experiments in which conditions can be sufficiently closely controlled that the results may be rigorously interpreted. Further, the inter-relation of some of the band spreading processes is so subtle that their magnitude, and sometimes even their existence, is often open to question. Nevertheless, particularly from the practical point of view, much benefit has derived from such studies. For convenience, it is best to consider first some results relating to extra column parameters, since any interpretation of column performance is of no value if there are significant external contributions to the theoretical plate height.

9
EXPERIMENTAL
TESTS
OF THE
RATE
THEORY

THE EFFECT OF SAMPLE SIZE ON COLUMN PERFORMANCE

As a general rule, concentration independent partition coefficients can

165

only be expected in the most dilute solutions (p. 10). A curved partition isotherm must lead to a variation of retention volume within a given solute band as it passes through a column and, thus, represents an extra band spreading mechanism. This situation, non-linear non-ideal chromatography, is clearly undesirable, and every effort should be made to avoid it

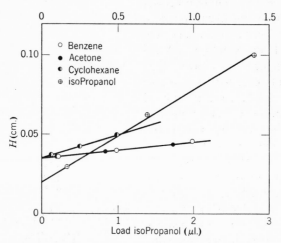

FIG. 1. Experimentally determined dependence of H upon injected sample size. Lower scale is for isopropanol. Solutes were eluted from a 20 per cent w/w polyethylene glycol—100 to 140 mesh (A.S.T.M.) Sil-O-Cel column by N_2 at 47°C. *By courtesy of the New York Academy of Sciences.*

in practice. On this basis, it is to be anticipated that a reduction of sample size must lead to an improvement in column performance.

That this is the situation in practice was first demonstrated by Mellor (1) who found a threefold improvement in column performance on reducing the sample size eight times, and by Pollard and Hardy (2) who observed a linear dependence of H upon the volume of liquid samples. These sample sizes were quite large, and since this might have introduced an extra effect of excessive feed volume, the problem was restudied by Bohemen and the author (3, 4) who, however, also found a linear relationship between H and sample size over the range 0.1 to about 5 μl. of liquid. These results are illustrated in Figure 1. Since the sample size is unlikely to affect the magnitude of the A, B_o and C_g^o terms of the van Deemter or extended equations this change in H must reflect a similar change in C_l. Presumably, sample size might bear on the value of the partition coefficient, but we then have non-linear non-ideal conditions and the van Deemter equation is inapplicable. Alternatively, D_l might be concentration dependent, although it would be surprising if this dependence were linear. There are no published data from which the effect of sample size on C_l can be deduced, although this seems a problem well worth investigation, since it has a direct bearing on the elucidation of the form of chromatographic process involved.

The only subsequent study has given results which appear to conflict with those discussed above. Bethea and Smutz (5) have studied the effect of sample size on H for a variety of solutes with columns containing either dibutyl phthalate or dibutyl sebacate. According to these authors, with the dibutyl phthalate column, the theoretical plate height passed through a minimum at liquid sample sizes between 4 and 7 μl., the exact value depending upon the solute in question. With columns containing dibutyl sebacate the minimum occurred in the region of 10 to 12 μl. Since the columns used had diameters between 5 and 7.5 mm., and were thus comparable with those of the studies cited earlier, it seems likely that their results reflect not so much column performance as the effect of excessive feed volume and the lengthy times of evaporation consistent with the use of liquid samples of 5 to 25 μl.

Some idea of the sample size which is consistent with linear non-ideal conditions can be gained from a very simple calculation. If a column, 1 metre in length, has an efficiency equivalent to 1000 theoretical plates, then, since $H = 0.1$ cm., from equation 7.37 we have

$$H = l^2/L \quad \text{and hence,} \quad l^2 = 10 \text{ cm.}^2$$

Thus, the emergent solute band is about 6.5 cm. wide (y) at the inflexion points. If the feed band is also Gaussian and its width is to have a negligible effect on the theoretical plate height, the injection band must have $y = 1.5$ cm. Its permissible base width is thus roughly 3 cm. which represents 3 per cent of the column length. If the column contains 1 g. of solvent of molecular weight 400, the permissible feed band width in terms of column length takes in only 7.5×10^{-5} moles of solvent. A 1-mg. sample of a solute of molecular weight 100 corresponds to 10^{-5} moles and if this can be injected in the permissible feed volume and has a high partition coefficient the resulting concentration in solution is about 12 moles per cent. This value is much above the limit below which Henry's law may be expected to apply to most solutions and a reasonably safe estimate of this limit would be about 1 mole per cent. To comply with this, therefore, the maximum sample size for the column quoted would be about 0.1 mg. This is very considerably smaller than is commonly used.

The concentrations calculated above occur only at the beginning of the elution and at the injection end of a column, of course, but even so, if the whole column is to be used to the best advantage the sample size limitation must be close to that suggested here. With more efficient columns, still smaller samples must be used, since the eluted peak width and, hence, the permissible feed width diminishes inversely as the square root of the number of plates in the column. It is not to be wondered, therefore, that the highest efficiencies appear only to be attainable with samples of the order of a few microgrammes.

From the example just given it follows that the sample size must be proportionated to the weight of solvent in the column and so, also, it may be varied in proportion to the square of the column diameter if the proportion of solvent to support is maintained constant. On this basis it seems likely that with capillary columns, or very lean packed columns, sample sizes of the order of hundredths of a microgram may be necessary if the high efficiency potential of such columns is to be realised. With such restrictions on sample size it seems certain that only detectors of the very highest sensitivity are of real use with highly efficient columns.

INJECTION VOLUME REQUIREMENTS FOR MAXIMUM EFFICIENCY

The necessary conditions such that the feed band width contributes only a negligible proportion of H have been discussed in Chapter 7 and the previous section. It should be remembered that, for a mixture, the appropriate band width is most likely to be that of the first substance eluted. In order to eliminate feed band effects it is necessary to have an effective injection method. For gas samples it appears that some form of hypodermic injection usually represents an adequate approach, although, for liquids the problem is rather more difficult.

A liquid sample may, of course, be hypodermically injected directly into the packing at the column head, and at first sight it appears that this is the ideal way. However, this is only true if the sample subsequent to injection is rapidly taken uniformly into solution. In the absence of stirring this may not occur readily. On the whole, it seems most probable that, with this form of injection, uniform distribution of sample liquid will be effected only after vaporisation in the column. If this is true it is probably best to vaporise the sample before or immediately after injection into the system. Care is evidently needed to ensure that complete vaporisation in the preheated sample chamber is possible.

This is not as simple as it sounds. For example, as little as 1 mg. of benzene represents about 0.5 ml. of vapour at 100°C. and 1 atm. pressure. If the sample vaporising chamber is smaller than this, the benzene cannot completely vaporise and the feed volume will be time and flow rate dependent. Similarly, if the chamber volume is big but the temperature low, rapid and complete vaporisation may not be possible. Thus, at 50°C., the saturation vapour pressure of benzene is only about one-third of 1 atm.; thus the volume occupied by 1 mg. becomes 1.5 ml. The 0.5 ml. chamber, which was adequate at 100°C. is deficient under these conditions. It is important to remember that the volume of a vaporised sample is occupied at its saturation vapour pressure at the preheater temperature, and so high boiling liquids which may have saturation vapour pressures of only 1 mm. of Hg or less even at 200°C. must meet the feed volume requirement at a proportionately low concentration, which in turn sets further limits on sample size. A further point is that the high temperature must extend up to the column packing if there is not to be condensation. Finally, vaporisation may become diffusion controlled if the pressure in the heated chamber is high due to the presence of carrier or other gas. This, again, would lead to a time dependence of vaporisation. Thus, the pressure should either be reduced or sufficient time allowed for mixing.

Experimental studies at high temperature support the above views. For example, Orr and Callen (17) found that even when the preheater was 150°C. hotter than the column, increasing this differential was beneficial, as is seen from Table 1.

TABLE 1

EFFECT OF INJECTION TEMPERATURE ON COLUMN
EFFICIENCY

Preheater Temperature °C., Column at 200°C.	Number of Theoretical Plates for Methyl Stearate
350	1460
300	1380
250	1230
200	920

It may well be, in fact, that some of the effects attributed to excessive sample size are connected with feed volume and slow vaporisation problems rather than high concentrations in solution in the column. It seems certain that this is a very important matter in connexion with attempts to use very large samples for preparative purposes. The result of using preheater temperatures which are too low was illustrated in Figure 9 of Chapter 7. A rough idea of the power needed in a preheater can be gained from the fact that to vaporise completely 1 mg. of benzene requires about 0.1 cal., while to vaporise an alcohol or high molecular weight compound twice this quantity may be needed. Evidently, the preheater must be able to provide this amount of energy per milligram rapidly and without appreciable change in temperature in the process. It is highly probable that preheater deficiencies are important practically and, in particular, in the field of preparative scale chromatography.

A somewhat unexpected source of excessive feed band width is the identity and properties of the material of which the injection system is constructed. Bohemen (6) has compared identical by-pass systems constructed in glass, stainless steel, copper and brass. The results obtained with glass and stainless steel were virtually identical but wider and more asymmetric elution bands were obtained with the copper and brass systems. The explanation appears to lie in adsorption, or, in some cases, even some chemical action, on the copper or brass surface. This leads to a time dependent exponential desorption which, in turn, results in the appearance of fairly long tails on the eluted chromatographic peaks. Of interest in this connexion is the observation of Porter (7) that columns constructed in copper tubes and used for the analysis of oxygenated compounds such as aldehydes and fatty acids rapidly develop a green layer on the copper surface. This is, presumably, the result of chemical interaction with the sample. This result would seem to substantiate the work of Bohemen, and it suggests that only glass, aluminium or stainless steel are really suitable for use in chromatographic apparatus.

Similar difficulties may be experienced with non-metallic components of injection systems such as plastic or rubber parts, grease or other lubricant. Bearing in mind that such substances are often good chromatographic solvents, this is not surprising, and the result of exposure of sample to such materials is again the appearance of tailed peaks, the tails sometimes being very long indeed, and often virtually ruining a separation. Sorption of sample may, in fact, be so pronounced that sometimes not only is there a long desorption time from a sampling system, but samples may even disappear completely.

Figure 2 shows some results which illustrate this phenomenon. The experiments were carried out with a chromatographic system which employed a stainless steel sampler drawing vapour from an all-glass vacuum system. The connexion from metal to glass was effected with about 2 inches of P.V.C. plastic tube. The system was originally used to calibrate a detector for the pentanes and subsequently, after several days' continuous evacuation, experiments were started with benzene and cyclohexane. In the first run (Figure 2a) much pentane, a little benzene and no cyclohexane appeared through the column, but as further runs (Figures 2b and 2c) were carried out, the pentane peaks progressively diminished, while those of benzene and cyclohexane increased. The vacuum system was then flooded with the vapours of the latter, pumped out and refilled. Only then (Figures 2d and 2e) were the pentanes reduced significantly and reproducible results obtained. When the P.V.C. was replaced by a metal-glass seal the phenomena could not be reproduced.

It seems certain that there was considerable competitive sorption in the P.V.C. when the benzene and cyclohexane vapours were first introduced into the system, the vapours being strongly sorbed and pentane desorbed.

This seems to be proved by Figure 2*f*, which shows the chromatogram obtained when the supposed vacuum was sampled, no vapours having been introduced. It is significant that the P.V.C. tube had been exposed for some time to high vacuum, since this suggests that a normal partition process could not have been operating; something in the nature of a cage effect being indicated. There is no published evidence of comparable effects in columns of any type, except, of course, when molecular sieves are

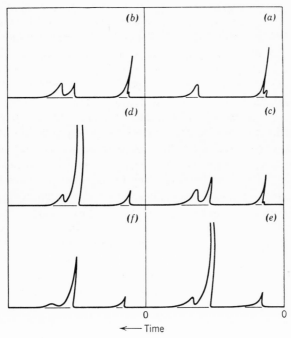

FIG. 2. Chromatograms of benzene/cyclohexane mixture showing loss of sample and introduction of impurities held back from previous runs by a short length of PVC tube connecting the sample source with the sampler. Sequence of elution is isopentane, *n*-pentane, cyclohexane, benzene. Curvature of peaks derives from use of galvanometer recorder.

used, but it is reasonable to suppose that they must at least be considered when rubber septums or, for example, plastic capillaries are used.

Pre-column configuration may make an important contribution to the theoretical plate height. It is evident that the injection system should be as close to the column head as possible, and that the system should contain no crevices, bulges or other regions from which material cannot be directly swept out, since these all enhance the diffusional mixing problem.

THE DEPENDENCE OF H UPON SOLVENT/SUPPORT RATIO

Before proceeding to the discussion of this topic it is worthwhile to emphasise again that almost all experimental tests of the rate theory have so far involved evaluation of only three coefficients through application of the simplified van Deemter equation. Thus, a mass transfer term, usually designated C, has been calculated, and has tacitly been identified with C_l. It is clear from the discussions of the last chapter that this is unlikely to be generally correct and so, in the following pages, allowance must be made for the fact that we are unable to separate the individual contributions of C_l and C_g^o to H and can speak only of a composite C term. It must also be borne in mind that the evaluation of the mass transfer coefficients as one term must also, almost certainly, lead to errors in the derived values of B_o and A, particularly the latter, experimental determinations of which could conceivably reflect mainly the inadequacies of the simplified approach.

The earliest studies of the dependence of C upon solvent/support ratio were those of Keulemans and Kwantes (8) who eluted propane and n-butane from hexadecane/Sterchamol columns. C appeared to vary linearly with solvent/support ratio (k') in the range 15 to 40 per cent w/w, but, at lower ratios, C fell off considerably faster than linearly. Calculation suggests that at the lowest ratio studied by these authors, their evaluated C term was close to what might be expected of C_g^o alone. In this case, since C rose rapidly at low k', and then more or less linearly with k', the results could be taken to substantiate the extended rate equation, since they were in general agreement with predictions based on a combination of Figures 2 and 5 of Chapter 8. However, this view demands that solvent distribution was at all times of the continuous film type. The general trend towards increasing column efficiency (decreasing C) with decreasing solvent/support ratio has also been observed by other workers (3, 9, 10) but the work was in each case no more than qualitative, and was conducted only over limited ranges of k' values. It seems unlikely, however, that any simple dependence of C upon k' would have been found since, for example, in the case of isopropanol elution from polyethylene glycol columns (3) the theoretical plate height was reduced only by about a factor of 2 on going from 20 per cent through to 2 per cent by weight of solvent.

The most comprehensive study of the effect of solvent/support ratio on column efficiency to date is that of Cheshire and Scott (14). They determined N as a function of carrier gas velocity for about twelve solutes eluted at 78°C. from a series of 152 × 0.36 cm. columns containing C.22 firebrick coated with Apiezon Oil A. The proportion of the oil varied from 2 to 30 per cent w/w. They plotted their results as N_{max} versus retention time, N_{max} being the maximum column efficiency attainable for a given solute and corresponding to the minimum on the more conventional H versus u

plot. It thus reflects the situation at any velocity. The data indicated a progressive improvement on going from 30 to 20 per cent w/w of solvent, but below this there was a progressive fall in efficiency. The curves for the lowest proportions of solvent appear to cross those for higher values at high retention times. It is not immediately apparent what these results mean in terms of the dependence of C upon solvent/support ratio but they show that a 20 per cent column is the most efficient.

It is, however, possible to make some interesting deductions if the data are replotted in another way. Insufficient information is given to permit

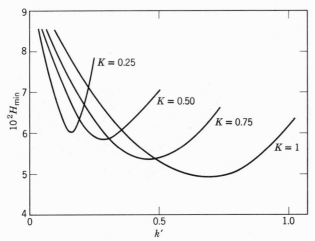

FIG. 3. Plots of H_{min} versus k' (units defined in text) derived from literature data (14).

calculation of an absolute value of either k' or the partition coefficient K but we can arbitrarily assume each to be unity for the unknown solute described as being eluted at 30 minutes from the 30 per cent w/w column. This seems likely to have been either benzene or n-heptane. We can now go further by evaluating the efficiency corresponding to the elution of this solute from every column on the assumption that the retention volume per gm. of solvent is constant and that the weight per cent ratio from column to column is reasonably close to the weight ratio. Thus, with the 15 per cent column its retention time would be 15 minutes, and so on. It is equally possible to do this for other solutes having retention times of, say, 22.5, 15 and 7.5 minutes when eluted from the 30 per cent column. The four solutes thus have K in the ratio $4:3:2:1$. Each set of data for a given solute gives the variation of column efficiency with k' since $D_g{}^o$ and D_l are presumed constant for a given solute. Figure 3 illustrates plots of the derived values of H_{min} against the relative values of k' for the four solutes. Their form is extremely interesting. It will be recalled (p. 126) that

$$H_{\min} = \acute{A} + 2\sqrt{BC}$$

which is true even if we include a Golay radial diffusion term $C_g{}^o$ in C. Hence the graphs represent effectively a plot of C against k' since, for a given solute, B_o is constant and it may be assumed that A varies little because the support particle size was the same for all columns. For each curve there is a definite minimum in the value of $H_{\min}$ and hence in C. The corresponding value of k' increases with increasing K. These results cannot immediately be reconciled with any existing theory.

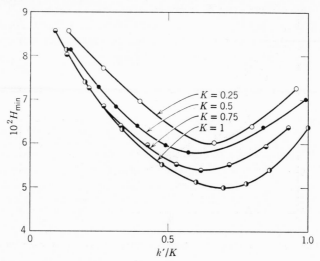

FIG. 4. Data of Figure 3 replotted in the form $H_{\min}$ against k'/K.

If the data from Figure 3 are plotted as $H_{\min}$ against k'/K, as in Figure 4, an even more surprising result is obtained. The value of $H_{\min}$, and hence $C_{\min}$ is seen to occur at the same value of k'/K irrespective of the value of K. The value of $(k'/K)_{\min}$ is about 0.6 which corresponds to an 18 per cent w/w column in agreement with the statement made earlier as to the most efficient column of the series. Since, by definition, $k'/K = V_l/V_a$, the position of the minimum is apparently dictated by the solvent/support ratio.

These results are explicable, even if $C_g{}^o$ is assumed to be zero, if it is accepted that, at low solvent support ratios, solvent is distributed as droplets. As the solvent weight increases there is no increase in d_f, and C diminishes as expected up to the point where all the pores are filled. Beyond this, the droplets must either increase in size or a surface film must form. In this condition $d_f \propto k'$ and there is a transition of behaviour, C now, instead of being proportional to $1/k'$, becoming proportional to k', that is, the solvent/support ratio. The net effect of this whole situation would be to produce, as shown in the theoretical discussion (Figure 7, Chapter 8), a minimum value of C which would depend upon the identities of solvent and support and also the temperature, and which would be the same for all solutes.

This argument, therefore, accords with the results of Cheshire and Scott and with data obtained for the dependence of C upon d_p which is discussed later. It is an interesting point that, if this view is substantiated, it may explain the conflicting data both for the effect of solvent/support ratio and that of temperature upon column efficiencies. A further consequence would be the existence of maxima in the curves of Figure 4 at very low values of k'. It was not possible to check this from the published graphs owing to the large error involved in the transposition, and no other work appears to have been carried out in this region. An alternative explanation, however, is clearly possible, since we have ignored the possibility of a sizeable contribution of $C_g{}^o$ to C. Thus, the combination of the dependence of $C_g{}^o$ (Figure 2, Chapter 8) and that of C_l upon k' for droplet distribution (Figure 6, Chapter 8) might also lead to a minimum on a plot of C versus k'.

Results which quite certainly conflict with the rate theory as its stands are those of McKenna and Idleman (12) who found a minimum value of H at 30 per cent w/w solvent. This result, however, accords with the above discussion of the work of Cheshire and Scott, as also did those of Eggertsen and Knight (11), who presented data for several solvent/support systems. In the range 1 to 20 per cent by weight of solvent, column efficiencies changed little and randomly, but at 40 per cent, efficiencies were generally very low, while below 1 per cent tailed peaks, attributed to adsorption by the support, were obtained. These results may be taken to agree with those cited earlier in that they probably reflect a C-k' relationship having a broad minimum of a type comparable to that found recently by Bohemen (6) for acetone and benzene with polyethylene glycol columns. Over a wide range of values of k', in such systems, C appears to be independent of the solvent/support ratio.

The most recent attempt to determine the dependence of the composite mass transfer constant C upon solvent/support ratio is that of Desty, Godfrey and Harbourn (13). These authors found that if C diminished with reduction of solvent weight, the fall was much less than the "film" distribution view predicts. In most cases, C increased. The results are complicated somewhat, since, inexplicably, both the molecular and eddy diffusion constants, A and B_o, of the simplified van Deemter equation appeared also to change markedly from column to column, although these differed only in solvent weight.

Some of their results are listed in Table 2.

The variations in A and B are so considerable and so unexpected that the calculated values of C must be suspect. There are several possible explanations, the first of which is that the method used to evaluate the constants was unreliable. Secondly, it is not stated which carrier gas velocity was used in the calculations, and if this was not properly corrected for gas compressibility the data from column to column would be incompatible, if, as the authors state was the case, there were marked differences in permeability to gas flow.

TABLE 2

EXPERIMENTALLY DETERMINED RATE THEORY CONSTANTS

Support	BSS Mesh	w/w % Solvent	A cm.	B cm.^{2} sec.$^{-1}$	C sec.
Celite	30–44	10	0.053	0.173	0.034
		20	0.037	0.126	0.024
	72–100	10	0.049	0.092	0.005
		20	0.033	0.136	0.006
	100–120	10	0.004	0.136	0.005
		20	0.006	0.109	0.005
Firebrick	30–44	10	0.029	0.089	0.011
		20	0.034	0.077	0.017
	72–100	10	0.010	0.097	0.008
		20	0.015	0.071	0.005

The situation is perhaps clarified if from the data in Table 2 the value of H at $u = 10$ cm. per sec. is evaluated. These figures are given in Table 3. While the values of A and B may be suspect there can be no doubt that those of H are accurate.

In the case of the two finer meshed Celite columns, change of solvent weight leaves both C and H unchanged, while with the coarse Celite column, C and H increased by 50 per cent on halving the solvent weight. These results could be adequately explained on the basis of the extended rate equation since, for droplet distribution of solvent, C_l should be independent of support particle size, while C_g^o varies as d_p^2. Thus, with the two finer meshed columns it is possible that $C_l \gg C_g^o$ and hence C would be independent of d_p. Also, because the relevant k' was quite high, C would change little between 10 and 20 per cent w/w solvent/support.

With the coarse column, C_g^o would be greater and more nearly comparable with C_l. Hence, on going from 100 mesh to 44 mesh support, an increase in C would be expected. The k' dependence of C for the coarse column is that to be expected for droplet distribution, its observation with this column and not with the others possibly being due to considerable differences in d_f. There is no obvious explanation of this, but it has recently also been observed by Bohemen and the author (25). The explanation suggested is obviously only speculative, especially since, although it accounts also for the behaviour of the finer meshed firebrick column, it cannot apply to the data listed for the coarser firebrick column.

The published data indicate that there is need for further study of the role of solvent/support ratio in determining H, particularly in the region of $k' < 1$ where, as seen from Figure 6 of Chapter 8, the most spectacular

TABLE 3

Support	BSS Mesh	w/w % Solvent	H cm.
Celite	30–44	10	0.41
		20	0.29
	72–100	10	0.108
		20	0.107
	100–120	10	0.068
		20	0.067
Firebrick	30–44	10	0.148
		20	0.212
	72–100	10	0.100
		20	0.072

changes in both C_g^o and C_l may be expected. On the whole, the evidence indicates that when the mass transfer coefficients are evaluated simply as C, this may either appear to be more or less independent of k', or may have a minimum value at some particular solvent/support ratio as a consequence of the interplay of the various contributing processes. This view, and the explanations offered here, must be considered as unproven, but there is little evidence to support any alternative view.

It is reasonable to suppose that if two mechanisms for solvent distribution are available, both will operate to some extent. The relative contributions of each can only be guessed, and may vary by orders of magnitude from system to system, or with change of temperature in a given system. They thus introduce considerable uncertainty into a theory which in any case hinges very firmly on the constancy of D_l. At constant sample size this is equivalent to saying that D_l is independent of solvent/support ratio, and hence of k'. There is always a possibility that this may not be the case, especially in view of the known behaviour of solutes in polymeric solvents. A concentration dependence of D_l could well lead to results such as those discussed, and would probably cause the theory to become intractable.

COMPARATIVE STUDIES OF SOLID SUPPORTS

It is difficult to specify the properties required of an ideal solid support without recourse to experimental studies, but, at least to a good approximation, it may be anticipated that the following are desirable:

a. The solid should be able to absorb large quantities of viscous liquids and still run freely and pack into a column offering the maximum permeability to gas flow.

b. It should be possible to separate it into fractions of well defined particle size within the approximate range of diameters 0.05 to 0.5 mm.

c. The particles should be sufficiently robust to withstand the usual procedures of preparation and column construction without deterioration.

d. The solid should offer a large surface area per gram, but nevertheless be completely non-adsorbing and chemically unreactive.

In so far as the solid support contributes to the theoretical plate height of a column it may be expected to do so in consequence of departure from one or more of the above criteria. For example, if the material is wet when carrying solvent it will pack badly and probably leave channels through which gas and sample will preferentially travel; the same being true if the material crumbles during packing. In consequence, only the grosser parts of the column will actually be used; eddy diffusion may then be considerable and solvent overloading is highly likely. The most serious problem, however, appears to be that associated with the adsorptive capacity of the solid, since if this is considerable, even the presence of large amounts of solvent may not inactivate the surface, and the column then becomes a combined gas-liquid/gas-solid system. The efficiencies attainable with gas-solid systems seem to be far lower than with gas-liquid columns, and hence any adsorption may contribute a great deal, not only to band spreading, but also to band assymetry.

Few materials are able to meet, even approximately, the requirements outlined. Those which have proved satisfactory in some degree or another are glass powder or spheres, powdered Teflon, Kel-F moulding powder, the low activity carbon Pelletex, crystalline salts and the numerous diatomaceous earth products such as Celite, Dicalite, Fosalsil, Chromosorb and the firebricks Sil-O-Cel (C-3, C-22) and Sterchamol. Glass spheres have not proved popular, and the polymeric supports have been used only in corrosive systems.

The earliest studies employed Celite 545 but the various firebricks were introduced at an early date (8, 18, 19) since they were found to hold solvents better than Celite, and also because it was suggested (8, 26) that the use of Sterchamol, for example, gave more efficient columns than did Celite. This was assumed to result from better packing properties and, in fact, it has been suggested (26) that Sterchamol columns exhibit no eddy diffusion. According to Grant and Vaughan (27) microscopic examination of Celite shows that it consists of clusters of small particles, which means that it is not possible to attribute a definite size to the aggregate. The consequence of this, according to these authors, is that there is little change in column efficiency with Celite particle size. For example, they found that a column of particles of less than 50 B.S.S. mesh gave an efficiency of 360 theoretical plates while a similar column of 100 to 120 mesh material gave only 400 theoretical plates.

This view conflicts with the findings of Mellor (1) and of Desty, Godfrey and Harbourn (13), the latter of whom found, as seen from Table 3, that coarse Celite may give theoretical plate heights up to three times those obtained with a comparable grade of Sil-O-Cel firebrick, while with particles finer than about 70 B.S.S. mesh there was virtually no difference between them. Zlatkis, Ling and Kaufman (47) have recently stated that after boiling Celite with *aqua regia* the particles are discrete and rounded.

On the basis of the evidence it would appear that, on balance, materials of the firebrick type are to be preferred to the Celites, particularly for academic studies where it is important that there should be no ambiguity about particle size. Both supports, however, appear to be superior to glass beads since the latter, being non-porous, can hold satisfactorily no more than about 3 per cent by weight of solvent (28). On the other hand, the symmetry and certain size of glass beads makes them attractive for theoretical studies.

The most important difference between firebrick supports and the Celites is said to be in the available surface area and adsorptive characteristics. Conner (19) states that C-22 firebrick adsorbs strongly even in the presence of an added liquid phase, and also brings about the isomerisation of α-pinene to camphene; a reaction which is normally acid catalysed. Conner takes this to indicate the importance of residual acid sites on the brick, the inertness of Celite then being attributed to its having been treated with an alkaline flux. Liberti (20) also claims to have observed isomerisation of terpenes with Sterchamol columns, but not with columns of Celite, and attributed the activity of the former to the presence of iron and aluminium hydroxides. Tuey (21) while stating that Sil-O-Cel, but not Celite, is catalytically active in columns has, at the same time, pointed out that, on analysis, these substances show the same iron and aluminium content. In contrast to other workers, Johns (18) in a study of a wide variety of solid support materials, found that the pH of the support was unimportant and, in addition, concluded that Chromosorb and C-22 firebrick were less adsorptive than Celite. Finally, Janak and Cvrkal (22) found that, in fact, terpenes were isomerised and decomposed by both Celite (160°C.) and Sterchamol (140°C.).

There is evidently a considerable difference of opinion on this subject, and this undoubtedly arises from the fact that the conclusions are all based on chromatographic experiments carried out under widely different conditions and with different adsorbates. Since elimination of adsorptivity of the support is important, Perrett and the author (23) have made a direct study by frontal analysis of the adsorption of acetone and benzene by various support materials. Figure 1 of Chapter 11 illustrates several adsorption isotherms for acetone from which it is seen that the order of adsorptivity is Chromosorb (acid washed) $\gg$ Chromosorb $\simeq$ Sil-O-Cel $>$ Chromosorb-W $\simeq$ Celite; the same sequence being found for benzene. Acid washing, which is widely practised, is clearly of little value for these adsorbates, at least, and there seems no doubt that, in the natural state, Celite represents the most inert material. The adsorption was in every case of Type B (p. 15) and excellent B.E.T. plots were obtained. Heats of adsorption between 10 and 12 kcal. per mole were calculated and the surface areas deduced were about 2 m.^{2} per g. for Sil-O-Cel and Chromosorb, while for Celite it was about 1 m.^{2} per g. These areas agree reasonably with others cited (11, 37) and fairly closely parallel the adsorptivities and the ability to take up solvent and remain free running. Thus, Sil-O-Cel, which takes up roughly twice as much solvent as Celite, while still flowing freely, exhibits about twice as much adsorption. What differences there are indicate that the adsorption sites on the two types of support are not entirely the same.

One point which emerges from Figure 1 of Chapter 11 is that with any of these materials the extent of adsorption at 50°C. is so small that it is almost unbelievable that, at higher temperatures, in the short time a solute spends in a column, it should react catalytically in any way. It might even be queried whether the extent of adsorption even with lean columns would be great enough to produce the peak tailing which is experimentally observed.

The extent to which the presence of a solvent reduces adsorption by the support is a matter of conjecture. For example, Eggertsen and Knight (11) found that chromatographic peak tailing was eliminated by addition to Celite of 1 per cent by weight of water, ethylene glycol or squalane, while a similar result was obtained by addition of 1.5 per cent of squalane to Pelletex. On the other hand, an apparent elimination of tailing undoubtedly cannot be taken as the criterion, either of the occurrence of or the elimination of adsorption. However, it has been fairly certainly shown (9) that even when mixed with 25 per cent by weight of polyethylene glycol, Sterchamol still weakly adsorbs a number of substances and also that when mixed with as much as 20 per cent by weight of squalane, Sil-O-Cel adsorbs acetone (24). The clearest proof of residual adsorption is obtained by studying the dependence of specific retention volumes (p. 207) on the proportion of solvent in a column. The specific retention volume should be independent of solvent/support ratio, but as shown in Table 4, (25) this is not always so. Even at 10 per cent by weight of solvent the support clearly contributes something to the over-all retention, and thus also to the theoretical plate height. It seems most reasonable to suppose that this is

TABLE 4
DEPENDENCE OF SPECIFIC RETENTION VOLUME ON SOLVENT WEIGHT

G. Polyethylene Glycol/100 g. Sil-O-Cel	Specific Retention Volume		
	Cyclohexane	Acetone	Benzene
2.0	54.7	103.2	195.0
5.0	36.5	90.0	176.0
10.2	31.8	86.7	168.3
20.1	29.9	85.8	165.0

an adsorption effect. Mass transfer in solids almost certainly is less efficient than in liquids and so any residual adsorption should reduce column efficiencies. The problem of eliminating, so far as possible, the adsorptivity of the support appears, thus, as one of importance.

The earliest approaches to support pre-treatment designed to achieve this aim were to add small amounts of highly polar and involatile liquids to the column (16, 18, 24) or to acid and then alkali wash the support (17, 20, 29, 30) to remove iron and aluminium (20). Neither of these methods seems to provide the answer, and more recently there have been attempts to deposit solids such as silver or gold (31) or polymeric material (32) on the support surface. Both these treatments are beneficial, but are slightly suspect, since the solids may themselves adsorb, or, more important, react chemically. Silver, for example, obviously cannot be used in the presence of sulphur compounds.

An alternative approach is to assume that the adsorptive sites are hydroxyl groups and to attempt to replace these by groups which will yield a feebly adsorbing surface. Trimethyl chlorosilane (33) and dimethyl dichlorosilane (34) have been used with success, the residual surface then being effectively a silyl or a chlorinated silyl ether. In both these reactions hydrogen chloride is liberated, and in the latter a hydrolysable chlorine remains on the surface; further, both reagents are volatile, toxic and inflammable. To overcome these drawbacks Bohemen, Langer, Perrett and

Purnell (24) have used hexamethyl disilazane to modify the support surface. The result is the same as when trimethyl chlorosilane is used but the technique appears to have several practical advantages.

The results of this treatment are shown in Figure 2 of Chapter 11, in which isotherms for the adsorption of benzene by treated supports at 50°C. are shown (23). Adsorption is not eliminated entirely but the point of saturation is reduced more than ten times while the saturation plateau is the same for Celite, Sil-O-Cel and Chromosorb. The adsorptivity remaining after treatment can be further suppressed by addition of about 0.05 per cent by weight of polyethylene glycol (24). The practical importance of this treatment is not only that it reduces the amount of adsorption, but, equally important, it makes firebrick and Chromosorb identical with Celite in this respect. This is an interesting point, since it suggests that the residual adsorption is independent of surface area. After such treatment, therefore, taking everything into account, Sil-O-Cel, Chromosorb and like materials are probably to be preferred to Celite, since they have a greater surface area and are considered by some to be structurally stronger. It is an interesting question as to whether or not treatment of a material such as silica gel, with its enormous surface area, might not reduce its adsorptive capacity sufficiently that it would become a very effective support for gas liquid chromatography.·

COLUMN DIMENSIONS AND EFFICIENCY

The rate theory as advanced up to this point takes no account of column dimensions. In practice, it is often found that H varies with column dimensions, although there have been few really quantitative studies of the supposed effects.

Column Diameter. It is widely accepted that, above about 10 mm., H increases rapidly with diameter. Such wide columns find their main use in preparative work and their reputed lack of efficiency may have slowed down development in this field. That it is possible to operate wide columns with reasonable efficiency is indicated by the work of Evans et al. (41, 48) and Kirkland (42); the former used columns up to 75 mm. in diameter, while the latter has worked up to 30 mm. diameter. Some of Kirkland's data and comparative values for a 5 mm. column are listed in Table 5, and it is seen that the column performances are comparable.

While it must be admitted that the analytical columns with which comparison is made are of very low efficiency, these results indicate clearly that failures in attempts to operate wide columns may stem largely from procedural error. Kirkland, for example, stresses the importance of effective preheater vaporisation systems and of a proper appreciation of the permissible sample size.

Significant contributions to column inefficiency may stem from the type of packing used and its mode of preparation. It is known (36) that the preparation of large quantities of packing in a single operation results in maldistribution of solvent. It has been found also (4) that during the packing of a column with material composed of particles differing widely in size, a size separation occurs. Both these factors would lead to poor column performance, since the net result obtained with the single, wide column would correspond to the combined performance of a number of parallel

TABLE 5

COMPARISON OF ANALYTICAL AND PREPARATIVE COLUMN EFFICIENCIES

Packing	Column Temperature (in °C.)	Theoretical Plates per Metre (Diameters)	
		5 mm.	30 mm.
Carbowax/Celite	50	320	410
Silicone grease/firebrick	185	260	260
Silicone grease/firebrick	225	170	140

operated columns differing widely both in efficiency and retention time for a given solute. This situation might be overcome if there were perfect lateral mixing in a column, but this has been shown to become less probable with increasing diameter (38). The very large volume of packing required for wide columns may thus well be an important cause of their relative failure. Recently (see Chapter 14) theoretical attempts have been made to take account of column inhomogeneities. Since the theory rightly or wrongly suggests that these are only important at fairly large diameters, this work is discussed in detail in a later chapter devoted to preparative methods.

In so far as analytical columns are concerned (1 to 10 mm.) most workers employ columns of 3 to 6 mm. internal diameter. There is no real evidence of any great variation of efficiency in this range, although Scott (15) has suggested 2 mm. as an optimum value, and McKenna and Idleman (12) have recommended 4 mm. It should be borne in mind that for effective packing the diameter of the containing tube of the column should be at least eight times that of the solid support particles.

Column Length. If we consider the extended rate equation in the form

$$H = A + \frac{B_o}{u_o} + C_g{}^o u_o + C_l f u_o$$

we can predict the theoretical effect of change of column length on H. Two columns compared at equal u_o will differ only in the contribution of the last term, and since f decreases with increasing length, so too will H. On the other hand, if the columns are compared at equal $\bar{u} = fu_o$ the net result depends entirely on the velocity region, since this determines whether $B_o/u_o > C_g{}^o u_o$ or vice versa.

Increasing column length, at constant $\bar{u}$, means increasing u_o; thus, at low velocities H should diminish, whereas at high velocities H should increase. Experimental studies of the effect of length on H and statements of the results have never been expressed in other than the most general terms, and so it is not surprising that while most workers have found that H appears to increase somewhat with increasing column length, Mellor (1) observed the reverse trend. In only two instances has constancy of H been reported. The first of these (4) was only qualitative, but Scott (15) has shown a plot of N against packed column length which was linear up to 50 feet. Beyond this, efficiencies apparently fell off and it has been suggested (15, 39) that this is due to the accompanying high pressure drop which yields a wide spread of velocity throughout the column and, hence, a reduced efficiency.

There is no reason to doubt that all these results are compatible with theory in that it is possible, at least qualitatively, to reconcile them with each other. Thus, at constant u_o, since f changes quite slowly with p_i/p_o and usually only over the range 1.0 to 0.4, H should be more or less additive with length. This opinion is to some extent borne out by the fact that a packed column, from the point of view of pressure and gas flow, is conventionally regarded as a bundle of capillaries, and recent work with capillary columns of as much as one mile in length (43, 50) has not revealed any length restriction. These conclusions suggest that any failure to achieve this near additivity in practice is probably due to constructional and configurational difficulties. The author, for example, has found that quite small gas leakages at the connexions between column sections can reduce column efficiency very markedly.

SUPPORT PARTICLE SIZE AND SIZE DISTRIBUTION

The dependence of column efficiency upon solid support particle size has been studied on a number of occasions. For Celite it has been suggested (27) that, due to its structure, coarse particles are as good as finer ones, but Mellor (1) found a definite improvement in column performance when using finer grades. More recently (13) further evidence has substantiated Mellor's findings. With firebrick type supports some authors (8, 18) have reported an optimum particle size in the region of 60 to 80 A.S.T.M. mesh, while others (4, 14, 43, 44) have found a progressive improvement in column efficiency with diminishing particle size over the whole range studied. These latter results are the most recent, and are probably reliable, particularly since great care was taken to use closely size graded material. The importance of this has been clearly demonstrated (3, 4, 43).

Figure 5 illustrates plots of H versus $\bar{u}$ for a series of firebrick supports of varying particle size (4). There is an approximately fourfold improvement in efficiency on going from 20 to 30 B.S.S. mesh to 100 to 150 mesh. A similar conclusion can be deduced from the data contained in Table 3 (13). A further significant point is that the fine particle columns have $H/\bar{u}$ plots

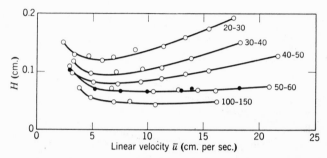

FIG. 5. Experimental data for the dependence of H upon $\bar{u}$ for packed columns of different d_p. B.S.S. mesh range quoted. (closed circles are duplicate column data.) *By courtesy of Butterworths.*

which are more or less parallel to the velocity axis at high velocities. This means that in addition to being more efficient, such columns permit faster analysis.

Figure 6 (3, 6) shows the effect on column efficiency of the use of a support of broad particle distribution; the closer size graded material undoubtedly gives better results. In fact, it appears as though H is determined primarily by the coarser material of the mixture. Cheshire and Scott (43) observed very marked improvement in column performance with reduced particle size, and also the deleterious effect of a broad size spread; both 100 to 120 and 120 to 160 B.S.S. mesh columns were markedly superior to one of 100 to 200 mesh.

According to equation (8.40)

$$H = 2\lambda d_p + \frac{B_o}{u_o} + C_g{}^o u_o + C_l \bar{u}$$

We may consider first the particle size dependence of the eddy diffusion term. In the earliest work Klinkenberg and Sjenitzer (51) suggested that "normal" values of λ might be 8 for 200 to 400 mesh particles, 3 for 50 to 100 mesh, and 1 for 20 to 40 mesh. Keulemans and Kwantes (8) found for Sterchamol columns that at 20 to 30 mesh A.S.T.M., $\lambda = 1.4$, while for 30 to 50 mesh, $\lambda = 1.2$. These values appear to agree with prediction. de Wet and Pretorius (52) found a minimum at $d_p = 0.1$ mm. on a plot of H versus d_p but did not evaluate λ. Brennan and Kemball (53) plotted $H/\bar{u}$ versus $1/\bar{u}^2$ and found such excellent linearity that they suggested that $A = 2\lambda d_p \simeq 0$. Following this, Bohemen and Purnell (3, 4) made a detailed study of the relation of H with d_p of Sil-O-Cel firebrick columns and found that while with coarse particles values of $\lambda \simeq 1$ were obtainable, depending on the method of evaluation, the data for fine supports yielded

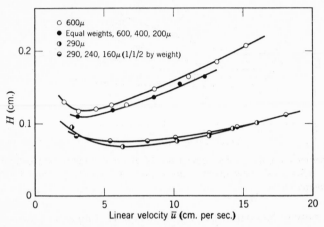

FIG. 6. Illustration of the deleterious effect of wide spread of d_p in column packing. *By courtesy of Butterworths.*

extremely small and often negative values for A. They too found that $H/\bar{u}$ versus $1/\bar{u}$ plots, and those of $H\bar{u}$ versus $\bar{u}^2$, were linear, and so concluded that A might possibly be zero, since it cannot be negative. Similar results were quoted by Rijnders (35) for columns of Sterchamol brick and by Littlewood (55) for glass bead columns. These results are now regarded as evidence for the inadequacy of the simple form of rate equation.

The data of Desty et al. quoted in Table 2 illustrate again the curious variation of A with d_p. A 30 to 44 A.S.T.M. mesh Celite column carrying 10 per cent by weight of solvent had $A = 0.053$ cm., whereas a similar column of 20 per cent solvent had $A = 0.037$ cm. For both, λ is near unity, but it is surprising that the lower solvent weight yielded a bigger value of A since it might be supposed that, if it had any effect at all, reduction of solvent would ease the problem of regular packing and so reduce A, as was, in fact, observed with a 72 to 100 mesh firebrick column. With the other columns studied, A changed hardly at all with solvent weight. These authors suggested that for Celite, A was virtually independent of d_p for particles coarser than 100 B.S.S. but found that it fell by a factor of 12 between 72 and 120 mesh. For firebrick, on the other hand, the value of A decreased linearly with d_p, extrapolating to zero at about 120 mesh. This result accords with those cited earlier (3, 4, 54, 55).

Glueckauf (56) has pointed out that the only safe way to evaluate the inter-relation of A and d_p is through studies with packed columns in which no sorption occurs. He studied the frontal elution of hydrogen, methane, oxygen and sulphur dioxide from glass bead columns, and showed plots of H versus $1/u$ which are linear. In the apparent absence of a mass transfer term we have

$$H = A + \frac{B_o}{u_o}$$

and, hence, the intercept of the plot yields A. It was found that for hydrogen $\lambda \simeq 1$ but for the other gases $\lambda = 0.5$. The latter value agrees with that predicted earlier by Glueckauf (57) and with the deduction of equation (8.48). Bohemen (6) has carried out similar studies by the elution technique with firebrick columns containing polyethylene glycol. He eluted permanent gases and also worked at extremely low flow rates in order to make the mass transfer terms as small as possible. He found that for carbon dioxide when $d_p = 0.32$ mm., $\lambda = 0.6$; when $d_p = 0.16$ mm., $\lambda = 0.75$; and when $d_p = 0.10$ mm., $\lambda = 1.15$. For hydrogen, the comparable values of λ were 0.5, 0.75 and 1.5. These results clearly substantiate Glueckauf's findings, but Bohemen found that there was, in fact, adsorption or solution of these gases by the packing and, further, that allowance was necessary for resistance to mass transfer in the gas phase. The latter approximated to $d_p^2/24D_g^o$ since k' was so small. The variable value of λ was then to some extent accounted for. Further experiments in which, in addition, acetone and benzene vapours were eluted in similar conditions yielded an average $\lambda = 0.75$ for fractions through the whole B.S.S. mesh range 20 to 150.

The work of Bohemen and of Glueckauf seems to establish that the eddy contribution to theoretical plate height is close to d_p as theory predicts. The variation in the results previously presented almost certainly arises from the use of inappropriate methods of evaluation and perhaps also from feed volume and sample size effects. Bohemen has concluded that A cannot readily be evaluated from H versus $\bar{u}$ data either by calculation or graphical means and that it is necessary to work at extremely low velocities and even then to evaluate the separate contributions to H of the mass transfer terms C_g^o and C_l. This process is extremely laborious and, in addition, necessitates very stringent experimental control of conditions since A is so small.

Turning now to the effect of particle size on the mass transfer term, it must be admitted that there is very little work from which to draw any conclusions. The data of Desty et al. given in Table 2 show a very sharp fall of C between 40 and 80 B.S.S. mesh Celite, but only a small linear fall for firebrick up to 100 mesh. Beyond this, the values for Celite and firebrick are the same, and do not change with further reduction of d_p. The author (3) has also shown that for firebrick columns containing 20 per cent by weight of polyethylene glycol the value of C is roughly proportional to d_p in the range 20 to 150 B.S.S. mesh. There is no obvious reason to expect this, but Bohemen (6) has recently obtained results which may provide an explanation. He studied the performance of columns containing particles ranging in diameter from 0.32 mm. to 0.10 mm. and evaluated both C_l and C_g^o. The latter was found to vary more or less as the square of the particle diameter, as predicted by equation 8.40, and it was then found that C_l appeared to be linearly dependent upon d_p.

However, a true check of the inter-relation of C_l and d_p must be made at a constant value of k' and as a result of small variations in packing density and solvent weight from column to column the function $k'/(1 + k')^2$ may vary quite considerably, although it may be meant to be constant. This may, of course, be accurately allowed for, and then the ratio d_f^2/D_l may be evaluated equally accurately. On doing this it was found that it decreased about 2.5 times on reducing d_p from 0.32 to 0.16 mm., but with further diminution of d_p, d_f^2/D_l was unchanged. These results indicate that with fine supports d_f is independent of particle size, a conclusion which supports the idea that solvent may be primarily distributed as droplets and not as a film. If the latter were the case, we see from equation 8.18 that C_l, corrected for changes of k', should vary as d_p^2. With coarse particles this appears to be true to some extent although the change is less than theory predicts and implies that both droplet and film formation may occur. These results agree with the interpretation of the dependence of C upon solvent/support ratio advanced earlier.

There is little doubt that, provided reasonable precautions are taken, the best column performance is consistent with the use of the smallest support particle size of the narrowest possible size spread. It must be admitted that the use of such material markedly increases the working pressure in the system and, in practice, most workers effect a compromise between efficiency and pressure in order to ease sampling problems. However, this only emphasises the need for the development of effective high pressure sampling systems. With this problem solved there seems no reason why support solids as fine as 400 mesh might not find wide application and so, possibly, lead to the attainment of theoretical plate heights in the region of 0.1 mm.

DIFFUSION IN THE GAS PHASE
The Role of the Carrier Gas. It is to be expected from the simplified van

Deemter equation that, from the point of view of diffusion, carrier gases of low molecular weight (high diffusivity) will be inferior to those of high molecular weight. We can illustrate this by assuming the reasonable value $B_o = 0.1$ cm.^{2} sec.$^{-1}$ for a solute eluted from a column operating with nitrogen, when the same column, using hydrogen, should give $B_o = 0.4$ (p. 50). Thus, if $A = 0.01$ cm. and $C = 0.01$ sec. we have, at an outlet velocity of 8 cm./per sec., ignoring the compressibility correction, the approximate results

$$H_{N_2} = 0.01 + 0.1/8 + 0.01 \times 8 = 0.102 \text{ cm.}$$

and

$$H_{H_2} = 0.01 + 0.4/8 + 0.01 \times 8 = 0.140 \text{ cm.}$$

The column efficiency should thus be about 40 per cent higher with nitrogen as carrier than it is with hydrogen. On the other hand, as seen on p. 126, the velocity corresponding to the minimum theoretical plate height is

$$u_{\min} = (B/C)^{\frac{1}{2}} \quad \text{while} \quad H_{\min} = A + 2(BC)^{\frac{1}{2}}$$

Thus

$$(u_{\min})_{N_2} = 3.2 \text{ cm./sec.}; \quad (H_{\min})_{N_2} = 0.074 \text{ cm.}$$

while

$$(u_{\min})_{H_2} = 6.4 \text{ cm./sec.}; \quad (H_{\min})_{H_2} = 0.138 \text{ cm.}$$

The ratio of $H_{\min}(N_2/H_2)$ is about 2, but it is seen that if the best result were required when using hydrogen, the column in the above example would have to be operated at a velocity twice that used for nitrogen.

However, if we accept that the simplified van Deemter equation is inadequate in most cases, and that $C_g{}^o u_o$ must be included, as has already been shown (p. 145), the interplay of B_o and $C_g{}^o$ means that $H_{\min}$ is more or less independent of the carrier gas, although $(u_0)_{\min}$ is directly dependent on $D_g{}^o$ At velocities other than $H_{\min}$, on the other hand, the identity of the carrier gas is important in determining H, since at low velocities $B_o/u_o > C_g{}^o u_o$ while at high velocities $C_g{}^o u_o > B_o/u_o$. Thus, at low velocities, carrier gases of high molecular weight will yield the lowest H, while at very high velocities the reverse is the case.

This conclusion is the same as that arrived at on the basis of the simplified equation. If for any reason, therefore, it is not possible to work at high velocity, nitrogen or argon, for example, are better choices than hydrogen or helium. Figure 7 illustrates experimental proof of this statement (4) but, equally, shows that the hydrogen elution data are converging on the same value of $H_{\min}$ as was observed with the other gases. The data thus go to substantiate the extended rate equation (3) and the view that for fastest analysis hydrogen will prove to be the most suitable carrier gas.

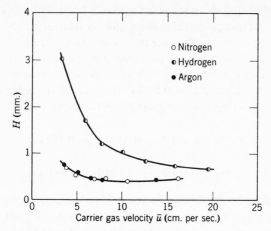

FIG. 7. The dependence of H upon carrier gas identity. Solute was acetone eluted in stated carrier with $p_o = 1$ atm. *By courtesy of Butterworths.*

Values of the constant B_o were calculated from the data shown in Figure 7 and are listed in Table 6. It must be pointed out that the plots in the figure and the derived data are only approximate, since the graph utilised $\bar{u}$ and the evaluations were conducted on the assumption of the validity of the simplified van Deemter equation.

Since the data were evaluated using the average velocity, B_o for nitrogen will be too low since $\bar{u}_{N_2}$ will be much lower than $\bar{u}_{H_2}$ in consequence of the greater pressure gradient (higher viscosity). Thus, the agreement between the two ratios is reasonable and substantiates the form of the molecular diffusion term since we would expect $D_g^o(H_2)/D_g^o(N_2)$ to be close to 4.

The Operating Pressure. Most work is conducted with the column outlet opened to the atmosphere but in early work sub-atmospheric pressures were sometimes used (45). This expedient leads to increased signals from concentration sensitive detectors, since for a fixed sample size concentration in the carrier is increased when the pressure of the latter is reduced. It is clear from equation 3.7, however, that saturation vapour pressures of solutes are

TABLE 6

VALUES OF $2\gamma D_g$ FOR ELUTION BY N_2 AND H_2 FROM POLYETHYLENE GLYCOL/FIREBRICK COLUMN AT 50°C. D_g^o FROM LITERATURE

Solute	$B_{H_2}^o$ cm.^{2} sec.$^{-1}$	$B_{N_2}^o$ cm.^{2} sec.$^{-1}$	$B_{H_2}^o/B_{N_2}^o$	$D_g^o(H_2)/D_g^o(N_2)$
Cyclohexane	0.74	0.168	4.35	3.91
Acetone	0.92	0.220	4.20	3.90
Benzene	0.76	0.185	4.15	4.26

virtually unaffected and so reduced pressures offer no advantage from this point of view. Where sampling and injection methods are inadequate, of course, the reduced inlet pressures consequent upon reduced outlet pressures facilitate injection.

On the basis of the simplified van Deemter equation reduction of p_o would be expected to lead to increased H. Thus, operation of columns at elevated outlet pressures would be beneficial. As we have already seen in

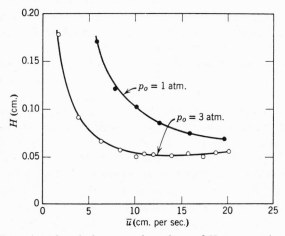

FIG. 8. Illustration of marked pressure dependence of H upon p_o at low velocities with hydrogen as carrier. *Courtesy of the New York Academy of Sciences.*

the previous section, the occurrence of gas mass transfer resistance leads to a situation in which $H_{\min}$ is independent of carrier gas identity and hence of p_o. Again, however, at velocities other than $(u_o)_{\min}$ the appropriate choice of p_o is important. Thus, at low velocities where B_o/u_o is more important than $C_g{}^o u_o$, elevated outlet pressures increase column efficiency while at very high velocities sub-atmospheric pressures may be beneficial since A and C_l should be pressure independent. Whatever pressure is employed $H_{\min}$ is a fixed quantity.

Figure 8 illustrates some data for elution of acetone by hydrogen at different outlet pressures (4) which substantiate what has been said. Over the whole range studied the higher operating pressure yielded the lower H but, again, it is seen that the curves are likely to have much the same $H_{\min}$. These curves, like those of Figure 7, suffer the defect of being H versus $\bar{u}$ and so are only approximate. Even so, they clearly show the general effect of pressure and, further, if the crossing point of the curves were realised it would permit evaluation of $C_g{}^o$, since it is the existence of this term which causes crossing.

The results depicted in the figure are those found generally. Thus, Mellor (1) and Brennan and Kemball (53) have shown that, most often, increasing p_o leads to a reduction of H. Scott and his associates (14, 15) have utilised the effect to achieve high efficiencies at low velocities, working in some instances with inlet pressures of 200 p.s.i. High pressure operation obviously is beneficial only at normal working velocities and in the future, as higher speeds of analysis are aimed for, it is likely as already stated that reduced pressures may once more be favoured. This aspect awaits exploration but from what was said on p. 156 we see that the velocity of operation of a column at high speeds is dependent almost entirely on C_g^o and C_l, the former of which is inversely pressure dependent.

Tortuosity in Packed Columns. Whatever form of rate equation is considered to apply, we must consider the possibility that the contribution of longitudinal diffusion to H is determined not only by D_g^o but also by γ. In principle, therefore, if γ could somehow be reduced, the role of molecular diffusion might be diminished. It is not possible to predict how tortuosity might be enhanced or even if it is a realistic concept; it was suggested on p. 120 that, in fact, the labyrinth constant might really be unity. The values of γ reported in the literature are highly conflicting. For instance, Rijnders (54) quotes values of γ between 0.5 and 1.0 without any details. Littlewood (28), who used glass bead columns, quotes values of the ratio $B/D_g = 2\gamma$ for ten solutes eluted from the same column. These lay mostly in the range 0.5 to 0.65 with one value as low as 0.35. Going hand in hand with these values, however, were some quite remarkable changes in A. Thus, from solute to solute, A changed over the range 0 to 0.8 mm., d_p being only 0.1 mm. There is no obvious reason for either A or B/D_g to vary with the solute, and it suggests that A may, in reality, have been smaller (it was unlikely to have been bigger), when B/D_g, that is γ, would have been bigger.

Glueckauf (56), as described on p. 187, studied frontal development of some permanent gases from dry glass bead columns. He quotes B/D_g values obtained from plots of H versus $1/u$ but points out that u was calculated as though the tube were empty, and is therefore always too small. If it is assumed that the porosity of his column was normal, the actual velocities would be greater than he states by the approximate factor 62/38, and so, equally, would the ratio B/D_g. Table 7 lists Glueckauf's values and those recalculated on the above basis. The recalculated values of γ agree reasonably with those mentioned by Rijnders. It is noticeable that Littlewood's values of B/D_g are comparable with the original ones of Glueckauf, and it seems possible that he too used an uncorrected velocity. It is not clear as to how velocities were calculated by any of these workers. If air peak velocities ($\bar{u}$) were used, the values of γ found by them would merely be an

TABLE 7
MOLECULAR DIFFUSION AND LABYRINTH CONSTANTS

	H_2	CH_4	O_2	SO_2
B/D_g original	0.8	0.6	0.6	0.8
B/D_g recalculated	1.3	1.0	1.0	1.3
$\gamma = B/2D_g$ recalculated	0.65	0.5	0.5	0.65

average of the compressibility correction f over the velocity range studied. The values of γ found are quite compatible with this situation and if, in fact, $\bar{u}$ was used, the results then imply that γ lies near unity.

Bohemen and the author (72) have carried out studies by the elution technique using gas liquid columns. Some data obtained by them are given in Table 8.

The values found for γ are somewhat higher than any previously reported and, on the whole, indicate that $\gamma \simeq 1$. Values higher than this quoted in the table may derive from experimental error or mistakes in the literature values of $D_g{}^o$. One point which favours these values over others is that they were evaluated in full cognisance of the extended rate equation with its several pressure dependences, and after a most careful study of the magnitudes of A and $C_g{}^o$ (p. 197). If A, in particular, is overestimated, it has the effect of making γ look small. If the view that $\gamma = 1$, in a reasonably

TABLE 8
DIFFUSIONAL PARAMETERS DETERMINED BY ELUTION IN N_2 FROM 20 PER CENT w/w POLYETHYLENE GLYCOL/FIREBRICK COLUMNS AT 50°C. VARIOUS SUPPORT PARTICLE DIAMETERS; $D_g{}^o$ FROM LITERATURE DATA $p_o = 1$ atm.

Solute	Support Particle Size B.S.S. Mesh	B	$B/2D_g{}^o = \gamma$
Hydrogen	20–30	1.72	0.95
	50–60	1.85	1.02
	100–150	1.75	0.96
Carbon dioxide	20–30	0.335	0.86
	50–60	0.380	0.95
	100–150	0.344	0.89
Acetone	20–30	0.205	0.85
	50–60	0.230	0.96
	100–150	0.254	1.06
Benzene	20–30	0.175	0.83
	50–60	0.205	0.98
	100–150	0.224	1.07

well packed column, is verified, it means that the contribution of B_o to the theoretical plate height can only be minimised by action directed at suppressing molecular diffusion. This course is then limited by the growing importance of C_g^o and there are, as discussed earlier, optimum pressure regions determined by the relative magnitudes of B_o and C_g^o.

Consideration of $H\bar{u}$ against $\bar{u}^2$ plots led Bohemen and the author in early work (4) to suggest that the B term was particle size dependent and that the simplified van Deemter equation might be written

$$H = \frac{\bar{B}' + nd_p}{\bar{u}} + C\bar{u}$$

Rijnders (54) suggested that this resulted from a failure to appreciate the pressure dependence of B_o. The data for acetone and benzene listed in Table 8 again could be interpreted as meaning that B_o might be particle size dependent, and in this case the pressure correction was applied. However, the variation appears to be of the same magnitude as the possible experimental error, and is not, therefore, conclusive. In the original work it was suggested that the additive part of the B_o term might possibly represent an inverse velocity dependence of eddy diffusion. In the present instance this cannot be true, since the term is negative. Whether the molecular diffusion term is particle size dependent or not is a matter of opinion. If γ is not unity it might well show such a dependence. It seems certain that further studies in this direction are desirable.

TEMPERATURE AND COLUMN EFFICIENCY

The probable effect of temperature change on H was briefly discussed earlier (p. 147). The molecular diffusion constant B_o must increase with temperature approximately as $T^{1.5-2.0}$. Thus over the range 30 to 160°C., for example, B_o would be approximately doubled. A, of course, should not change, and so if H were to be reduced by increased temperature, C would have to be very seriously affected. The net effect must be rather complex and the only unequivocal study would be one of the individual dependences of A, B_o and C upon temperature. Desty, Godfrey and Harbourn (58) have made such a study and quoted values which are shown in Table 9.

In each case, increased temperature leads to improved performance, as is seen from the column containing values of H_{min} computed from the other data. The variation of B_o with temperature for the three pairs of results is proportional, respectively, to $T^{3.00}$, $T^{1.05}$ and $T^{1.7}$. The data are clearly inconsistent and only the last in any way accords with theoretical prediction. It is a point of interest that an unexpectedly high value and variation of A are recorded for the first two pairs. As mentioned earlier, errors in estimating A affect B_o much more than C. It seems possible that this might account for the results and, in fact, the anomalies in A were commented on by the authors. In each case, C was reduced by raising the temperature. Unfortunately, however, the results are complicated by the fact that at the lower temperature the column was more than 20° below the melting point of the wax. However, this in itself is very interesting, and indicates a problem which might be explored further. Other workers have reported effective separations with solvents, usually inadvertently, below their melting point. The author, for example, has experienced this with paraffin wax at room temperature and has also successfully used gels in columns (59).

TABLE 9

EXPERIMENTAL VALUES OF RATE EQUATION CONSTANTS AT TWO
TEMPERATURES, COLUMNS OF 20 PER CENT w/w *IG* PARAFFIN WAX Z;
SOLUTE UNSTATED

Support	Mesh B.S.S.	Temperature °C.	A cm.	B_o cm.²/sec.	C sec.	H_{min} cm.
Firebrick	72–100	78.5	0.015	0.046	0.005	0.049
		134.0	0.015	0.071	0.005	0.048
Celite	72–100	78.5	0.020	0.079	0.012	0.082
		134.0	0.033	0.092	0.006	0.059
	100–200	78.5	0.002	0.085	0.018	0.080
		134.0	0.006	0.109	0.005	0.052

Littlewood has shown plots of H versus column temperature for the elution of *n*-octane over the range 30 to 100°C. H again progressively diminished; more or less linearly. Littlewood's data refer to the optimum flow rate, that is, u_{min}, at which value, $H_{min} = A + 2\sqrt{B_o C}$ and so, since B_o must increase with temperature, the results again imply that C decreases more rapidly. If we make the simplifying assumption that A may be neglected and that $B_o \propto T^2$, we get approximately

$$\frac{C_{100°}}{C_{30°}} \simeq 0.42$$

Thus, over 70°C., C is about halved, a result which compares reasonably with those in Table 9. We can go further now, and assume as Littlewood did that the simplified van Deemter equation is applicable and that the evaluated C is in fact C_l. We may then say that, with only the slight approximation introduced by ignoring the temperature dependence of d_f, that

$$C_T = C_0 e^{\Delta E/RT}$$

which is a reasonable hypothesis since, at high values of k', we can write $C_l \propto (KD_l)^{-1}$ and both K and D_l have this type of temperature dependence (3). From the above value of C_{100}/C_{30} we then get

$$C_T = C_0 e^{1950/RT}$$

The activation energy term has a positive sign since C decreases with increasing temperature and, if the assumptions made are correct, represents the difference in the heat of solution and the activation energy of diffusion (equation 4.14). This implies an activation energy of diffusion of 10 kcal./mole or so, a very high figure. The results may be taken, therefore, to indicate the inadequacy of the assumptions made and, in particular, of the simplified van Deemter equation. The most likely explanation of the commonly observed diminution of H with increasing temperature is thus to be

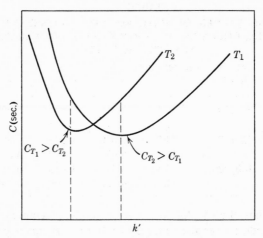

FIG. 9. Hypothetical plots for two temperatures of values of C (assuming $C_g{}^o \simeq C_l$) against k'. The crossing of the plots shows how the experimentally observed effect of temperature on C may depend upon the value of k' relevant to the column and conditions.

looked for in the extended rate equation. The dependence of the various C terms on k' was illustrated in Figures 4, 5 and 6 of Chapter 8. $C_g{}^o$ undoubtedly must be reduced with increasing temperature provided k' is less than about 10, while the effect on C_l depends both upon k' and the form of solvent distribution.

It is clearly the case that the precise effect of temperature on a block C term depends entirely on experimental conditions and that, in appropriate circumstances, it may either increase or decrease. This is illustrated in Figure 9 which shows hypothetical plots against k' of values of C calculated by compounding $C_g{}^o$ and C_l and assuming them to be roughly equal. Curves for two temperatures are shown and it is clear that there is a change over in the effect of temperature with changing k'. It may well be some such effect as this which has led to the situation where some workers (1, 8, 60) have reported increases in H as the temperature is raised, in contrast to the work discussed here. Evidently, temperature studies must be carried out over a range of solvent/support ratios if they are to be correctly interpreted.

EXPERIMENTAL EVALUATION OF THE RADIAL DIFFUSION TERM

All the work discussed up to this point has involved only the three constant simplified van Deemter equation and in almost every instance the results provided evidence for the extended equation. In consequence, Bohemen and the author (25) have attempted a detailed study of column performance in terms of the extended rate equation. Processing of the data was according to the methods outlined on p. 159 and values of C_l and C_g^o

TABLE 10
MASS TRANSFER COEFFICIENTS

Sil-O-Cel Support Size d_p in cm.	Carrier Gas	$10^3 \times C_g^o$ (sec.)		$10^3 \times C_l$ (sec.)	
		Acetone	Benzene	Acetone	Benzene
0.032	H_2	1.4	1.3	2.4	2.9
	N_2	5.8	6.2	2.4	2.9
0.016	H_2	0.3	0.3	1.1	1.6
	N_2	1.3	1.4	1.1	1.6
0.010	H_2	0.1	0.1	1.2	1.5
	N_2	0.4	0.4	1.2	1.5

(corresponding to 1 atm. outlet pressure) obtained by them for the elution of acetone and bezene in nitrogen and hydrogen from 20 per cent w/w polyethylene glycol columns at 51°C. are given in Table 10.

These results fully bear out the need for introducing a C_g^o term into the general equation. In fact, as is seen, it was more than twice as great as C_l when nitrogen was used as carrier with the coarsest support. With the finest support, however, C_g^o contributed only about one quarter of the whole C term for nitrogen elution and less than 10 per cent for hydrogen elution. The results also substantiate the view that for maximum speed gas chromatography, hydrogen is superior to other gases since it confers the lowest total C for any column. Further, since with coarse support $C_g^o \gg C_l$, while with fine support $C_l \gg C_g^o$, the column conditions for maximum speed analysis are different in the two cases (p. 150).

Thus, the detailed theory of maximum speed analysis is very complex and the abridged theory presented earlier is probably adequate until more specific information about the dependence of C on experimental parameters becomes available. Further point is given to this by the listed data for C_l. The halving of d_p from 0.032 to 0.016 cm. roughly halved C_l but no further change occurred on going to $d_p = 0.010$ cm. It will be recalled that roughly comparable results were reported by Desty, Godfrey and Harbourn (Table 2). Thus, on the basis of the rather limited data it appears that with fine supports, d_f is independent of d_p. This again, like most of the evidence previously discussed, indicates a droplet type solvent distribution.

Confidence in the data of Table 10 comes from calculation of χ of equation 8.40. For the twelve values of $C_g{}^o$ quoted, χ varied only between 1.1 and 1.7, having a mean of 1.5. Further, the relative values of $d_f{}^2/D_l$ computed from the C_l data for acetone and benzene were constant at 2.2 for all the columns and both carrier gases. The assumption that D_l for acetone was 10^{-7} cm.^{2} sec.$^{-1}$ gave $d_f = 1.5 \times 10^{-3}$ cm. in reasonable accord with expectation.

The general conclusion drawn by Bohemen and the author was that the extended rate equation in the form

$$H = 1.5d_p + \frac{2D_g{}^o}{u_o} + \frac{[1 + 6k' + 11(k')^2] d_p{}^2 u_o}{16(1 + k')^2 D_g{}^o} + \frac{2}{3} \frac{k'}{(1 + k')^2} \frac{d_f{}^2 f u_o}{D_l}$$

gave a very close representation of their packed column results over the velocity range 1–80 cm. sec.$^{-1}$ for all the systems studied. It is to be noted that their conclusion that $\gamma = 1$, if verified, opens up the way unequivocally to interdiffusion coefficient measurements from chromatographic data. In so far as they represented $A = 1.5d_p$ it was their view that this was not necessarily evidence for eddy diffusion since the derived A was of a magnitude comparable with the overall errors inherent in the computation of the four coefficients. It must also be pointed out that the value of χ found is very big, which could indicate the existence of some gas phase effect not yet taken into account. For example, lateral inhomogeneity of flow or of solvent distribution would give a contribution to $C_g{}^o$ of the correct form (p. 408), although independent of k'. The values of k' pertaining to the systems of Table 10 were large and so would not readily allow observation of any dependence of a radial diffusion contribution to $C_g{}^o$ upon k' (p. 144).

The magnitude of the $C_g{}^o$ term obviously complicates very considerably the interpretation of many of the results discussed earlier in this chapter, and it seems not unreasonable to suggest that a fresh attack on the evaluation of rate equation coefficients is called for.

STUDIES WITH CAPILLARY COLUMNS

Following the theoretical studies of Golay (61, 62) he showed (63) that capillaries were capable of offering in practice the predicted high efficiencies; by today as many as one million theoretical plates have been achieved. The first attempted study of the effect of various experimental variables was that of Dijkstra and de Goey (64). They used columns of 0.3 to 1.0 mm. diameter, and achieved theoretical plate heights of several cms. They estimated solvent film thicknesses on the basis of a uniform film distribution and obtained rather erratic results. For example, the lowest efficiencies corresponded to the thinnest films, in contrast to the theoretical expectation. Their ratio of $H/r_0 \simeq$ 50–200 is far removed from the hoped for minimum (p. 145) of about unity. There is no doubt, as pointed out by Golay (65) that these workers were bedevilled by instrumental problems such as the large volumes of their injection and detector systems, and that their columns were, in fact, functioning very much better than appeared to be the case.

TABLE 11

COMPARISON OF CAPILLARY MATERIAL;
SOLVENT-SQUALANE, CARRIER GAS =
NITROGEN

	Stainless Steel	Copper	Glass
Diameter, cm.	0.028	0.028	0.015
Temp. °C.	20	72	20
H, cm.	0.18	0.07	0.037
H/r_0	13	5	4.9

Desty, Goldup and Whyman (66) have carried out the most comprehensive study to date. In the first instance they compared the performance of capillaries constructed in different materials. Table 11 gives an outline of their results.

With stainless steel capillaries containing other solvents values of $H/r_0 \simeq$ 5 were obtained, and so it is evident that, from the data listed, there is no clear cut difference between the various materials. The real difference lies in the finding that quite marked peak tails were obtained which were smallest with the glass capillary, and so Desty et al. (67) recommend this material. They attributed the peak tailing to adsorption by the metal, even when it carried solvent, a suggestion which accords with the result of Bohemen in injection system studies (p. 170). A microscopic study indicated that the glass had a smoother surface than the metals, and the solvent appeared to spread better. If this latter statement is true, it is evident that even in capillaries there may not be true film type distribution and the possibility of droplet formation cannot be ruled out. Further evidence for this is that Desty et al. described the occasional formation of droplets which completely blocked the capillary, rendering it useless for further work.

The value of H/r_0 achieved by Desty et al. is little removed from the ideal value (p. 145) calculable on the basis that mass transfer in the liquid phase is zero. Since this seems unlikely it suggests that this work represents a near ideal performance which can hardly be improved upon to any great extent. These authors, in fact, quote a value of $H/r_0 =$ 2.7 for a "typical" column, and show that operation at 10 atm. outlet pressure gives $H/r_0 = 1.5$. It is not clear whether this is a calculation or an experimental achievement. If it is the latter it is virtually the best to be hoped for.

The theoretical plate heights achieved by other workers also appear to be in the same range as those above. Scott (71), using nylon tube, obtained $H \simeq 0.04$ cm. for peaks eluted early and $H \simeq 0.12$ cm. for later ones. These give $H/r_0 \simeq 4 - 12$, both values only a factor of 8 removed from the ideal value for their respective values of k'. More or less identical results were obtained by Lipsky, Landowne and Lovelock (73, 74) while Zlatkis and Kaufman (50) achieved $H/r_0 \simeq 20$. It would appear then that the work on capillaries to date has been conducted in a region where mass transfer effects in solution are of negligible magnitude. This view would appear to be substantiated by the plots of H against retention volume shown by Scott (70) for his nylon columns. These were of the form shown in Figure 4 on p. 174. This state of affairs could result from the use of extraordinarily small amounts of solvent. It should be pointed out, however, that in such circumstances the theoretical plate requirement (equation 7.44) may become astronomical and even simple separations may need a million theoretical plates or more (68). A small theoretical plate height is not the only consideration in analysis, and it is pertinent to point out that a better appreciation of capillary column performance can be gained from the use of equation 7.44 than from H. On this basis it can readily be shown that by far the most effective capillary analyses yet performed are those of the m and p-xylenes by Golay (62) and by Desty et al. (69), both carried out with quite heavily solvent loaded columns of relatively large H. The major problem associated with capillary analysis appears to be that of obtaining a large V_R/V_d ratio without adversely affecting H. It has been suggested that a porous capillary might overcome this problem (63, 68), but it is not clear how this might be achieved. Another consideration which must be borne in mind is that of obtaining a sufficiently small sample in a representative and reproducible manner. All the work carried out up to now has been done with a simple T-splitting device, the splitting sometimes being in the ratio of 1000/1 or more. As Desty et al. point out, there is no guarantee that this splitting operation can be conducted without some fractionation. Some form of iso-kinetic device may, therefore, be needed and this may present a considerable development problem.

There can be no doubt that capillaries, with the enormous numbers of theoretical plates available, offer glowing possibilities for the analysis of mixtures of very great difficulty. However, it is important to point out that if a column has 1,000,000 theoretical plates which are to be usable, then analysis must take 1000 times as long as with a column of 1000 theoretical plates. In other words, there is a definite waiting time per plate for a given degree of separation. To overcome this by reduction of solvent weight or elevation of temperature is a retrograde step, and it would, in most cases, be better to use shorter capillary or, packed columns in multiple array if necessary.

It is certain that in the near future a great deal of work with capillaries will be described in the literature, and this will be awaited with great interest, in particular since theoretical studies will be facilitated by the absence of solid supports.

CONCLUSIONS

Considering first the extent to which experiment confirms or contradicts the theory it seems likely that, in fact, few if any of the experimental studies have been carried out in a sufficiently comprehensive way to test the theory thoroughly. This is a consequence of the fact that the number of variables which must be controlled is so large that definitive experiments may be virtually impossible. In addition, even for the most elementary studies, gas chromatographic measurements demand a very high degree of refinement and the attainable accuracy at this time is probably inadequate to justify very detailed investigations. It must be remembered also that the theories advanced to date involve numerous approximations, and so even their protagonists do not expect them to give an explicit account of the state of affairs in practice.

Broadly speaking, however, the basic premises of the theory have undoubtedly been substantiated and it is only in the details that differences are observed. Doubtless, other rate determining processes might be introduced into the theory, for example, account might be taken of the special situation at phase interfaces, but it is unlikely that experiments could be devised in the immediate future to study such effects, even qualitatively. Until such time as more precise experimentation is possible, and until general equations such as 8.38 and 8.40 have been positively shown to be quantitatively inadequate, further refinement of the theory seems pointless. As it stands at the moment, the rate theory almost certainly accounts for the major band spreading processes. Keulemans and Kwantes (8) have pointed out that the simplified van Deemter equation cannot be expected to do much more than give a semi-quantitative account of chromatographic mechanisms. In fact, one might conclude that it has been much more successful than this.

From the practical point of view, the experimental data obtained have been very valuable, since they have very convincingly shown the way to high efficiencies. It seems certain that the following expedients must always be beneficial.

a. The use of the minimum detectable sample.

b. Introduction of the sample as compactly and as rapidly as possible.

c. The employment of the narrowest capillaries and the finest and most uniform possible solid support in packed columns.

d. Using apparatus in which the only significant free gas space is that of the column.

e. Operation at the lowest convenient column temperature.

Other features which may be advantageous in the situation that high velocities are unattainable are:

f. The use of carrier gases of high molecular weight.

g. Elevation of the total column pressure.

There is undoubtedly much to be gained by appropriate choice of solvent/ support ratio in packed columns and solvent/free gas space in capillaries. The published experimental data are equivocal, but tend to suggest that there may, in fact, be an optimum condition. Until more detailed information is available, no definite view as to the probable location of this optimum can be offered. On the whole, it seems safe to suggest that in the "normal" working range, say 1 to 20 per cent w/w solvent/support, there is no significant change in column efficiency. Thus, the choice of solvent weight represents a compromise between separating power, efficiency and speed of analysis.

Experimental data relating to the effect of temperature on H mostly show an improved column performance at higher temperatures. This would appear to contradict (*e*) above. However, the observed improvements are relatively slight, perhaps factors of 2 or 3 over a range of 50°C. Retention volumes will almost always change faster than this, and the theoretical plate requirement for separation (equation 7.44) will do so too. In addition, relative retention volumes most often increase with reduced temperature. Low temperatures are, therefore, almost certain to be the best on the whole. The general trend of results obtained in studies of the effect of temperature and solvent weight on H suggest that the most urgent problem, from a practical point of view, is to devise ways of obtaining more uniform and film type solvent distribution. Achievement of this aim would lead not only to higher efficiencies but also to increased speed of analysis. The appropriate experimental approach is not very evident, but judging from the few data available, the addition of surface active agents to column packings seems to merit study.

REFERENCES

1. Mellor, N., *Vapour Phase Chromatography*, 1957, Butterworths, London (editor, D. H. Desty), p. 63.
2. Pollard, F. H., and C. J. Hardy (see ref. 1), p. 115.
3. Purnell, J. H., *Ann. N.Y. Acad. Sci.*, 1959, **72**, 592.

4. Bohemen, J., and J. H. Purnell, *Gas Chromatography*, 1958, Butterworths, London (editor, D. H. Desty), p. 6,

5. Bethea, R. M., and M. Smutz, *Anal. Chem.*, 1959, **31**, 1211.

6. Bohemen, J. (Ph.D. thesis, Cambridge, 1959).

7. Porter, K. (Ph.D. Thesis, Cambridge, 1959).

8. Keulmans, A. I. M., and A. Kwantes, *Vapour Phase Chromatography*, 1957, Butterworths, London (editor, D. H. Desty), p. 15.

9. Adlard, E. R. (see ref. 8), p. 98.

10. Ring, R. D., *Gas Chromatography*, Academic Press, N.Y., 1958 (editors, V. J. Coates et al.), p. 195.

11. Eggertsen, F. T., and H. S. Knight, *Anal. Chem.*, 1958, **30**, 15.

12. McKenna, T. A., and J. A. Idleman, *Anal. Chem.*, 1959, **31**, 1021.

13. Desty, D. H., F. M. Godfrey and C. L. A. Harbourn, *Gas Chromatography*, 1958, Butterworths, London (editor, D. H. Desty), p. 200.

14. Cheshire, J. D., and R. P. W. Scott, *J. Inst. Petrol.* 1958, **44**, 74.

15. Scott, R. P. W., *Gas Chromatography*, 1958, Butterworths, London (editor, D. H. Desty), p. 189.

16. Eggertsen, F. T., and S. Groennings, *Anal. Chem.*, 1958, **30**, 20.

17. Orr, C. H., and J. E. Callen, *Ann. N.Y. Acad. Sci.*, 1959, **72**, 649

18. Johns, T., *Gas Chromatography*, 1958, Academic Press, New York (editors, V. J. Coates et al.), p. 31.

19. Conner, A. Z. *ibid.*, p. 214.

20. Liberti, A., *Gas Chromatography*, 1958, Butterworths, London (editor, D. H. Desty), p. 214.

21. Tuey, G. A. P. (see ref. 20), p. 215.

22. Janak, J., and H. Cvrkal (see ref. 20), p. 329.

23. Perrett, R. H., and J. H. Purnell, *J. Chromatog.*, (in press).

24. Bohemen, J., S. H. Langer, R. H. Perrett and J. H. Purnell, *J. Chem. Soc.*, **1960**, 2444.

25. Bohemen, J., and J. H. Purnell, *J. Chem. Soc.*, **1961**, 360; 2630.

26. van Deemter, J. J., F. J. Zuiderweg and A. Klinkenberg, *Chem. Eng. Sci.*, 1956, **5**, 271.

27. Grant, D. W., and G. A. Vaughan, *J. Appl. Chem.*, 1956, **6**, 145.

28. Littlewood, A. B., *Gas Chromatography*, 1958, Butterworths, London (editor, D. H. Desty), p. 23.

29. James, A. T., *Research*, 1955, **8**, 8.

30. Cuthbertson, F., and W. K. R. Musgrave, *J. Appl. Chem.*, 1957, **7**, 99.

31. Ormerod, E. C., and R. P. W. Scott, *J. Chromatog.*, 1959, **2**, 65.

32. Knox, J. H. (private communication).

33. Kiselev, A. V., "The Structure and Properties of Porous Materials," *Vol. X, Colston Papers*, 1958, Butterworths, London (editors, D. H. Everett and F. S. Stone), p. 257.

34. Horning, E. C., E. A. Moscatelli and C. C. Sweeley, *Chem. and Ind.*, **1959**, 751.

35. Rijnders, G. W. A., *Gas Chromatography*, 1958, Butterworths, London (editor, D. H. Desty), p. 19.

36. Purnell, J. H. (unpublished work). See *J. Roy. Inst. Chem.*, 1958, **82**, 586.

37. Baker, W. J., E. H. Lee and R. F. Wall, *2nd International Symposium of I.S.A.*, Lansing, Mich., 1959.

38. Purnell, J. H., *Ann. N.Y. Acad. Sci.*, 1959, **72**, 614.

39. Wiebe, A. K., *J. Phys. Chem.*, 1956, **60**, 685.

40. Bernhard, R. A., *J. Assoc. Off. Agric. Chemists*, **1957**, 917.
41. Evans, D. E. M., W. E. Massingham, M. Stacey and J. C. Tatlow, *Nature*, 1958, **182**, 591.
42. Kirkland, J. J., *Gas Chromatography*, 1958, Academic Press, New York (editors, V. J. Coates et al.). p. 203.
43. Cheshire, J. D., and R. P. W. Scott, *Nature*, 1957, **180**, 702.
44. Dimbat, M., P. E. Porter and F. H. Stross, *Anal. Chem.*, 1956, **28**, 290.
45. Ray, N. H., *J. Appl. Chem.*, 1954, **4**, 21.
46. Purnell, J. H., and C. P. Quinn, *Gas Chromatography*, 1960, Butterworths, London (editor, R. P. W. Scott), p. 184.
47. Zlatkis, A., S. Ling and H. R. Kaufman, *Anal. Chem.*, 1959, **31**, 945.
48. Evans, D. E. H., *Gas Chromatography*, 1958, Butterworths, London (editor, D. H. Desty, p. 286.
49. van Deemter, J. J. (see ref. 48), p. 4.
50. Zlatkis, A., and H. R. Kaufman, *Nature*, 1959, **184**, 2010.
51. Klinkenberg, A., and F. Sjenitzer, *Chem. Eng. Sci.*, 1956, **5**, 258.
52. de Wet, W. J., and V. Pretorius, *Anal. Chem.*, 1958, **30**, 325.
53. Brennan, D., and C. Kemball, *J. Inst. Petrol.*, 1958, **44**, 14.
54. Rijnders, G. W. A., *Gas Chromatography*, 1958, Butterworths, London (editor, D. H. Desty), p. 18.
55. Littlewood, A. B. (see ref. 54), p. 23.
56. Glueckauf, E. (see ref. 54), p. 33.
57. Glueckauf, E., *Ann. N.Y. Acad. Sci.*, 1959, **72**, 614.
58. Desty, D. H., F. M. Godfrey and C. L. A. Harbourn, *Gas Chromatography*, 1958, Butterworths, London (editor, D. H. Desty), p. 211.
59. Purnell J. H., and M. S. Spencer, *Nature*, 1955, **175**, 988.
60. Littlewood, A. B., C. S. G. Phillips and D. T. Price, *J. Chem. Soc.*, **1955**, 1480.
61. Golay, M., *Anal. Chem.*, 1957, **29**, 928.
62. Golay, M., *Gas Chromatography*, 1958, Butterworths, London (editor, D. H. Desty) p. 36.
63. Golay, M. (see ref. 62), p. 53.
64. Dijkstra, G., and J. de Goey (see ref. 62), p. 56.
65. Golay, M. (see ref. 62), p. 66.
66. Desty, D. H., A. Goldup and B. H. F. Whyman, *J. Inst. Petrol.* 1959, **45**, 287.
67. Desty, D. H., J. N. Haresnape and B. H. F. Whyman, *Anal. Chem.*, 1960, **32**, 302.
68. Purnell, J. H., *Nature*, 1959, **184**, 2009.
69. Desty, D. H., A. Goldup and W. T. Swanton, *Nature*, 1959, **193**, 107.
70. Scott, R. P. W., *4th Informal Symposium of G. C. Discussion Group*, Imperial College, London, April 1959.
71. Scott, R. P. W., *Nature*, 1959, **183**, 1753.
72. Bohemen, J., and J. H. Purnell, *J. Chem. Soc.*, **1961**, 360.
73. Lipsky, S. R., J. E. Lovelock and R. A. Landowne, *J. Amer. Chem. Soc.*, 1959, **81**, 1010.
74. Lipsky, S. R., R. A. Landowne and J. E. Lovelock, *Anal. Chem.*, 1959, **31**, 852.

It was shown in Chapter 7 that the most useful measure of the rate of movement of a solute through a two phase partitioning system is the apparent retention volume (V_R'). Provided the compressibility correction equation 5.21 is applied, V_R' is related to column volumes and operating conditions by the retention volume equation (7.10)

$$V_R' = N\Delta V_g + KN\Delta V_l$$

or in terms of total column volumes,

$$V_R' = V_d + KV_l = V_d + V_R \quad (10.1)$$

each volume corresponding to that measured at the column temperature.

If the literature contained values of K for gases or vapours dissolved in the type of solvent normally used in gas chromatography, a knowledge of V_d and V_l would immediately permit calculation of retention volumes, and hence the drawing up of tentative chromatograms. Nothing would be known of the widths of the peaks, but their maxima could, in principle, be precisely located. In fact, no such data are available at this time, and so this aspect of the problem awaits development.

As it stands, equation 10.1 might appear not to apply to gas-solid chromatography. However, this is untrue, since adsorption can be described in terms of a volume or surface area partition coefficient. Unfortunately, the value of such coefficients depends primarily on the nature and extent of the available surface of adsorbent, and unless this can be reproduced from sample to sample, the value of K has little meaning. In addition, as a consequence of the variation of structure and nature of the

10
THE THERMODYNAMICS OF GAS CHROMATOGRAPHY

surface, unlike most gas-liquid systems, gas-solid systems often have partition coefficients which are concentration dependent, although, as pointed out earlier, it is vapours rather than gases which usually have such non-linear partition isotherms. In consequence, measured values of K are often highly specific to a system and the conditions in which they were determined. This is a great pity, since the literature contains a vast fund of adsorption data which could otherwise be gainfully employed in gas chromatography to limit the amount of experimental study necessary. Even so, much useful qualitative information may be drawn from the literature in this field.

While, therefore, in principle any thermodynamic treatment of gas-liquid chromatography, appropriately modified, is equally valid for gas-solid chromatography, it may be expected that general experimental agreement with theoretical predictions will be observed less often.

Considering equation 10.1, we see that when $K = 0$

$$V_R' = V_d$$

and so the value of V_d corresponds reasonably closely to the retention volume, of for example, air, hydrogen or an inert gas. V_d obviously, in practice, may contain extra-column free space, and so any thermodynamic study of sorption processes must not include this quantity. In consequence, the retention volume used for thermodynamic purposes must be the true retention volume V_R. No great error is normally involved, if this is taken to be V_R' minus the retention volume of air, for example.

THE RETENTION VOLUME AND SATURATION VAPOUR PRESSURE OF A SOLUTE

The relationship, already established, between retention volume and the partition coefficient, is not very informative as it stands. However, it can be cast into a more suitable form by considering the question of the dependence of the partition coefficient on other parameters such as the saturation vapour pressure. A start is made by using equation 2.11, deduced earlier

$$p = p^0 \gamma x \tag{10.2}$$

If the solute vapour is ideal, then according to the gas laws

$$p = \frac{N_g{}^s RT}{v_g} = c_g{}^s RT$$

v_g being the volume of the gas phase, $N_g{}^s$ the number of moles of solute in the gas phase, and $c_g{}^s$ its molar concentration in the gas phase.

The mole fraction of solute x is given by

$$x = \frac{N_l{}^s}{N_l + N_l{}^s} \simeq \frac{N_l{}^s}{N_l}$$

where N_l^s is the number of moles of solute in solution in N_l moles of solvent. The approximation is good in highly dilute solution, say $x \simeq 0.01$. However, $N_l = V_l/V_l^m$, that is, the ratio of the volume of solvent to its molar volume, hènce

$$x = \frac{N_l^s V_l^m}{V_l} = c_l^s V_l^{m.} \tag{10.3}$$

Substituting for p and x in 10.2 yields

$$\frac{c_l^s}{c_g^s} = K = \frac{RT}{V_l^m \gamma p^0} \tag{10.4a}$$

Since $V_R = K V_l$, then,

$$V_R = \left(\frac{RT}{\gamma p^0}\right) \frac{V_l}{V_l^m} = \frac{RTw}{\gamma p^0 M_l} \tag{10.4b}$$

w being the weight of solvent in the column and M_l its molecular weight. Thus, the *retention volume per gram of solvent* at the column temperature, V_g^T, is given by

$$V_g^T = \frac{RT}{\gamma p^0 M_l} \tag{10.5}$$

Flow rates are normally measured at room temperature and so a correction is necessary. Since this is so, it is just as useful to correct V_g^T to 0°C., a process which has a number of advantages, not least of which are the elimination of T from equation 10.1 and the fact that values reduced to 0°C. will usually be closer to the practically observed room temperature value than will be the value corrected to the column temperature. The elimination of T from equation 10.5 follows, since the retention volume per gram of solvent at 0°C., known now as the *specific retention volume* (Ambrose, Keulemans and Purnell, 1) and designated V_g, is given by

$$V_g = \frac{273 V_R}{Tw} = \frac{273 V_g^T}{T}$$

Hence,

$$V_g = \frac{273R}{\gamma p^0 M_l} \tag{10.6}$$

If V_g is in milliliters and p^0 is in millimeters of mercury, $R = 6.3 \times 10^4$ ml. mm./mole deg. and

$$V_g = \frac{1.7 \times 10^7}{\gamma p^0 M_l} \tag{10.7}$$

The advantage of using V_g rather than V_R or V_g^T is obvious since it reduces considerably the amount of calculation necessary. It follows from the fore-going equations that the activity coefficient γ can readily be calculated from experimental data, since on rearrangement of 10.7, we get

$$\gamma = \frac{1.7 \times 10^7}{V_g p^0 M_l} \tag{10.8}$$

If the saturation vapour pressure is expressed in atmospheres, V_g being again in milliliters, R becomes 80.5 atm. ml./mole deg., and 10.8 becomes

$$\gamma = \frac{2.24 \times 10^4}{V_g p^0 M_l} \tag{10.9}$$

Equation 10.7 is the most convenient form of expressing the inter-relation of retention volume and vapour pressure. However, because γ may not be unity, and may also be temperature and concentration dependent, we cannot assume the simple inverse relationship which is indicated by 10.7. A general equation, however, was deduced by Hoare and Purnell (2) who used the expression for the general form of the activity coefficient given by equation 2.13. Then 10.7 can be written

$$V_g = \frac{1.7 \times 10^7}{\gamma_a \gamma_t p^0 M_l} \tag{10.10}$$

Now, we know from equations 3.2 and 2.17 that in the simplest case

$$p^0 = e^{-\Delta H^v / RT} e^{2.3C}$$

and that

$$\gamma_t = e^{-\Delta H^m / RT}$$

Thus,

$$\gamma_t p^0 = e^{2.3C} \exp\left[-\frac{(\Delta H^v + \Delta H^m)}{RT}\right] = e^{2.3C} \exp\left(-\frac{\Delta H_e^{\,s}}{RT}\right)$$

If we define a constant a by

$$a = \frac{\Delta H_e^{\,s}}{\Delta H^v}$$

we can write

$$\gamma_t p^0 = e^{2.3C} e^{2.3aC} e^{-2.3aC} \exp\left(-\frac{a\,\Delta H^v}{RT}\right)$$

$$= e^{2.3C(1-a)} \exp\left[-a\left(\frac{\Delta H^v}{RT} + 2.3C\right)\right]$$

$$= (p^0)^a e^{2.3C(1-a)}$$

Substitution in 10.10 gives

$$V_g = \frac{1.7 \times 10^7}{\gamma_a \, M_l \, (p^0)^a \, e^{2.3\,C(1-a)}} \qquad (10.11)$$

or taking logarithms

$$\ln V_g = -a \ln p^0 + \ln \frac{1.7 \times 10^7}{\gamma_a M_l} + 2.3C(a-1)$$

or

$$\log V_g = -a \log p^0 + \log \frac{1.7 \times 10^7}{\gamma_a M_l} + C(a-1) \qquad (10.12)$$

The validity of equation 10.12, first demonstrated by Hoare and Purnell (2, 3), has subsequently been further established for a wide range of chemical types of both solvent and solutes (11, 12, 13, 19). In so far as data are available there seems to be no recorded exception to the rule. Figure 1

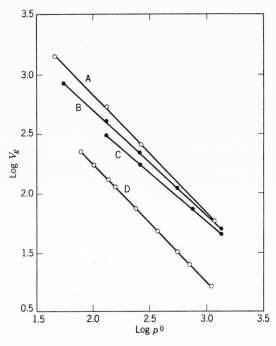

FIG. 1. Plots of log V_g against log p^0 for: A, fluoro, chloro, bromo and iodo benzenes eluted from benzyl diphenyl at 100°C. (20); B, n-butyl, n-propyl, ethyl and methyl benzenes and benzene eluted from 7,8-benzoquinoline at 100°C. (21); C, solutes as in B eluted from di-n-propyl tetrabromophthalate at 100°C. (21); D, ethyl, n-propyl and n-butyl alcohols eluted from medicinal paraffin each at several temperatures in the range 30° to 110°C. (2).

shows typical plots of log V_g against log p^0 for a variety of solutes eluted from columns containing several solvents.

It is apparent that theoretical values of log V_g can be calculated from equation 10.7 or 10.12 if it is assumed that the solutions are ideal, that is $\gamma_a = \gamma_t = 1$. The ideal solution equations then become

$$V_g = \frac{1.7 \times 10^7}{p^0 M_l}$$

and

$$\log V_g = -\log p^0 + \log \frac{1.7 \times 10^7}{M_l}$$

Examples of a comparison of calculated ideal and experimental values of log V_g are shown in Table 1, which contains data for C_5 hydrocarbons eluted from dioctyl phthalate (11) and a wide range of acetate and formate esters and n-alcohols eluted from a column of tricresyl phosphate. In each case, the retention volume has been calculated as that at the boiling point

TABLE 1

CALCULATED IDEAL AND EXPERIMENTAL RETENTION VOLUMES

Retention Volume at the Boiling
Point of the Solute

Solvent	Solute	Calculated	Found	γ_a	Reference
Dioctyl	neopentane	57.20	36.73	1.562	(11)
phthalate	isopentane		43.65	1.310	
	n-pentane		48.07	1.190	
	2-pentene		54.95	1.042	
	1-pentene		57.68	0.992	
Tricresyl	esters	62.10	53.70		(4)
phosphate	n-alcohols		59.60		

of the solute concerned ($\log p^0 = \log 760$). The agreement is reasonably good, and since for the hydrocarbons experiment shows that $a = 1$ (athermal solution), this provides good reason for the introduction of the temperature independent coefficient γ_a at this point. The ratio of calculated to experimental retention volume for the hydrocarbons is clearly numerically equal to γ_a since $\gamma_t = 1$.

While such theoretical calculations of V_g are only approximate even for such substances as the hydrocarbons, esters, ethers and ketones eluted from non-polar or weakly polar solvents, that is, systems which do not deviate too greatly from ideality, they can sometimes be of some value in making a preliminary assessment of the possibilities of any system.

RETENTION DIAGRAMS

Some interesting regularities in the form of log V_g versus log p^0 plots (retention diagram) have been pointed out by the author (11). Generally, retention diagrams for series of homologous or related compounds fall into one of three classes:

a. In which the retention diagrams for all members of the series fall on a common line or "family" plot.

b. In which retention diagrams for individual members are separate, but for which isothermals drawn across the retention diagrams are also linear, thus giving a grid. When the solutes of highest vapour pressure have the highest activity coefficient the slope of the isotherms is greater than that of any retention diagram. When the substance of lowest activity coefficient has the highest vapour pressure the slope of the isotherms will be less than that of any retention diagram.

c. In this class there is no regularity in the disposition of the retention diagrams.

Family Plots. Family behavior has been demonstrated to occur (1, 2, 3, 11, 19) with all types of hydrocarbons, esters, alcohols, ethers and ketones eluted from solvents differing as widely in character as liquid paraffin, the silicone oils and tricresyl phosphate. Figure 2 (*a*, *b* and *c*) illustrates some data for such systems. In most cases the slope of the plot is near unity, in other words, the temperature dependent activity coefficient γ_t is also near unity, and so separation of homologues is based only on differences in saturation vapour pressure, since γ_a is the same for all, although not unity. The process is thus a distillation with the ideal degree of separation. Solvents which show family behaviour with a range of solute types may, nevertheless, be excellent type separators because γ_a may vary considerably from unity and differ from type to type. For example, each of the classes of C_5 hydrocarbons listed in Table 1 gives a family plot of unit slope ($a = 1$) when eluted from dioctyl phthalate, but the activity coefficients, in this case γ_a, range from 1.56 for *neo* type paraffins to about 0.99 for 1-olefins.

Should the slope of the family plot be greater than unity the relative retentions of successive homologues is greater than would be predicted on the basis of their vapour pressures. The process is then a sort of "superdistillation." Few, if any, such systems are as yet known, but there is no doubt that they are worth looking for since they represent the best that gas liquid chromatography can offer.

A slope less than unity means that the separation is less effective than would theoretically be expected, and so, unless there are cogent reasons for doing otherwise, such systems should not be employed for the separation of homologues.

Grid Plots.   Figure 3 (*a* and *b*) illustrates grid-type plots of the two possible types (11).   The alcohols, eluted from silicone oil, show a grid in which solution and vapour pressure effects assist each other, and so, although the individual alcohols exhibit marked positive deviation from Raoult's law,

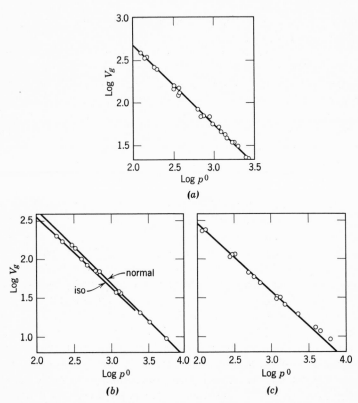

FIG. 2. Family retention diagrams (11) for alkyl (C_3 to C_6) esters eluted from (*a*) silicone 702, (*b*) tricresyl phosphate, (*c*) *n*-alcohols (C_1 to C_4) eluted from tricresyl phosphate. *By courtesy of Butterworths.*

the isotherms for the series, and these are after all the things of importance to the analyst, have slopes very close to unity.   Thus, as a series, the alcohols appear to be close to ideal if the data for a single temperature only are considered.   It is only when data for a number of temperatures are available that any idea of the complexity of the system is gained.   If for no other reason, therefore, a study of the effect of change of elution temperature on the retention characteristics of the solutes under study is worthwhile.

A grid system in which solution and vapour pressure effects oppose each other is obtained when certain aromatics are eluted from tricresyl phosphate. The effect is so considerable that, depending on the elution temperature, the separation may vary from poor to negligible, despite large differences in vapour pressure. In certain circumstances, with a grid of this type the substance of highest vapour pressure might well be eluted after one of lower vapour pressure. Clearly, such systems should be avoided in practice.

Other systems which exhibit complicated grid effects have been reported by Hardy (12) and Harrison (13) while the family plot for ketones eluted

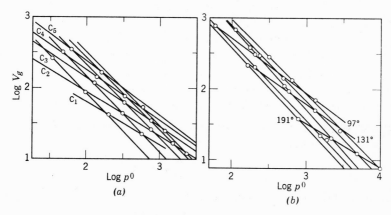

FIG. 3. Grid type retention diagrams (11) for (a) alcohols eluted from silicone oil 702 (35 to 110°C.) and (b) aromatics eluted from tricresyl phosphate (97° to 191°C.). *By courtesy of Butterworths.*

from dinonyl phthalate reported by Young (19) is, according to him, in reality a very narrow grid. It seems certain that if more quantitative data were available, many more grid systems might be discovered.

Irregular Plots. When the retention diagrams for a number of solutes exhibit no obvious regularity they are less useful, but they can still be used to extrapolate data well outside the temperature range studied, and so obtain a great deal of information with a minimum of experimentation. In addition, they serve a very useful purpose in indicating the crossing of retention diagrams. Vapour pressure curves rarely cross, and so the crossing of retention diagrams usually means that, while a solute A may be eluted before a solute B at some high temperature, there will be a lower one at which B is eluted first. In between there is some temperature at which they are eluted simultaneously, and always will be, irrespective of the length of column. It is obviously desirable to avoid working at or very near such a temperature. Examples of such behaviour are to be found in the work of Littlewood, Phillips and Price (4) and concern the elution of *o*-xylene, isopropyl benzene and mesitylene from tricresyl phosphate columns. The retention diagrams of the former two cross at a point corresponding to a temperature of about 200°C., while those of the latter two cross at about 120°C. Thus, the order of elution would vary in the following way with column temperature:

Above 200°C.:   o-xylene, mesitylene, isopropyl benzene.

At 200°C.:   o-xylene, $\begin{bmatrix} \text{mesitylene} \\ \text{isopropyl benzene} \end{bmatrix}$

120–200°C.:   o-xylene, isopropyl benzene, mesitylene.

At 120°C.: $\begin{bmatrix} o\text{-xylene} \\ \text{isopropyl benzene} \end{bmatrix}$, mesitylene.

Below 120°C.:   isopropyl benzene, o-xylene, mesitylene.

Evidently, in the absence of a detailed knowledge of this behaviour, not only could an unsuitable elution temperature be chosen but errors in the identification of the chromatographic peaks are also likely.

THE TEMPERATURE DEPENDENCE OF RETENTION VOLUME
Using the fact that

$$2.3a \log p^0 = -\frac{a \, \Delta H^v}{RT} + aC$$

equation 10.12 can be transformed into

$$\log V_g = \frac{a \, \Delta H^v}{2.3RT} + \log \frac{1.7 \times 10^7}{\gamma_a M_l} - C \qquad (10.13)$$

$a \, \Delta H^v$ is, by our earlier definition, the differential molar heat of evaporation from solution ΔH_e^s, hence 10.13 can be written

$$\log V_g = \frac{\Delta H_e^{\,s}}{2.3RT} + \text{constant} \qquad (10.14)$$

The earliest work which demonstrated the wide applicability of equation 10.14 was that of Littlewood, Phillips and Price (4). It was they also who showed that, provided adequate experimental precautions were taken, the specific retention volume was a constant for a given solute/solvent system at constant temperature, and it is to them that we owe the introduction of this most important function into gas liquid chromatography. Subsequently, a number of workers (1, 2, 3, 5, 6) verified their findings and showed that, at least to a good approximation, equation 10.14 held for all the systems studied. Figure 4 illustrates data plotted in accord with the equation, that is, $\log V_g$ against $1/T$. Since, also

$$V_g = \frac{273 V_R}{Tw}$$

$$V_R = K V_l$$

and

$$V_g = \frac{273KV_l}{Tw} = \frac{273K}{T\rho_l}$$

where ρ_l is the density of the solvent at the column temperature. Thus K/T can be substituted for V_g in equation 10.14, or any other for that matter, and a plot of $\log K/T$ against $\log p^0$ or $1/T$ should be approximately

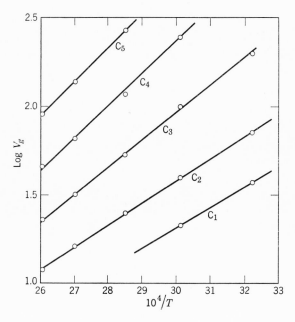

FIG. 4. Plots of $\log V_g$ against $1/T$ (1) for the elution of n-alcohols from silicone oil 702 (30° to 110°C.). *By courtesy of Analytical Chemistry.*

linear. Porter, Deal and Stross (5) used such plots but they are of restricted value since, K must be separately calculated from V_R, V_g^T or V_g for every experimental point. Again, and more important, the resultant diagram must be more curved than the corresponding $\log V_g$ plot, in consequence of the inclusion of $\log \rho_l/273$ in the constant term, since ρ_l, of course, has a small temperature dependence of the form

$$\rho_l = \rho_l^0(1 + kt^0)$$

The latter drawback also applies to plots of $\log V_g^T$ against $1/T$.

The data presented by Pollard and Hardy (7) indicated that some systems exhibit marked curvature of $\log V_g$ against $1/T$ diagrams. In order to reduce these data to a convenient linear form, Ambrose, Keulemans and

Purnell (1) employed Antoine type equations. More recently, Ambrose and Purnell (10) have extended this approach to all the data available in the literature up until early 1958. While $\bar{B}$ rarely falls outside the range 200 to 300 in vapour pressure equations, values considerably outside this sometimes had to be introduced into the gas chromatographic Antoine equations. This might well be expected since deviations from ideality in solution

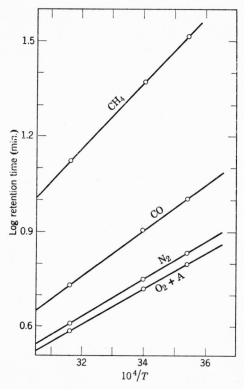

FIG. 5. Plots of log (retention time) against $1/T$ for the elution of some permanent gases from active charcoal. *By courtesy of the Journal of Physical Chemistry.*

may be superimposed on those in the pure liquid solute. A point of importance which arises is that the deviations may not be superimposed but act in opposite senses. Should this occur values of $\bar{B}$ might be found in the gas chromatographic equations which were closer to the ideal value 273 than in the corresponding vapour pressure equation. In consequence, the vapour pressure characteristics of a solute should be closely studied before use is made of gas chromatographic Antoine constants to attempt to evaluate solute/solvent interactions.

So far as is known, there has been no attempt yet made to fit log V_g data to a Kirchhoff type equation, although it is clear that if Antoine equations are used there must be a sufficient temperature dependence of $\Delta H_e{}^s$ to merit this approach.

The applicability of equation 10.14 to gas solid chromatography is widely accepted and Janak (8), for example, has used the method to determine the

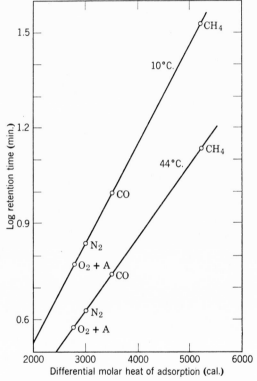

FIG. 6. Illustration of the dependence of log (retention time), in fixed experimental conditions, on the heat of adsorption of some permanent gases adsorbed by active charcoal. *By courtesy of the Journal of Physical Chemistry.*

heats of adsorption which replace $\Delta H_e{}^s$ in the equation. Figures 5 and 6 illustrate data due to Green and Pust (16) which relate to the elution of some low molecular weight gases from charcoal. The heats of adsorption calculated from these plots lie in the expected region, between about 3 and 6 kcal./mole and individual values are said to be in reasonable agreement with static measurements. The second of the diagrams shows how the logarithm of retention time depends on the heat of adsorption. Adsorption (persorption) by molecular sieves also obeys equation 10.14 (16).

THE USE OF RELATIVE RETENTION VOLUMES

More often than not, specific retention volumes are not measured and published data are presented in the form of relative retention times or volumes. Some solute is arbitrarily chosen as having unit retention and those of all others are measured relative to this. This approach has certain practical advantages. Thus, provided all measurements are made under identical column pressure conditions it is unnecessary to apply the compressibility correction equation 5.21, or to know the weight of solvent in the column. Further, the retention times can be measured in any units, such as, for example, cms. of chart, and it is not even necessary to know the carrier gas flow rate provided it is maintained constant.

That such data are also amenable to thermodynamic treatment is readily seen if we write equation 10.13 for any two solutes X and Y eluted from a column

$$\log (V_g)_X = \frac{(\Delta H_e^s)_X}{2.3RT} + (\text{constant})_X$$

and

$$\log (V_g)_Y = \frac{(\Delta H_e^s)_Y}{2.3RT} + (\text{constant})_Y$$

whence

$$\log \frac{(V_g)_X}{(V_g)_Y} = \frac{(\Delta H_e^s)_X - (\Delta H_e^s)_Y}{2.3RT} + [(\text{constant})_X - (\text{constant})_Y]$$

Since the reduction factors of retention volume for both X and Y are the same we can equally well write

$$\log \frac{(V_R)_X}{(V_R)_Y} = \frac{(\Delta H_e^s)_X - (\Delta H_e^s)_Y}{2.3RT} + (\text{constant})$$

Plots of $\log [(V_R)_X/(V_R)_Y]$ against $1/T$ are simpler to construct for a series of solutes than are all those of $\log (V_R)$ against $1/T$. However, they are no more likely to be linear. An illustration of curved relative plots is shown in Figure 7 (9). The origin of such curvature is hard to define, since it could arise, for example, out of non-equivalent curvature of individual $\log (V_R)$ against $1/T$ plots. In the extreme case, it might well result entirely from the characteristics of the chosen standard solute. Again, it could be caused entirely by experimental error such as might be involved in temperature control and measurement or in adsorption by solid support. The relative method of recording information must thus be regarded, not as superior to, but only more convenient than the absolute method.

Although there is, apparently, no recorded example, it is clear that a plot of $\log [(V_R)_X/(V_R)_Y]$ against $\log p^0$ could also be linear.

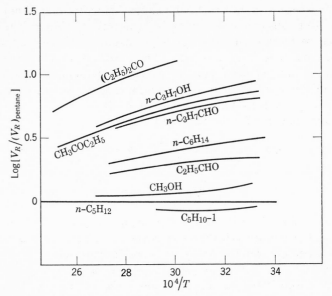

FIG. 7. Illustration of data for systems for which log relative retention versus $1/T$ plots are curved. *By courtesy of Butterworths.*

RETENTION VOLUME, BOILING POINT AND MOLECULAR STRUCTURE

It was shown earlier (p. 39) that for many homologous series of compounds there was often a linear relationship between boiling point and the number of structural units in the molecule. Equation 3.8 read

$$T_b = k_7 + k_8 \bar{n}$$

The generality of Trouton's rule was also illustrated (p. 38) and since this is written approximately as

$$\frac{\Delta H^v}{T_b} = 23$$

$$\Delta H^v = 23 T_b = 23(k_7 + k_8 \bar{n})$$

Consider equation 10.11. If $a = 1$ and C and γ_a were the same for all members of a series of homologues, the equation for any member X of the series would read

$$\log (V_g)_X = \frac{\Delta H^v}{2.3RT} + \text{constant}$$

which, on application of the Trouton rule, becomes

$$\log (V_g)_X = \frac{10 T_b}{RT} + \text{constant} \qquad (10.15)$$

This relationship, which was first pointed out theoretically by Grant and Vaughan (14) means that a plot of $\log (V_g)_X$ against T_b for members of a series would be linear, the line having a slope close to $5/T$ since R is approximately 2 cal. per mole deg. The actual value of the slope would vary somewhat with the value of the Trouton constant for the solute series, but it should not differ significantly from that given. The constant term would, of course, be the same as that given in equation 10.12.

Substituting now for T_b in equation 10.15 gives

$$\log (V_g)_X = \frac{10(k_7 + k_8\bar{n})}{RT} + \text{constant}$$

$$= \frac{10k_8\bar{n}}{RT} + \text{constant} \qquad (10.16)$$

In this case, a plot of $\log (V_g)_X$ for series members against, for example, the number of carbon atoms in the molecule should be linear, of slope about $(5k_8/T)$, the constant term differing from that in equation 10.15 by the addition of $(10k_7/RT)$. An example of a plot of this kind was given by James and Martin in the first paper on gas liquid chromatography ever published (15).

If either equation 10.15 or 10.16 holds for a homologous series for more than one solvent then it is clear that a plot of $\log (V_g)_X$ for the series for one solvent, against $\log (V_g)_X$ values for another solvent will also be linear. This follows since equation 10.15 can be written for each of two solvents (designated by the subscripts W and Z).

$$T_b = \frac{RT}{10} \left[\log (V_g)_W - (\text{constant})_W\right] = \frac{RT}{10} \left[\log (V_g)_Z - (\text{constant})_Z\right]$$

or

$$\log (V_g)_W = \log (V_g)_Z + [(\text{constant})_W - (\text{constant})_Z]$$

The difference in the constants can readily be deduced from 10.11, which yields

$$\log (V_g)_W = \log (V_g)_Z + \log \frac{M_Z}{M_W} - \log \frac{(\gamma_a)_Z}{(\gamma_a)_W} \qquad (10.17)$$

In the event that $(\gamma_a)_Z/(\gamma_a)_W$ were unity, the constant in 10.17 should be the logarithm of the ratios of the molecular weights of the solvents while the slope of the plot of $\log (V_g)_W$ against $\log (V_g)_Z$ would be unity. It is also true that a plot of $(V_g)_W$ against $(V_g)_Z$ would be linear, of slope $(M)_Z/(M)_W$ and zero intercept.

The relationships deduced here could equally well have been based on the linear variation of heat of vaporisation with molecular structure illustrated in Chapter 3 and typified by equations 3.9 and 3.10 or, alternatively, on the validity of equation 3.11 connecting $\log p^0$ with $\bar{n}$. Had the former approach been adopted, it would not have mattered which type of vapour pressure equation was used in the derivation of the basic equations 10.9 and 10.11 since the possibility of the linear dependence of Kirchhoff and Antoine constants on molecular weight within a series has also been established (p. 42). The various relationships, however, clearly cease to hold immediately the constants a, γ_a and C vary in an irregular manner. Fortunately, C does not vary much from the value 7.8 for a very wide range of compounds, as shown in Chapter 3, and, as shown earlier, in a number of instances when it does increase with molecular weight, does so linearly with the number of structural units in the homologous molecules. Changes in C are often, therefore, either insignificant or result in the introduction of another constant into each equation. For example, using the nomenclature of Chapter 3

$$C = k_{11} + k_{12}\bar{n}$$

and so, equation 10.16 would become

$$\log V_g = \frac{\bar{n}(10k_8 - k_{12}RT)}{RT} + \log \frac{1.7 \times 10^7}{\gamma_a M_l} + \frac{5k_7}{T} - k_{11}$$

In the event that a were not unity, but the same for all members of the series, it would only be necessary to multiply the first term throughout by a. As shown earlier, equation 2.19, there is a certain amount of evidence to substantiate the view that a sometimes increases linearly with the number of structural units in a homologous series. In this situation, it is necessary to introduce a further expression of the type

$$a = k_{13} + k_{14}\bar{n}$$

into the derivations. The only effect of this is to modify the values of the slopes of the various possible plots.

Retention Volume—Boiling Point Plots. Equation 10.15 has been verified by a large number of workers and is probably the most popular method of presenting data in a compact form. However, the majority of workers utilise relative retention data and it follows from earlier discussion of these that 10.15, in this situation, becomes

$$\log \frac{(V_g)_X}{(V_g)_Y} = \frac{5T_b}{T} + \text{constant}$$

$(V_g)_Y$ is taken as the standard for all other solutes, whether or not these are homologues of Y. The effect of using relative data is to leave the slope of the log plot unchanged but to alter the constant in equation 10.15 by some arbitrary amount which can only be calculated if comprehensive experimental details are given.

The use of the coefficient $5/T$ in the above equation depends upon the substances in question having a Trouton constant of 23. If this were 21, as is the case with the n-paraffins, the coefficient would be $4.55/T$, while for highly associated liquids such as the fatty alcohols and acids it would be $6.30/T$. Since plots of $\log V_R$ (or V_g) are illustrated in Chapter 13, at this point Table 2 is used to illustrate the generally observed linearity of such

TABLE 2
SLOPES OF LOG V_R VERSUS BOILING POINT PLOTS; ELUTION AT 100°C.

Solvent	n-Paraffins	Alkyl Benzenes	n-Alcohols	Ketones	Esters
Theoretical	0.0123	0.0130	0.0164	0.0134	0.0134
[b]Squalane	0.0115	0.0118			
[b]2-Ethyl hexyl sebacate	0.0113	0.0118	0.0154		
[b]Convachlor-12	0.0115	0.0120	0.0182	0.0137	0.0137
[a]Dinonyl phthalate	0.0119	0.0144			
[d]Tricresyl phosphate	0.0109	0.0145	0.0145		
[c]Polyethylene glycol 400	0.0087	0.0085	0.0125	0.0115	0.0090
[c]Polypropylene glycol 425	0.0112	0.0106	0.0160	0.0112	0.0117
[d]Silicone 702		0.0112	0.0163		

[a]Grant and Vaughan (14).
[b]Tenney (20).
[c]Adlard (18).
[d]Littlewood, Phillips and Price (4).

graphs. Listed in the table are the slopes of a number of plots to be found in the literature for a wide variety of systems.

There is clearly general agreement between the calculated and experimental values. This is particularly true of the n-paraffins and it is interesting to see that the n-alcohols give a value reasonably close to the calculated one, except when eluted from polyethylene glycol 400. The implication, although this may not be the true explanation, is that they are associated in all but one of the solvents quoted. This may possibly be the reason for the very marked tailing observed when alcohols are eluted from most solvents, since association in the liquid phase would result in a non-linear partition isotherm. The value obtained for the alcohols eluted from polyethylene glycol is very close to that expected for a non-associated liquid, as can be seen by comparison with the data for the *n*-paraffins, and it may be significant that in this case they emerge as reasonably symmetrical peaks.

Another point of interest which is brought out clearly in the table is the very considerable difference in properties of polyethylene and polypropylene glycols of about the same molecular weight. The polyethylene glycol

TABLE 3

SLOPES OF LOG V_R AGAINST BOILING POINT PLOTS

Solvent	Temperature	*n*-Paraffins		Alkyl Benzenes		Alcohols	
		Calculated	Experimental	Calculated	Experimental	Calculated	Experimental
[b]Squalane	100°	0.0123	0.0115	0.0130	0.0118		
	150°	0.0109	0.0102	0.0115	0.0109		
[d]Silicone 702	56°					0.0188	0.0196
	77°					0.0177	0.0180
	97°					0.0163	0.0163

Reference letters refer to Table 2.

shows marked deviations from normal behaviour with all but the ketones, while the polypropylene glycol is, relatively, normal and, in fact, differs little in performance from, for example, the hydrocarbon squalane, or Silicone 702.

At first glance it would appear from Table 2 that, with the exception of the polyethylene glycol, there is nothing to choose between the solvents listed for the separation of any of the solute types under discussion. However, this view would almost certainly not be upheld in practice, since there are other criteria of suitability. For example, one must consider also the question of the time of retention of a given solute, and, thus, both the theoretical plate requirements and the speed of analysis, both of which of course depend on the absolute value of the partition coefficient. Again, the selectivity of separation of molecular types; the vapour pressure, and hence the rate of loss of solvent from a column; and the theoretical plate height attainable, must all be taken into the reckoning. Much of this uncertainty would be eliminated if log V_g values were presented in published work instead of relative data, since then a quantitative comparison of the calculated and experimental constants in 10.15 would be possible.

That there is agreement between theory and experiment over a wide range of temperatures is shown by the data in Table 3.

Retention Volume—Molecular Structure Plots. The wide applicability of the boiling point equation implies that in so far as boiling point is a function of molecular weight within a series, an equally good agreement with equation 10.16 should be observed. That this is, in fact, so, is well known and, if anything, plots of $\log (V_R)_X$ against $\bar{n}$ show less scatter of experimental

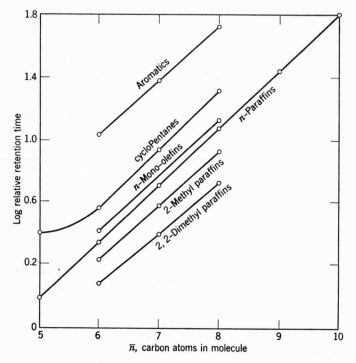

FIG. 8. Carbon number plots for various solute types eluted at 78.5°C. from a column containing benzyl diphenyl. *By courtesy of Analytical Chemistry.*

points than do plots of $\log (V_R)_X$ against T_b. This may well be due to the fact that many recorded boiling points are slightly in error. Figure 8 illustrates plots of the data of Desty and Whyman (26) for the elution of a variety of solute types from benzyl diphenyl at 78.5°.

These diagrams are typical and it is clear that much useful information can be presented in this form. It is particularly suitable as a compact method of compiling isothermal retention data, more so perhaps than by boiling point plots, since identification of points on the boiling point diagram does require a knowledge of the boiling points concerned. However, if all the solutes have the same number of carbon atoms, a boiling point plot is necessary, and that an approximately linear diagram of this sort can be obtained has been demonstrated by Sullivan, Lotz and Willingham (22) in their studies of the separation of isomeric hexenes and hexanes. Perhaps the most remarkable demonstration of the linearity of log $(V_g)_X$ versus $\bar{n}$ plots is afforded by the work of Ogilvie, Simmons and Hinds (23) whose results are illustrated in Figure 9. The column contained asphalt as solvent

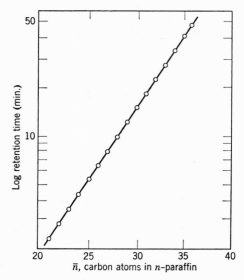

FIG. 9. Carbon number plot for n-paraffins eluted from a column containing asphalt at 320°C. This plot illustrates linearity of the data for an unexpectedly large range of $\bar{n}$ (21 to 35) at an extremely high temperature.

and despite the fact that the elution temperature was as high as 320°C., the data for n-paraffins from C_{21} to C_{35} yielded a straight line.

It has been pointed out earlier that the slopes of plots of log V_R against T_b and $\bar{n}$, respectively, should be connected simply by the constant k_8 of equation 3.8. Values of k_8 for several series of compounds were tabulated in Table 4 of Chapter 3 and we can check some of the literature data with the aid of these. Table 4 in this chapter lists values of the slopes of boiling point and carbon number plots for four types of solute eluted from two solvents. The data used are those of Adlard (18) and were chosen for presentation since they pertain to systems showing very considerable differences between the calculated and experimental values of the slope of the boiling point plot. If the theory holds here it may confidently be expected to do so in more favourable cases.

It is only to be expected that there would be some measure of agreement between the calculated and experimental values in the above table since the calculated data are derived entirely from experimental measurements, but it is gratifying to find such consistency, since this substantiates the relationships deduced earlier. A point which is illustrated is that it is unnecessary to know the boiling points of solutes in detail in order to construct a boiling point plot since this can conveniently be done by reference to k_8 and the

TABLE 4

COMPARISON OF SLOPE OF LOG V_R AGAINST T_b AND $\bar{n}$ PLOTS; ELUTION AT 100°C.

| | | Polyethylene Glycol 400 | | | Methoxy Polyethylene Glycol 350 | |
| | | | Slope of n Plot | | | Slope of $\bar{n}$ Plot |
Solute Type	k_8	Slope of T_b Plot	Calcu-lated	Experi-mental	Slope of T_b Plot	Calcu-lated	Experi-mental
n-Paraffins	27.3	0.0087	0.236	0.241	0.094	0.255	0.258
n-Alkyl ketones	23.4	0.0115	0.268	0.269	0.090	0.210	0.210
n-Alcohols	19.6	0.0125	0.245	0.251	0.014	0.275	0.280
n-Alkyl esters	23.2	0.0090	0.210	0.227	0.010	0.232	0.254

slope of the $\bar{n}$ plots. k_8 values can be very conveniently tabulated in a small space, and so this may represent a less laborious and time consuming approach.

Before concluding this discussion it would be of interest to speculate on how far gas solid chromatographic systems are likely to follow the boiling point and molecular structure relationships. In principle it might be surprising if they did since, as deduced here, the equations depend to a large extent on the applicability of Trouton's rule. As an extra factor it is often also necessary that activity coefficients should vary regularly with molecular parameters. Neither of these considerations can be expected to apply widely in gas solid chromatography and for such systems to exhibit regularities would require that the heat of adsorption was in some way a function of molecular weight within a homologous series. In the region of physical adsorption this might be expected, but when chemisorption occurs, many factors, difficult to evaluate, could contribute to the process.

Experimental data in this field are sparse, but a few workers, notably Janak (8) and Patton, Kaye and Lewis (24) have pointed out regular behaviour. The data of the latter authors for elution of n-paraffins from alumina at 60°C. are illustrated in Figure 10, which shows plots of the logarithm of retention time against both the boiling point and the number of carbon atoms in the paraffin. A result calculable from these graphs is that the experimentally measured slope of the boiling point plot (0.0142) is virtually identical with the value calculated on the basis of an ideal Trouton constant (0.0138). This indicates that the process occurring is a physical one and that the ease of condensation is a controlling factor in determining

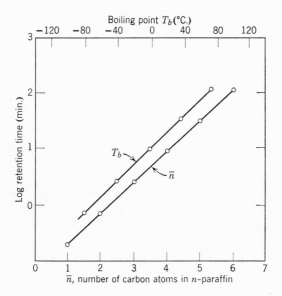

FIG. 10. Illustration of the applicability of boiling point and carbon number equations to gas-solid chromatography. Data relate to the elution at 60°C. of *n*-paraffins from alumina. *By courtesy of Analytical Chemistry.*

the extent of adsorption. This result may be compared with the data illustrated in Figure 3 of Chapter 2.

TWO SOLVENT DIAGRAMS

Equation 10.17 can be written in either of the two ways

$$\log (V_g)_W = \log (V_g)_Z + \log \frac{M_Z}{M_W} - \log \frac{(\gamma_a)_Z}{(\gamma_a)_W}$$

or

$$(V_g)_W = \left[\frac{M_Z(\gamma_a)_W}{M_W(\gamma_a)_Z} \right] (V_g)_Z$$

if the coefficient *a* is unity for the solute in both solvents. The slope of the logarithmic plot should then be unity and Figure 11, taken from the work of James and Martin (25) shows how closely true this is for a variety of hydrocarbon types eluted from hydrocarbon solvents. The slopes are so

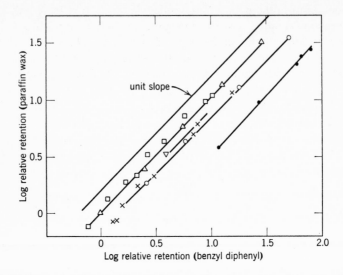

FIG. 11. Two solvent plots of log relative retention data. △, straight chain aliphatics; □, branched aliphatics; ○, naphthenes; ▽, naphthenes with side chains; ●, aromatics; ×, olefins. *By courtesy of the Journal of Applied Chemistry.*

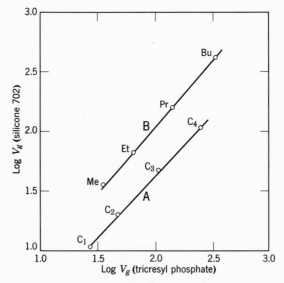

FIG. 12. Two solvent plots of log V_g at 78°C. for A, *n*-alcohols and B, *n*-alkyl acetates. Solvents are silicone 702 and tricresyl phosphate.

close to unity that the best way to demonstrate this is by drawing a comparison line of unit slope on the diagram. That equally good agreement between experiment and theory may be obtained when either solutes or solvent are polar is shown in Figure 12, in which data for some n-alcohols and n-alkyl esters eluted from both tricresyl phosphate and silicone 702 are plotted. The slopes of the logarithmic plots for the alcohols and esters are 0.98 and 0.94 respectively, which must be considered good agreement. The corresponding slopes of the non-logarithmic plots are 2.18 and 0.92, and since the molecular weight of the silicone is indeterminate, it is not possible to make any quantitative comparison with theory. However, the graphs pass through zero, as predicted.

REFERENCES

1. Ambrose, D., A. I. M. Keulemans, and J. H. Purnell, *Anal. Chem.*, 1958, **30**, 1582.
2. Hoare, M. R., and J. H. Purnell, *Trans. Faraday Soc.*, 1956, **52**, 222.
3. Hoare, M. R., and J. H. Purnell, *Research*, 1955, **8**, S41.
4. Littlewood, A. B., C. S. G. Phillips, and D. T. Price, *J. Chem. Soc.*, **1955**, 1480.
5. Porter, P. E., C. H. Deal, and F. H. Stross, *J. Amer. Chem. Soc.*, 1957, **78**, 2999.
6. Pollard, F. H., and C. J. Hardy, *Vapour Phase Chromatography*, 1957, Butterworths, London (editor, D. H. Desty), p. 115.
7. Pollard, F. H., and C. J. Hardy, *Analytica Chim. Acta*, 1957, **7**, 535.
8. Janak, J., *Vapour Phase Chromatography*, 1957, Butterworths, London (editor, D. H. Desty), p. 247.
9. Cvetanovic, R. J. and K. O. Kutschke, (see ref. 8), p. 87.
10. Ambrose, D., and J. H. Purnell, *Gas Chromatography*, 1958, Butterworths, London (editor, D. H. Desty), p. 369.
11. Purnell, J. H., *Vapour Phase Chromatography*, 1957, Butterworths, London (editor, D. H. Desty), p. 52.
12. Hardy, C. J. (see ref. 11), p. 61.
13. Harrison, G. F. (see ref. 11), p. 332.
14. Grant, D. W., and G. A. Vaughan, *J. Appl. Chem.*, 1956, **6**, 145.
15. James, A. T., and A. J. P. Martin, *Biochem. J.*, 1952, **50**, 679.
16. Greene, S. A., and H. Pust, *J. Phys. Chem.*, 1958, **62**, 55.
17. Tenney, H. M., *Anal. Chem.*, 1958, **30**, 2.
18. Adlard, E. R., *Vapour Phase Chromatography*, 1957, Butterworths, London (editor, D. H. Desty), p. 98.
19. Young, J. R., *Chem. and Ind.*, **1958**, 594.
20. Langer, S. H., C. Zahn, and G. Pantazoplos, *J. Chromatog.*, 1960, **3**, 154.
21. Langer, S. H., and J. H. Purnell (unpublished work).
22. Sullivan, L. J., J. R. Lotz, and C. B. Willingham, *Anal. Chem.*, 1956, **28**, 495.
23. Ogilvie, J. D., M. C. Simmons and G. P. Hinds, *Anal. Chem.*, 1958, **30**, 25.
24. Patton, H. W., J. S. Lewis, and W. I. Kaye, *Anal. Chem.*, 1955, **27**, 170.
25. James, A. T., and A. J. P. Martin, *J. Appl. Chem.*, 1956, **6**, 105.
26. Desty, D. H., and B. H. F. Whyman, *Anal. Chem.*, 1957, **29**, 320.

GAS
CHROMATOGRAPHIC
PRACTICE

THE PREPARATION OF SOLID SUPPORT

Size Grading. Siliceous solid supports can nowadays be bought ready graded for use as column packings, but are usually expensive and, further, there is no absolute guarantee that the true particle size spread corresponds to the value quoted, which is normally a sieve range. For many purposes, and theoretical studies in particular, it is probably safest always to size grade from the bulk material.

Size grading is facilitated by a preliminary sedimentation through water in a large tube or beaker. This removes dust and fine particles. Following this, the material can be dry sieved either manually or mechanically. This process certainly gives a size separation but, because of the softness of the solid, there may also be considerable destruction of the particles. Thus, prolonged sieving should be avoided since in the worst case it is readily possible to recover nothing but powder, while even at best the sieves easily become clogged, in consequence of which the effective mesh size not only becomes smaller, but also very variable.

After recovery of the sieved fractions they should again be allowed to fall through water, the first and last fractions reaching the bottom of the container being rejected. In principle, the time of fall of a fraction could, through Stokes' law, be used to determine the mean particle size. The results obtained in this way differ considerably from the apparent mesh size derived from the sieve dimensions, since particles pass through the latter by virtue of their smallest cross-section, whereas in free fall they

11

EQUIPMENT AND MATERIALS

expose their maximum cross-section to the direction of motion. The evidence suggests that particles pack in columns with their longest axis parallel to the column length, hence the Stokes law size is inappropriate. The sedimentation procedure can be repeated any number of times in order to achieve closer size grading.

A more tedious but almost certainly better method of grading is to sieve the solid while wet. Sieves can either be used singly or in cascade. In the former case, the best procedure is to immerse the sieve in water and gently raise it clear, particles being pulled through by suction. If used in cascade a moving stream of water is directed into the top sieve, the whole assembly being slowly tilted from side to side. The water flow must be adjusted to the rate of passage through the finest sieve used, which may well be very slow.

A method which has possibilities but has been little used is that of continuous elutriation. The apparatus for this consists of a series of tubes each several feet long, inter-connected top to bottom, the diameters increasing progressively along the series. The ungraded material and a continuous water flow enter at the bottom of the first, and narrowest, vessel, the water flow rate being adjusted so that the coarsest particles just fall to the bottom. Particles of different size come to a stationary state at different heights and some are swept on into the second vessel, where the upward velocity is smaller, and so on to further vessels. If the flow of water had a uniform radial velocity this method would give very exact separations.

However, the velocity profile is parabolic (equation 5.1) and so there is a fountain-like motion of particles up the centre, out and then rapidly down the sides where the velocity tends to zero. Despite this, a stationary state in terms of particle size can be set up in each vessel, and so a continuous process can be operated. The drawbacks of the method are that the narrowest tube has to take the bulk of the material and that the radial velocity is non-uniform. If these could be modified suitably the method would become very attractive indeed, particularly for the recovery of very fine fractions. Glueckauf (49) has described the use of this method to produce solid which gave remarkably small theoretical plate heights and it has been employed with some success by the author.

Whatever method of fractionation is employed, or if commercial material is used, the graded solid should be intensively dried at very high temperature and, preferably, under high vacuum. It can then be stored in a desiccator. Drying in ovens may not be very effective, and the use of those with air circulating fans should be avoided, since the vibration causes particle disintegration. The author has, inadvertently, lost a whole fraction being dried on its sieve in such an oven. This result illustrates an important aspect of size grading of solid supports. Their tendency to crumble is so great that rough treatment after grading can very quickly nullify the precautions and care taken in the grading process, and prepared support should, therefore, be very carefully handled.

Other types of support are, on the whole, more robust than the siliceous ones. Glass beads, for instance, can be sieved with few precautions, as also can such solids as alundum or carborundum, which may find use in the future with lean columns. Plastic supports such as Teflon have usually to be ground as well as graded. The grinding can be readily carried out in a coffee mill, solid CO_2 being added to the material to aid the process (1).

A new type of solid support has recently been described by Decora and Dinneen (66). They started with a commercial detergent powder which was originally made by spray drying a mixture of liquid detergent in an inorganic matrix of sodium sulphate, sodium triphosphate, sodium pyrophosphate and sodium silicates. Strong heating removed water and left a petroleum ether soluble film on the porous, sponge-like inorganic matrix. Washing with the ether removed 99 per cent of the original detergent. The residual solid could hold up to 50 per cent w/w of solvent and still flow freely, and gave very efficient columns. The solid appears to adsorb basic materials strongly, a property attributed to acidic residues from detergent breakdown, but addition of 10 per cent w/w of solid potassium hydroxide from solution largely eliminated this. It seems possible that this support material may find general use, and that the spray drying technique, in general, may find future application. Another support recently described consists of a highly porous fluorocarbon polymer, Fluoropak. This has a surface area and porosity comparable to that of Celite 545 and is claimed to be non-adsorbing even to highly polar materials. It is, of course, chemically inert in addition.

Surface Modification Methods. The numerous methods of pretreatment of supports were discussed earlier, and apply almost exclusively to siliceous type materials. Acid washing, to be effective at all in removing impurities, should be carried out in very hot acid. This procedure is both unpleasant and of possible danger, since the concentrated acid froths alarmingly if any small particles are present. Following treatment, washing with copious amounts of water is needed, the wash can be tested for iron with thiocyanate solution. Several acid washes are needed, thiocyanate checks being used each time. Alkali washing is commonly carried out with a 10 per cent methanolic solution of sodium hydroxide (2, 3, 4). The procedure can be carried out in the cold or under reflux. After treatment the material is washed with methanol and copious amounts of water.

Adsorptive studies suggest that neither of these methods is of any great benefit for many gas chromatographic purposes, and acid washing may well worsen matters, possibly because of the difficulty of acid removal.

However, the procedure does seem to be of value in the analysis of high boiling organic acids and esters.

Silane Treatment. Trimethylchlorosilane has been successfully used to reduce the activity of high surface area silica gels (5) and also other siliceous solids (7, 8, 9) and even active carbon (5). The ratio of the adsorptivity before and after treatment of silica gels (150 m.^{2} per g.) is comparable to that found (6, 13) for firebrick (<3 m.^{2} per g.) treated with hexamethyldisilazane. The surface reaction is of the type

$$
(CH_3)_3SiCl \; + \; \overset{\displaystyle OH}{\underset{\displaystyle |}{-Si-}} \; = \; \overset{\begin{array}{c} CH_3 \\ | \\ CH_3-Si-CH_3 \\ | \\ O \end{array}}{\underset{\displaystyle |}{-Si-}} \quad + \; HCl
$$

the hydroxyl group being converted to a silyl ether. The paraffinic surface formed may be expected to be a much less active adsorbent than the original.

The treatment is usually carried out with the silane in the gas phase but a benzene solution can also be used. For a highly active silica, complete treatment at 20°C. requires eight days and results in considerable loss of the reagent in consequence of its high vapour pressure. No information is available as to the time needed for treatment of low area materials but it is probably several hours. Intensive drying of the solid before treatment is essential, since the reagent reacts preferentially with water. Removal of the HCl formed is not an easy matter, particularly since the solid is unwettable by water.

Dimethyldichlorosilane (Drisil) has been more widely used than trimethylchlorosilane for chromatographic support treatment purposes. The former reagent was first employed by Martin (10, 11) and has since been used by others (6, 50) with some success. The treatment is usually carried out with the reagent in the gas phase admixed with nitrogen and requires twelve hours for completion with Celite, presumably at room temperature (12). That the treated material is undoubtedly superior to the original as a support has recently been verified by direct adsorptive studies (6). The drawbacks to the use of either silane are that they are both very volatile, toxic and inflammable and appear to be most effectively used in the gas phase. The dichloro compound has the additional disadvantage of being bidentate, thus requiring two hydroxyl groups to be very close together if all the chlorine is to be eliminated. If this is not possible the surface compound formed is a chlorosilyl ether which might be both more active than a true paraffinic one and also susceptible to hydrolysis of the chlorine back to a hydroxyl group. There appears to be some evidence that support treated in this way deteriorates with time. Of the two chlorosilanes, therefore, trimethyl would seem to be preferable.

Silazane Treatment. Hexamethyldisilazane reacts quantitatively with hydroxyl groups in most compounds (14) and was used in gas chromatography by Langer, Perrett, Bohemen and Purnell (13), since when it has been used to treat most of the common solid supports (6). The surface reaction is similar to that of the silane being stoichiometrically representable by

$$
(CH_3)_3SiNHSi(CH_3)_3 \; + \; \overset{\overset{\displaystyle OH}{|}}{-Si}-O-\overset{\overset{\displaystyle OH}{|}}{Si}-
$$

$$
= \; CH_3-\overset{\overset{\displaystyle CH_3}{|}}{\underset{\underset{\displaystyle -Si-}{|}}{\underset{\displaystyle O}{|}}}Si-CH_3 \quad CH_3-\overset{\overset{\displaystyle CH_3}{|}}{\underset{\underset{\displaystyle Si-}{|}}{\underset{\displaystyle O}{|}}}Si-CH_3
$$

$$
-Si\text{------}O\text{------}Si-
$$

The surface compound is thus identical with that obtained from trimethylchlorosilane. The apparent bidentate character of the silazane is no drawback since the free radial $(CH_3)_3Si\overset{.}{N}H_2$ appears to be formed in the first step of the reaction and then itself reacts with hydroxyl. The great advantage of the silazane is its low volatility and toxicity and the consequent ease and convenience of treatment with a solution. Details of this are as follows.

Twenty-five g. of well dried solid is placed in a flask while still warm and is covered completely with 60° to 80° petroleum ether. The flask is fitted with a reflux condenser down which 7 ml. of the silazane is poured. The mixture is refluxed for about 10 hours for firebrick and 6 hours for Celite. The solid is then separated by decantation and washed with several portions of *n*-propanol and petroleum ether. After filtration it is dried by heating under vacuum. The decanted petroleum ether/silazane solution can be reused since less than 10 per cent of the silazane reacts.

A rough check of the extent of treatment can be made by adding the solid to water, when it should all float indefinitely. On a more quantitative level, the ammonia liberated during treatment can be continuously entrained by nitrogen into an acid solution, the volume and strength of which have been calculated to correspond exactly to the number of hydroxyl groups treated. The indicator change marks completion.

The value of the treatment is illustrated in Figures 1 and 2. The former shows isotherms for the adsorption of acetone vapour by untreated Sil-O-Cel, Chromosorb, Chromosorb-W and Celite at 50°C. The latter shows a comparison of the isotherms for adsorption of benzene vapour at 50°C. for treated and untreated Sil-O-Cel and Celite 545. After treatment the adsorption plateau is considerably lower but, equally important, the pressure corresponding to the saturation point is reduced by about a factor of ten. No quantitative information of this sort is available for other forms of treatment. The addition of 0.1 per cent polyethylene glycol suppresses

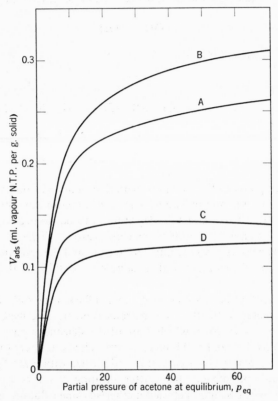

FIG. 1. Isotherms for the adsorption at 50°C. of acetone vapour by A, Sil-O-Cel and Chromosorb; B, acid washed Chromosorb; C, Chromosorb-W; D, Celite 545. ·

residual adsorption of a treated firebrick sufficiently that air and acetone are eluted simultaneously from a dry column (13).

The silazane can also be used successfully to treat glass beads, or, in fact, any glass apparatus. The treated supports are thermally stable at 200°C. and it seems possible that they may well be so up to much higher temperatures, since they should have comparable stabilities to silicone polymers.

Metal Deposition.   Ormerod and Scott (19) have developed the method of metal deposition, in particular that of silver. They saturate the solid with a solution of silver nitrate and then reduce this at high temperature with hydrogen. The process can be conducted in a packed column, a feature which has some advantages. There is a significant reduction in the peak tailing observed in the chromatography of polar solutes with non-polar solvents. The treated packing cannot, however, be used with sulphur containing compounds or anything else which might react with silver. On the

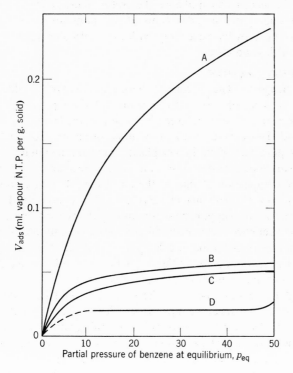

FIG. 2. Isotherms for the adsorption at 50°C. of benzene vapour, first by Sil-O-Cel (A, before and C, after treatment with hexamethyldisilazane), and second by Celite 545 (B, before and D, after treatment).

other hand, it should be thermally stable to the highest temperatures, which is unlikely to be true of some chemically treated surfaces.

Other Methods. A number of workers have suggested the possibility of coating solid surfaces with polymeric substances, but nothing has as yet been published in this connexion. The principle of the method is evident, however, and treatment would probably take the form of soaking the solid support in monomer and then heating. Alternatively, some form of emulsion polymerisation could be used.

Several chemical reagents might be expected to be useful in surface modification, anything which reacts readily with hydroxyls will undoubtedly have some potential. Such things as acetyl chloride or benzoyl chloride should react, but would probably not give as inert or as thermally stable a surface as the silanes or silazanes. Alternatively, calcium hydroxide, alcohols, diazomethane and thionyl chloride are possibilities which have already been tested by Boehm and Schneider (20) with very active solids. It would appear that the reagents most likely to be useful, in fact, contain a reactive chlorine, although gas solid adsorbents of the montmorillonite clay type have been modified by base exchange with low molecular weight aliphatic amines (74) with good effect.

COLUMN PREPARATION

Coating the Support.   The stationary phase is almost always added to the support in the form of a solution in some volatile liquid. The graded support is best spread out in a large dish such that the layer of solid is not too thick and then covered with the volume of solution containing the calculated requirement of stationary phase. The volatile liquid is then removed by heating or forced evaporation. The surface area of the support is so great in comparison to that of the containing dish that only an insignificant amount of stationary phase is lost in this operation. It is often recommended that the support be stirred during the coating operation. In the author's experience this does nothing to aid distribution of stationary phase and causes considerable break up of the solid. This then reduces column efficiency. If large quantities of packing are to be coated it is best to carry this out in a number of operations (p. 183).

Following the coating operation the packing should be heated under vacuum for several hours at a temperature at least 20° above that at which it is to be used. This process removes lower boiling liquids which may be present in the stationary phase and seems also to redistribute it more uniformly to some extent. The removal of volatile materials is advantageous since otherwise they are eluted from a column for many hours and make it very difficult to stabilise the detector system. This problem can be very serious with high sensitivity detectors.

Janak and Komers (44) have described a method for the distribution of solid sugars on Celite by prior mixing of the two solids, packing of the column and then raising this to a temperature at which the sugar melts. The liquid sugar appears to spread reasonably uniformly since satisfactory column efficiencies were obtained.

Occasionally, it is suggested that the stationary phase might be added to the packing *in situ*. There seems no obvious advantage to be derived from this approach other than that it may seem possible to pack support more regularly when dry than when coated with solvent. Its use would, however, probably require extensive standardisation of procedure if reproducible column packing were to be achieved and it seems unlikely anyway that a uniform solvent distribution could result.

Column Configuration.   The simplest configuration is obviously a straight column, but it is not readily possible to use one which is longer than about five feet. The alternative, for longer columns, may be either a series of connected U-tubes, a spiral or a helix. If a 5-ft. straight column can be accommodated in an apparatus, a 10-ft. U-column can obviously be used without trouble. This length offers considerable separating power. Longer columns can be made, of course, Bohemen and the author (15) for example, have constructed connected U's up to 50 ft. in length entirely in glass, sections being fused to each other through very short pieces of thick walled capillary. Joints involving thick walled glass do not need to be blown and can be fused by use of a small flame directed always half on a point where fusion has already taken place or where there is very close contact. Metal column units can be connected through conventional threaded unions and Scott (22) has used 50-ft. copper columns, while McKenna and Idleman (16) have used units up to 70 ft. long. One of the major problems in the use of such columns is that of ensuring that the unions are gas tight. Because of the considerable pressure drop across long columns even very small gaps become significant, and this is certainly an important source of efficiency loss with increasing length of packed columns. Unions should be carefully checked for leakage with soap bubble mixture.

Spiral columns offer a number of attractive features, in particular, the elimination of joints and the fact that great lengths take up little space in comparison to connected U's. The relative merits of the two types have several times been discussed, the most profitable discussion being that at the London Symposium of 1956 (17). Scott stated there that spiral columns were somewhat less efficient than U's, but Blom maintained that there was no significant difference. It is evident that there must be gas velocity differences between the inside and outside walls of the spiral, the question is whether or not this is great enough to affect column performance. Klinkenberg, Glueckauf and Martin concluded that since the magnitude of any effect is determined, first, by the ratio of the spiral radius to that of the column and secondly, by the rate of radial gas diffusion, in the normal course of events these were liable to be small. It seems likely, therefore, that any great difference in the performance of spirals and U's which may be observed in practice stems from packing differences.

Packing of a spiral is undoubtedly likely to be difficult and, if poorly done and the spiral is mounted with its axis vertical, then subsequent settling of the support will cause a channel to form along the top side from end to end of the column. Thus, a very much reduced efficiency may be observed. If there is any doubt it is probably better to mount spirals horizontally, since then packing shifts lead only to small free spaces at the top of each turn. While these are undesirable, they are less so than is a continuous channel. Pratt (18) has recently obtained support for the view that, provided care is taken in packing spirals, or better still, helices, they give efficiencies comparable with those of straight columns. Furthermore, he has found that the packing can be introduced with equal effect either before or after bending, although procedurally the latter is to be preferred.

It would seem, therefore, that any configuration is acceptable as long as care is taken in the packing operation. For theoretical studies the straight or U form is probably desirable, since there is little point in introducing the added complication of the extra radial non-linearity of flow to be expected of spirals.

Packing Procedure.   Packing of columns is a very simple process. A small funnel is connected to the open end of the column tube and the prepared support is poured in. It should flow freely into the tube when this is lightly tapped on its side. While this proceeds the column is bounced up and down on the floor or table to help consolidate the packing. James and Martin (24) initiated the technique of slowly rotating the column while it was pressed against a rotating disc; Martin (25) has pointed out that the column should always be rotated in the same direction. The author has found that this technique tends to lead to break up of the particles and does not always give a good packing. This point has been elaborated by Tuey (26) who, using a commercially available vibrator unit, found that the packing does not settle while being vibrated, and that the final consolidation must always be brought about by bouncing and tapping without vibration. The whole operation, according to Tuey, takes about four minutes per column.

This, in the author's experience, is not an unreasonable estimate of the time required to prepare a single U-tube column and the speed of the operation is helpful, since it reduces the size separation, which, it has been shown, may occur during packing (15). More important, however, is the possible deleterious effect of prolonged packing. There is no doubt that the final consolidation can be carried too far. Bohemen (21) has studied the rate of change of packing density with time of packing. He found that during the first ten minutes of tapping and bouncing the packing density increased steadily in fairly large but progressively diminishing amounts. A point was then reached when the rate of density change became constant over a long period of time; tests showed that at this point the permeability to gas flow started to increase rapidly, while column efficiency fell correspondingly. It thus appears that prolonged packing leads to disintegration of the support and reduced column performance.

Glass wool or other porous plugs are usually used at the two open ends to keep the packing tight, but when these are inserted, no pressure should be applied, or a blockage to gas flow can easily result through local crushing of the packing. The plugs should be inserted as near to the column ends as possible in order to minimise dead space.

Coating Capillaries. The deposition of solvent on the walls of a capillary tube is again effected by use of a solution in ether, acetone or other volatile liquid. In the earliest work by Golay (28) the capillary was filled, blocked at one end and then slowly passed, open end first, at constant speed through a furnace. This procedure is both cumbersome and tedious, and although likely to yield uniform films is little used now, recent work being conducted entirely by forcing the solution through the capillary at more or less constant rate. Dijkstra and de Goey (29) found that this was the most satisfactory of several procedures tried. In their method the column was filled and the solution then forced out by gas at speeds of 10 to 50 cm. per sec. Evaporation at the trailing edge of the solution leads to deposition of a film of solvent, a process which can be helped by use of a small local heater. A 20 per cent solution of Apiezon M grease in ether, for example, gave a film estimated to be of 5μ thickness, while silicone grease coatings of only 0.6μ were thought to be obtained in some instances. Golay has estimated that the film thicknesses pertaining in his experiments were of the same order of magnitude. Scott (30) and Desty, Goldup and Swanton (31) have also used the flow method of coating but employed much lower velocities than those cited above; the latter suggesting a maximum of 10 cm. per sec. It is very probable that a constant velocity is the most important requirement, and this then demands a continuously falling gas back pressure. That the flow method is effective is shown by the very high column efficiencies achieved by these workers.

SAMPLE INTRODUCTION

This is almost certainly the most significant practical problem remaining in the field of gas chromatography. Numerous methods of sample injection have been employed, but there is no single one which is universally applicable. The problem has been accentuated recently by the advent of high sensitivity detectors, and even more so by the introduction of capillary columns. The difficulties of obtaining, measuring and transferring to a column, volumes of liquid of the order of microlitres are great enough, but the corresponding problem of dealing with microgrammes or less is clearly one of considerable difficulty. Sampling systems can be classed as belonging to one of three groups:

a. Those designed for qualitative studies.

b. Those intended for quantitative work in the microlitre of liquid range.

c. Those designed for quantitative use at the microgram or smaller level.

Sampling devices of type (a) are relatively easy to devise. In fact, for most purposes some form of hypodermic injection suffices, and it is only necessary to equip the column head with a rubber serum cap or plug, through which the syringe needle or pipette can be inserted. Silicone rubber plugs can be used up to about 200°C. without deterioration, and some twenty syringe insertions can be made if care is taken. Microlitre quantities of liquid can be injected from micrometer syringes which are available commercially, or with specially constructed syringe pipettes such as those described by Langer and Pantages (32), Samsel and Aldrich (33), Tenney and Harris (34) and Stanford (59). The latter two involve some special construction at the column head, but this is not considerable.

It is surprising but true that quite remarkably quantitative work can be carried out with this form of injection; Tenney and Harris, for example, report a precision at the 95 per cent confidence level of ± 0.9 per cent for samples of 1.5 μl. Every effort should be made to get the needle tip close to the packing or well down into the heated zone ahead of the column. It is usually necessary to make a small allowance for the compressibility of the liquid in the syringe; the magnitude of this is quickly found by experiment. The hypodermic injection of gas samples in the milligram weight range is even simpler than that of liquids, since 1 μl. of liquid corresponds to something in the region of 1 ml. of gas, provided this can be obtained at atmospheric pressure. Thus, ordinary medical syringes can frequently be used.

For the injection of high boiling or even solid samples, solutions in volatile liquids can be used successfully (33, 36, 37, 52) and solids can also be temporarily liquefied by exposure to infra-red heat (35), the hypodermic also being heated, of course. A further alternative is to introduce a plug of solid in a notched hypodermic needle, the plug melting in a heated zone at the column head (51). The first seems the most convenient and reliable method.

For quantitative analysis involving introduction of microlitre samples of liquid, that is, type (b) samplers, as has been pointed out, hypodermic methods are often quite suitable with laboratory instruments. Several alternatives have been employed, however, which offer the possibility of greater precision.

An important point which determines the choice, is whether or not the description "quantitative" refers to data for sample components relative to each other, or on an absolute basis. In the former situation hypodermic injection is probably perfectly adequate, but for the latter it is often preferable to attempt to weigh the sample. To this end, Dimbat, Porter and Stross (41) weighed samples into glass ampoules, which were then sealed. An ampoule was then placed in a special heated chamber at the column head and a threaded crusher screwed down on it to liberate the liquid; this, at the same time, opened up carrier gas flow to the chamber. An alternative type of ampoule crusher system was described by McCreadie and Williams (38). In this the ampoule took the form of a small length of thin walled capillary which could be weighed on a torsion balance, and which was then introduced into the crusher chamber by removal of a stopper. An eccentric rod coaxial with the long axis of the chamber could be rotated to crush the ampoule at any time after its introduction, and so a sufficient interval could be allowed for the stabilisation of gas flow.

A similar technique was reported by Brennan and Kemball (23) who used, instead of a crusher, ampoules of such thin wall that, on being dropped into the heated zone at the column head, the pressure build up inside caused them to explode. Although there was a sufficient time lag to enable the stopper, which was removed to introduce the ampoule, to be firmly replaced, there was not always time for stabilisation of gas flow. Any interruption of gas flow is obviously undesirable.

The introduction of gas samples for quantitative work with injection systems of type (b) is almost always through the use of a "by-pass" system of some sort. In the simplest case this is merely a glass system of three stopcocks, between two of which there is a standard volume in which gas is trapped, and which may be interchangeable with others of different size. Filling with sample may be by syringe and septum, or through direct connection to the sample source. It is usually necessary in either case to have a mercury or other manometer in the system in order that the "volume" may be standardised.

Among many others, van de Craats has given fairly comprehensive details of the performance of such systems (39) while Hooijmeijer, Kwantes and van de Craats (45) have described a very complex device using six pneumatically operated on/off neoprene or Teflon diaphragm valves. This system gave gas samples reproducible to 0.25 per cent or better, and was successfully incorporated in an automatic analyser. Such an arrangement, however, is very cumbersome for laboratory purposes.

Glew and Young (40) employed an arrangement in which the multi-valve action was incorporated in a single stopcock, an approach which is obvious since, basically, these by-pass samplers are adaptations of conventional high vacuum "standard volumes." When constructed in glass, stopcock type systems suffer the very serious drawback that even when fitted with powerful springs they are not able to withstand pressures much above atmospheric without leakage. Thus, their use at the inlet end of long or impermeable columns is not usually possible. To overcome this, and to streamline the system, they can be made in metal; the majority of commercial chromatographs use metal rotary valves operating on such principles, being either of the stopcock or annular type. A common annular design employs two metal discs, not less than about 1/4 in. in thickness, which are ground together to give excellent contact. Each disc has a number of holes, in the simplest case four, drilled through it.

Figure 3 shows diagrammatically how such a valve operates. The left hand disc in the upper half of the figure has opposite pairs of ports connected across standard volumes 1 and 2. The right hand disc has one opposite pair of ports connected to the sample line, the sample flowing continuously or being taken intermittently from some source; the second pair

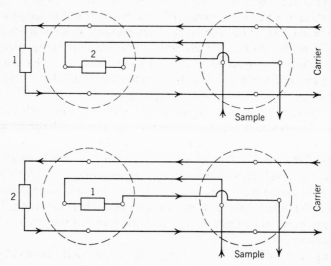

FIG. 3. Illustration of flow path arrangement in a typical rotary annular sampler.

of ports connects the carrier gas supply to the column. Rotation of the left hand disc through 180° brings the filled sample volume 2 into line with the carrier gas supply to the column, as shown in the lower half of the figure. Following the subsequent analysis, the next injection is brought about by a further rotation through 180° when the volume 1 comes into line with the column. If it is desired to use only a single standard volume and a 360° injection cycle, the disposition of the block holes must be appropriately adjusted such that the sample line does not come into line with the second connecting volume on the left hand disc at any time. The arrangement described can be considerably elaborated to provide greater flexibility.

Bohemen (21) and also Porter (42) have carried out a fairly detailed study of samplers of this type and have found that they behave very well provided the column back pressure is no greater than about two atmospheres gauge. Above this they leak badly across the faces of the discs, no matter how carefully these have been prepared. Experiments with different metals and O-ring inserts of different types showed that only occasionally was it possible to construct a reasonably leak free valve, and even then it failed to function when connected between a vacuum and a chromatographic system. This makes this type of sampler almost useless for gas kinetic studies.

Some improvement is effected if a layer of Teflon is sandwiched between the metal plates. However, the force of the holding spring causes the Teflon to spread and even a containing ring around the circumference is not altogether effective. Samplers of this general design, therefore, are, in the author's experience, adequate for quite accurate gas sampling only at moderate column and sample source pressures and not too high temperatures. One feature of the design which is, however, very attractive, is that the sample volume may be made very small indeed; a few cm. of 1-mm. tube, for example, has a volume of only about 10^{-2} ml. This corresponds to about 4 μg. methane at N.T.P., or, if measured at room temperature and at a pressure of, say, 10 mm. Hg, is only 0.05 μg.

Thus, within the limitations of the design, very small samples could be dealt with quite accurately and conveniently, through measurement of the sample pressure. Such samples could, therefore, be used with capillary columns. This advantage is to some extent lost in the conventional stopcock type of rotary sampler, since in this design gases have to pass through the key which increases the dead volume. In addition, the device requires greater and more frequent lubrication than a laminar valve. On the other hand, the much greater area of contact means that stopcock valves should be much more satisfactory than annular ones at high pressures. A sampler of this general design has been used in an automatic analyser by Atkinson and Tuey (27).

In principle, slide valves can be designed which would function on the same principles as rotary samplers. Their use has several times been indicated, but little is known of their performance.

Liquid sampling at the microlitre level can be reasonably carried out as described earlier by syringe injection. At high column back pressures and temperatures, however, this is not easy, and Scott (22) has devised a neat system to overcome the difficulties. The basic features are shown in Figure 4. The outer brass case contains a close fitting piece of heavy walled rubber tube which can be tightly closed by pressure from a cam operated plunger. The back pressure from the column seals the rubber against the brass containing tube. With the plunger screwed up, carrier gas enters and flows directly to the column, while the top cap can be removed without leakage. A small glass pipette of roughly microlitre capacity charged with liquid sample is placed inside the upper part of the rubber tube and the cap screwed back into place. On releasing the plunger, the pipette drops through the rubber tube, and sample is vaporised and is thus injected into

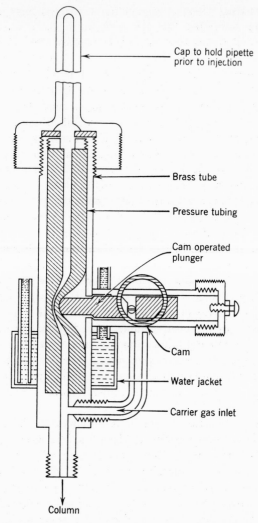

Cap to hold pipette
prior to injection

Brass tube

Pressure tubing

Cam operated
plunger

Cam

Water jacket

Carrier gas inlet

Column

FIG. 4. High pressure injection system (22). *By courtesy of Butterworths.*

the column. The empty pipette can be drawn back into the cap by a magnet
and the plunger once more screwed up.

The system has been operated effectively at column back pressures of
10 atm. or more, it is at least as quantitative as any pipette method, and
does not interfere with gas flow during injection. It is, therefore, within its
limitations, very successful. The main drawbacks associated with the
device are that first, it is a laboratory instrument only, secondly, since

liquid samples have to be taken in a pipette it can probably handle no less than 100 μg. quantitatively, and finally, the large volume of rubber actually in contact with the sample is very undesirable (p. 170). Of less importance is the need for water cooling of the upper part of the device to prevent vaporisation of sample before it is desired.

Ideally, it would be nice to have a sampler which combined the ability of the Scott method to work at high pressures with the simplicity of operation and the capacity to deal with very small samples of the rotary metal valve. Further, it would be desirable for it to be able to handle either gas or liquid samples (as vapour), to operate at any reasonable temperature and to have the small capacity and dead space of the annular valve. The conventional glass vacuum stopcock, suitably modified, would seem to present the best basis on which to start designing such a valve since, in metal, it offers the best chance of a pressure resistant system. The problems to be overcome are the need for grease of some sort, and also the elimination of the dead space of the connexion holes through the key.

A partial solution, at least, has been found by Pratt and the author (43) who have constructed a six way stainless steel stopcock working on the sloping O-ring principle. These sloping O-rings have the same function as the sloping bores of conventional multi-way vacuum stopcocks but offer the double advantage of needing no grease, and that the gas path across the stopcock is through the space between the key and barrel, and not through the key itself. Thus, passage of gas occurs through the volume which in the ordinary way would either contain grease or act as dead volume extra to the conventional bore.

Figure 5 shows the construction of the sampler. It has six ports, connected to the barrel at 60° intervals. The two at right angles to the page (numbers 1 and 2) are connected respectively to a vacuum system and the sample source. The standard volume is connected across 3 and 4, while 5 connects to the gas supply and 6 to the column. In the injection position, which corresponds to that shown in the diagram, gas flows in through 5, across the outside of the solid key between the appropriate O-rings into the standard volume at 3, back through 4, across the key again to 6, and hence directly to the column. Over the next 60° sector, which acts as a safety margin, the O-rings isolate all ports except 5 from 6. When the key is rotated further into the next 60° sector, the sample volume is pumped out through 4 and 2, while 5 and 6 are still connected. The next 60° sector again isolates all ports except 5 from 6, and then in the last 60° sector the sample volume is connected to the sample source through ports 1 and 3. A further 120° rotation brings the sample volume back into the injection position, when sample is directed into the column. At all times there is direct flow of carrier gas into the column, the valve is greaseless, it exposes only a tiny area of O-ring to the sample and can certainly be operated at temperatures well in excess of 150°C. with silicone rubber rings. The sample volume can be made very small, in fact, it could well be simply the free space enclosed between the barrel, key and O-rings. It is thus possible to inject with excellent reproducibility either gases or vapours in the weight range below 10^{-2} μg.

Quinn and the author (47) have operated a valve of this type for long periods of time in these conditions in connexion with gas kinetic and fast

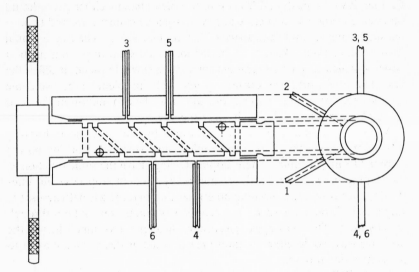

FIG. 5. Rotary high pressure sampler. *By courtesy of Analytical Chemistry.*

chromatographic studies, while Pratt and the author (48) have used it in a study of the pyrolysis of oximes, the products of which were very complex and ranged from permanent gases to liquids boiling at 150°C. or more. After many months of operation at high temperature, during which it was turned several hundred times weekly, it still held a high vacuum ($\sim 10^{-3}$ mm. Hg) on one side and a chromatographic column back pressure of 6 atm. or more on the other without leakage across the O-rings.

If it is desired, the sample source connexion can be replaced by a rubber septum for use with syringe injection into the sample volume used. The valve can, in this case, be simplified by elimination of the vacuum connexion. This design was employed by Bohemen and the author (21) who also studied the peak injection widths obtainable with the device and found them to approximate as nearly as any other method to plug injection. The small sample potentialities of this device and its ability to work at high pressure make it suitable for use with capillary columns, although this has not yet been done. This sampler can be described as being either of type (*b*) or (*c*).

An elegant sampling arrangement for gases has been described by Girling (73). A network of small bore nylon tubes is employed, each one being closed or opened to flow by actuation of a set of cam operated plungers. Gas flow can thus be diverted from a direct flow path through a tiny sample volume. Essentially, this arrangement is a simple by-pass system with external rather than internal closure and elimination of stopcocks. It can withstand very high pressures without leakage or bursting, but is restricted in use to fairly low temperatures.

An important experimental point in connexion with by-pass type samplers which has never, apparently, been brought out, is that since the sample chamber pressure is always smaller than the column back pressure, during switching of the sample chamber into the flow system there may be marked compression of the sample such that saturation pressures may be exceeded and condensation result. This compression or piston effect can readily be observed when a vacuum system filled with a saturated vapour is suddenly opened to the atmosphere when the incoming air, instead of mixing, forces the vapour along to condense at a point far removed from the air inlet.

The introduction of sufficiently small gas and liquid samples into capillary columns is a matter of great importance and is not easily achieved. The only samplers yet used are of the gas flow T-splitting type. Sample is first introduced by some or other of the methods already described, and then before entering the column meets a junction, one arm of which goes to waste while the other enters the column. A detailed description of such an apparatus has been given by Condon (58) and by Desty, Goldup and Whyman (31). The latter make the point that there is no guarantee that there is not some fractionation of sample as well as splitting in the desired ratio. The reproducibility of close boiling sample analyses was good but appeared less so with wide boiling range mixture. This led them to suggest that a more reliable method might have to be developed and based on what they describe as iso-kinetic principles. Condon, on the other hand, considers the T-splitting arrangement perfectly adequate and describes experiments carried out with a splitting ratio as high as 5000 to 1.

Even if this simple arrangement is found to be completely satisfactory it is clear that it has, potentially, one very undesirable feature; that of the tremendous carrier gas wastage. For a 5000 to 1 split it is necessary to vent to waste 4999 ml. per min. to achieve a flow through the column of only 1 ml. per min. While cylinder life is not in the ordinary course of events an important consideration, in this situation it could well be so, especially if the wastage were of an expensive gas such as helium, or even argon, which would become costly at 5 l. per min. More recently, Desty (70) and Boer (71) have stated that quantitative analyses good to ± 2 per cent can be carried out with simple T-splitters. Boer checked the analyses against conventional packed column/large sample analyses for verification. Since his mixtures had a boiling range of 50 to 150°C. it seems that the quantitative use of capillary columns is established.

There are several ways, of course, in which gas wastage might be avoided. For example, the splitting could be arranged to take place only during the short interval associated with the actual injection. However, this would introduce certain problems connected with sudden changes of pressure and flow at the column head and it might not be very easy to alter total flow virtually instantaneously from 1 ml. to 1 l. per min. Even if it were, it would undoubtedly introduce some complicated design features.

An alternative method which has sometimes been advocated is to dissolve the sample in a suitable solvent (or column packing) and then to take off the vapour. With a high enough solubility it should be possible to obtain extremely small samples in this way, and in a sense the sampler corresponds to the first theoretical plate of the column. Without a highly detailed knowledge of the relevant activity coefficients and saturation vapour pressures, it is difficult to see how this approach could be used for quantitative analysis. In addition, the sampler would have to be renewed for every injection.

Since splitting of minute liquid samples is likely to be almost impossible at the level employed with present day detectors and columns, it seems certain that complete conversion to vapour prior to splitting will ultimately become standard practice. How this will be achieved will depend very much upon circumstances, and it is unlikely that any one method will suffice to solve all problems. In the work done with the rotary valve described earlier (48) the whole sample was vaporised into a large volume in a vacuum system, but this will clearly not always be possible. Special vaporiser/saturator systems such as that described by Hooijmeijer, Kwantes and van de Craats (45) may have to be used, but these are hardly simpler than a vacuum system, and almost certainly less reliable.

For qualitative work, Pitkethly (46) has made considerable use of a dilution method in which microlitre volumes of liquid were first injected into large evacuated flasks where they vaporised completely, then diluted with carrier gas and, finally, sampled as fairly large volumes. In this way dilutions of a millionfold or more were readily achieved, and sub-microgramme quantities were conveniently contained in millilitres of gas. This method can obviously be made highly quantitative and it seems likely that some new facet of this technique, as opposed to direct flow splitting, may be the key to the solution of the quantitative micro-sampling problem. However, because of the stringent feed volume requirements (p. 168) it will still be necessary to inject volumes of diluted sample of the order of 10^{-2} ml. or so, and, in consequence, an adequate system for work with such volumes will still be required.

One aspect of the sample splitting method which has been suggested by the author (72) but has not apparently been investigated yet is the possibility of the use of "time" splitting as opposed to flow splitting. It may well be much simpler and more satisfactory to reduce sample size by actuating a valve for a short period than to use it to cut off a given small volume. Thus, for example, if a diluted gas sample flows at the rate of 1 ml. per min., exposure of this flow to a column for about 0.5 sec. would give a 0.01-ml. sample. This approach would have the added advantage of virtually eliminating carrier gas wastage and would considerably reduce the demand for miniaturisation of the sampler volume.

CONTROL AND MEASUREMENT OF CARRIER GAS FLOW

Almost without exception, carrier gases are derived from cylinders, and so a preliminary and sometimes sufficient control is provided by the cylinder reduction head. It is always advisable to pass the gas immediately through a drying column of silica gel and/or Linde 4A molecular sieve, a procedure which, in addition, provides some further buffering of flow and so helps further to maintain constancy.

For routine analysis, very close control of flow rate is not essential. Variations of ± 1 per cent are certainly tolerable, and so any type of pressure regulating valve, interposed between the drying agent and the column head, is adequate. Even the simplest orifice type needle valve functions satisfactorily at this level. If the pressures involved are not too great, a blow-off liquid manometer can be used, either in its simplest form or as some more elaborate modification, such as that described by James and Phillips (52). An alternative version incorporating a mercury monometer electrically operating magnetic on-off valves by contact with a metal strip has been used on occasion (2).

If, as is most common and convenient, needle or Bourdon type valves are used, it is undoubtedly best to employ very large pressure drops across each of them where this is possible, since then, small pressure changes affect flow very little. An added convenience is the addition of a valve at the column outlet, since this both permits the variation of total column pressure, and adds to the refinement with which the flow can be adjusted. An important point to be borne in mind is that small fluctuations in room temperature can lead to quite large changes in the flow of gas through an orifice, and it is for this reason that close flow control demands thermostatting of control valves. Thus, there is little point in utilising a precision controller in a system containing unthermostatted ordinary valves as well.

If retention volumes are to be used for identification or thermodynamic purposes, or an automatic analysis cycle is envisaged, a very rigid control of flow rate is desirable. In this situation, if the apparatus is not contained in a thermostatic room all parts of the flow system must be thermostatted. There are a number of commercially available pressure regulators which are suitable. The need for thermostatting follows immediately from equations 5.1 and 5.15. It is evident that constancy of pressure drop is no guarantee of constancy of flow rate if there is any possibility of temperature variation in the gas flow system.

Fortunately, in most cases the major restriction to gas flow occurs in the column itself, and if this is adequately thermostatted much trouble may be avoided. When it is possible, the flow regulator valves can be contained in the same thermostat. In elaboration of the point made earlier that large pressure drops through valves are advantageous, van de Craats (53) has discussed this in some detail and finds that if the column presents little resistance it is essential to incorporate restrictors between the cylinder and column, while Atkinson and Tuey (27) state that a cylinder pressure in excess of 800 p.s.i. is essential for steady flow. It is certainly true that flow stability diminishes as the cylinder pressure is reduced, but the value given may be somewhat excessive. In most cases it is worthwhile to include pressure gauges in the system, both near the column inlet and at the exit. These should have the minimum of dead volume and should have been calibrated reasonably accurately to be of value. Their inclusion is, of course, a necessity if compressibility correction factors (equation 5.21) are to be computed.

Measurement of gas flow rate is usually carried out with a rotameter, a capillary manometer, an orifice meter or a soap bubble meter. The first two can be included either ahead of or after the column, but usually the flow meter is sited after the column and measurement conducted at the prevailing atmospheric pressure. Rotameters are quite unsuitable to the accurate measurement of flow and are only useful as a rough guide. Capillary meters present certain constructional and calibration problems, and by far the most used and, in the author's view, the most accurate meters are of the moving bubble type.

Construction of these is extremely simple, a burette being modified by addition of a hooked T-piece in place of the stopcock. The precision of even the worst burettes is more than sufficient for the purpose. Before use, the hook is filled with bubble solution up to the point of gas entry at the T, the liquid sold for use by children being excellent for the purpose. The other end of the hook carries a small rubber bulb, which when squeezed sends a bubble up the burette. It is a simple matter to make measurements to better than 1 per cent in this way, and in fact, very much greater accuracy is possible even at flow rates of 500 ml. per min. Small changes in the measured value are observed at low flows if several bubbles occur in the burette simultaneously, and this should be avoided. Before use it may be necessary to send many bubbles through the burette in order to wet the walls sufficiently to allow stable bubbles to form, after which it is advisable to direct gas flow through the device only during a measurement to ensure that the walls are not dried out continuously.

It is very helpful if the burette is contained inside a wide outer glass tube filled with water in which a thermometer is placed. Then, the lens effect helps greatly in taking readings, while the water acts as a thermostat and its temperature is that of measurement of the gas volume. If accurate retention volumes are to be calculated, correction for the vapour pressure of water over the detergent solution must be made, since saturation of carrier gas in the meter is virtually complete. This is sensibly equal to the saturation pressure of pure water, since the solution is very dilute. The need to know, and if possible, standardise the temperature of flow measurement is thus evident on two counts.

The pressure drop/volume flow characteristics of a column provide the best means of measuring the mean particle diameter of the support solid or the mean radius of a capillary, and further, offer by far the best means of checking the reproducibility of packing procedures. For this reason, it is well worth determining the permeability of each new column made according to the method outlined in Chapter 5 (p. 65). The whole process takes only a matter of an hour or so, and may well obviate the need to make many chromatographic experiments before it is discovered that a column is substandard. Equally, extra-column blockages or leaks can be most readily detected in this way. If standard length and diameter columns, and fixed temperatures, are used, it is not even necessary to calculate permeability coefficients, but only to have available graphical data for pressure and flow rate.

COLUMN HEATING

As in the case of pressure, very close control of the column temperature is often unnecessary for routine analysis, and regulation to $\pm 1°C$. may be good enough. Thus, it is often the case that the analysis of permanent gases and liquids of high vapour pressure could be conducted at room temperature. While a $1°C$. change of column temperature may, in the extreme case, alter the absolute retention volume of substances by 5 per cent or so, those of all components will be more or less equally affected. Whether or not this approach can be adopted depends primarily on the detector used. The response of certain detectors may be quite seriously affected by retention volume change, especially if peak height calibration is employed, and so, for quantitative work in most situations, it is almost certainly worthwhile to employ some form of thermostat.

The simplest apparatus appears at first sight to be some form of vapour bath, and these have been very widely used. The constructional details of vapour jackets are so familiar as not to be worth repeating, but it is not always appreciated that constancy of boiling temperature depends upon the maintenance of constant total pressure and the absence of any chemical decomposition. It appears that the great majority of workers use vapour jackets without any form of pressure control; this can be deduced from the fact that in the literature the most commonly cited column temperatures correspond to the normal boiling points of the liquids used. It seems unlikely that atmospheric pressure would always be 760 mm. Hg., or that total pressure would always be adjusted to this value. Variations in atmospheric pressure of 50 mm. are commonly observed, not only from day to day, but during a single day. Such a variation would correspond roughly to a 2° change of boiling point. Evidently, some simple manostat should be incorporated into every vapour jacket arrangement. This has the added advantage that wide ranges of temperature can then be obtained with a given liquid; benzene, for example, boils conveniently over the range 50° to 80° at sub-atmospheric pressures.

Chemical decomposition of the boiling liquid is not a serious complication when the normal boiling point is fairly low, say below 150°. Higher boiling liquids, however, tend to break down fairly quickly, and the boiling point changes correspondingly. It is worthwhile immersing a thermometer or thermocouple in the vapour, if only to keep a check on this. However, vapour baths can be used successfully even at very high temperatures; Hawkes (54), for instance, has carried out experiments at 300°C. in this way, while Lewis and Patton (57) have worked up to 500°C.

There are a number of drawbacks to the use of vapour baths in addition to those mentioned. For instance, it is not easy to arrange the insertion of columns, particularly in glass jackets, and in addition, it is quite difficult to heat the system right up to the point of entry of the column. This may cause a cold spot to form there and sample may well condense at this point in or before the column. The mechanical difficulties and the instrumentation needed to provide constant temperature are, if anything, greater than those involved in the construction and operation of a conventional thermostatic bath and, for this reason, the author has found little use for vapour jackets.

The first alternative is to use a liquid bath. This represents a very simple constructional problem nowadays when combined heater/stirrer/controller units can be bought commercially for a small sum. Bath liquids are available for work at temperatures up to 200°C. or more, although for the highest

temperatures silicone fluids are necessary, and their cost may prove prohibitive. However, hydrocarbon and halogenated hydrocarbon oils are
cheap and perform satisfactorily up to at least 150°C. One constructional
requirement attending the use of oil baths is the use of coiled columns,
since an excessive oil volume requires considerable heating and is also very
heavy. Further, while a long narrow oil bath might be used for U columns,
temperature regulation is then generally inadequate. One way out of this
is to have the oil heating and temperature regulation in a separate bath
from which it is constantly pumped through the column container. This
works perfectly well, but increases the bulk of the apparatus considerably.

The second alternative is the use of an air thermostat. Such thermostats
are notoriously difficult to operate satisfactorily, but otherwise offer every
advantage. They require no liquids or special containing apparatus, they
can be operated at any temperature whatsoever, and consume very much
less power than vapour or liquid baths. From any point of view, air thermostats are the most desirable form of heating system, and every commercial
laboratory machine employs one. The simplest approach is to enclose the
column in a glass or metal pipe which carries an electrical heater winding.
One then relies either on the mains power supply for constancy of temperature, a rather unsatisfactory procedure, or uses a bimetallic or phase change
regulator. Many workers and several commercial instruments achieve
good results in this simple way.

A somewhat more refined and better approach is to use an insulated
metal box as the container and to circulate air with a fan of some sort.
Most commercial instruments are designed in this way, the box being
equipped with a door for easy access to column and detector. However,
while a constant temperature may well be maintained to better than 1° it is
usual to find quite enormous temperature gradients within the heated
cavity. These are commonly as much as 5° and in some cases may be as
great as 25°, depending on the geometry of the system and the location of
the heaters. Thus, the temperature registered by a thermometer placed
within the system may bear little relation to the column temperature. For
routine analytical purposes this is of little consequence provided temperature gradients are constant, but for accurate measurement of retention
volumes or solute identification, such instruments are obviously unreliable.
For an air thermostat to operate satisfactorily, it is absolutely necessary to
provide forced circulation of the air with sufficient power to achieve linear
velocities in excess of 35 f.p.s., at about which speed flow becomes turbulent at oridinary temperatures and pressures.

A very versatile air thermostat capable of working up to 350°C. has been
described by Ashbury, Drinkwater and Davies (55). The general features
are shown in Figure 6. The column passes through the containing case,

and is located centrally inside a metal cylinder, which in turn is contained within a glass vacuum jacket. The air space within the vacuum jacket is entirely closed off from the rest of the container, but has a valve to atmosphere through which hot air can be released when desired. A high temperature cut-off and resistance thermometer control element are located inside

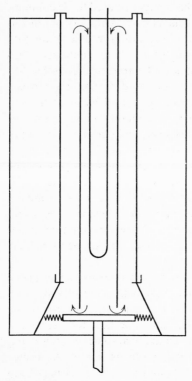

the protective vacuum jacket near the bottom and close to the radial fan, which is surrounded by heater elements. The fan sucks air at 50 f.p.s. down the inside of the metal cylinder and over the column, and then drives it back up through the space between the metal cylinder and the vacuum jacket.

The temperature control, which is based on the use of a proportional controller incorporating a resistance thermometer and a thyratron output stage, is better than 1° at 350°C. and the apparatus can be heated or cooled very rapidly indeed. For example, heating from room temperature to 200°C. requires ten minutes, with a power input of 1500 w. Cooling can be speeded up by use of the air release valve. This design seems to have by far the best characteristics of any described in the literature but, for ordinary purposes, is rather elaborate. It would seem to present a number of constructional problems, in particular, those associated with the use of a long vacuum jacket.

FIG. 6. Illustration of the main features of a versatile high temperature air thermostat. *By courtesy of Analytical Chemistry.*

Langer, Perrett and Quinn, in the author's laboratory, have simplified the above design very considerably in an attempt to produce an apparatus which would be both satisfactory and easy to fabricate. Their design is illustrated in Figure 7. An outer case of asbestos pipe is fitted with a thick insulating lid through which pass the carrier gas connecting piping, and from which projects downwards a centrally situated length of perforated metal angle strip. This carries the column, resistance thermometer element, thermocouples and a low power (10 watts) control heater. Between this and the outer wall is placed a cylinder of thin metal, underneath which is sited a vacuum cleaner fan driven through the outer case by the appropriate motor. The outside of the metal cylinder is fitted with asbestos rings which are glued on for work at low temperatures, but riveted for work over an extended range. These provide insulation to carry the zig-zag main heater windings. The whole unit is contained in an insulated container with about two inches of kieselguhr between walls. In order to maintain uniformity of temperature right up to the lid, the underside of this may need a small extra heater winding attached over its whole area and several thermocouples close by.

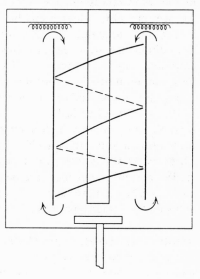

The main heater current is adjusted to bring the temperature up to that required, regulation is then effected by the on-off action of the central control winding. The current to this heater is monitored by the resistance thermometer which actuates a phase sensitive relay. The lid heaters, if needed, are adjusted to bring the temperature there to that of the body of the apparatus. This thermostat can be constructed in a day or two with reasonable workshop facilities, and has been found to work up to more

FIG. 7. Illustration of the main features of a simple and satisfactory forced circulation air thermostat.

than 200°C. with temperature regulation of 0.1° or better. At 150°C., during protracted use, and after careful adjustment, both temperature gradients throughout the system and temperature regulation of the order of ±0.01°C. could be maintained.

The final alternative form of thermostatting is the use of a large metal block on which the column is wound, usually as a spiral, the whole unit being enclosed within a metal dome or box. The central metal block can be drilled out to give cavities which contain heaters, flow control valves, the detector if desired, and temperature regulators. In the latter connexion, phase change devices are very suitable, since they are fabricated in small metal pots and give a degree of temperature control comparable with that of other methods. Their one disadvantage, that they can only operate at a single temperature, that of the phase change, limits their utility, but since the metal block design is best employed for process chromatographs or automatic machines this is not such a serious problem as might appear, since a range of regulators is available, and an appropriate temperature can usually be chosen. While the metal block configuration helps materially in smoothing out temperature fluctuations it has the disadvantage that rates of heating and cooling are relatively low and power consumption is high. Again, for process control instruments or for routine analysis under fixed conditions this is of no great importance and is more than counterbalanced by the compactness and ease of construction. Felton (56) has carried out analyses at 500°C. with a metal block unit and it seems likely to form the basis of most apparatus designed for work at extremely high temperatures. In addition, the arrangement seems particularly suitable for use with the enormous lengths of capillary, which are nowadays quite common, since these coil up neatly in a very small space (31).

Recent work has indicated that very effective thermostatting is achieved by the use of fluidised beds. There is no record of their use in gas chromatography, but for very high temperatures they would seem ideal, and it is probable that some attempt will soon be made to use them for this purpose. Thermostats of this sort are little more complicated than good air thermostats, what difficulties there are being of an entirely different nature, and have already been evaluated and largely overcome. Whether or not they will supplant other types of bath is speculative.

SAMPLE RECOVERY METHODS

It is sometimes desired to recover samples of materials which have been eluted from columns. The reasons may vary, but are commonly associated with a desire to investigate further the nature and properties of the substances. For example, in many well equipped laboratories, unknown substances are recovered for mass spectrometric or infra-red analysis. All recovery methods use up to this time have one thing in common, they almost all rely on refrigeration, that is, some form of cold trap arrangement. The only exception would appear to be where diluted sample recovery by direct flow through an optical cell of some sort is adequate. This would only be of value generally when the sample was diluted less than about 1000/1 by carrier.

In the simplest case of recovery by condensation it is only necessary to pass the column effluent through a U tube or trapping vessel immersed in dry ice or liquid nitrogen, this then should, in principle, retain everything which condenses at the chosen temperature. Often, however, it is desired to isolate individual components and then some modification of the collector is necessary. The obvious approach is to have a series of cold traps in parallel, each isolated by a stopcock from the column outlet. Gas can then be directed through any one at will at the appropriate time. The rotary valve sampler of Atkinson and Tuey (27) after suitable modification, has been used as the master control for recovery by parallel cold traps with considerable success, and is undoubtedly more convenient than a number of separate stopcocks, particularly for automatic operation. If only two or three fractions are to be collected, conventional three way vacuum stopcocks can obviously be used. Clearly, even here, it is again worthwhile to avoid the use of lubricant and for once this presents no problem, since there need be no pressure gradient across the stopcock, and lubricant is thus unnecessary if the key and barrel are not subjected to much force.

Craig, Mallard and Hoffman (60) have described a neatly fabricated system which employs hypodermic needles to carry gas flow into the cold traps, selection of gas path being made with a multi-way Teflon stopcock. Such a stopcock is very useful, since it is constructed in feebly adsorbing material, is self lubricating and easily worked mechanically. These authors, who reported quantitative recovery of a range of fatty acids, chose to evacuate the cold traps before collecting samples; gas flow was thus primarily due to expansion. Kronmueller (65) has described a twelve-position system of fundamentally similar design in which the stopcock was replaced by a rotating drum.

While such simple arrangements are undoubtedly convenient and satisfactory with what may be called conventional chromatographic systems, that is, where the recovered sample is present in reasonably large amount, say 1 μl of liquid, and has been eluted from a relatively inefficient column, it does not follow that they will function equally well at all levels. Consider the situation if recovery is to be attempted in an arrangement incorporating a capillary column of very many theoretical plates. The total sample will be less than 1 μg. and each component may be only 0.1 μg. After elution, the individual components may occur in the carrier gas at a concentration of 1 p.p.m. and so, if the carrier gas is at one atmosphere pressure the component partial pressure is only about 10^{-3} mm. Hg.

Even at liquid nitrogen temperatures, many substances have saturation vapour pressures of this magnitude and cannot, therefore, be frozen down. If the sample size were originally 10^{-3} μg., and several workers have described the use of such samples, the partial pressures of individual components would be as small as 10^{-6} mm. Hg, at which level it would be virtually impossible to freeze down anything. Furthermore, the stationary phase would probably have a saturation vapour pressure greater than this at the column temperature and would contaminate the sample. These theoretical considerations are important, but become even more so when practical experience is taken into account.

It is very difficult to obtain quantitative recovery of material in cold traps even when the temperature is extremely low. A major source of loss is the formation of fogs, the sample on entering the trap being immediately chilled to a supercooled mist or even a solid aerosol. n-Hexane, for example, boiling at 69°C., passes through a dry ice acetone trap quite readily (61) at quite low flow rates, and for good recovery it is essential to have slow flow through a series of traps, each well baffled or packed tightly with glass wool or other inert solid, offering a large surface area. Electrostatic precipitation may also be useful in this connexion and is commonly used for this purpose in gas kinetic systems (68).

A further point is that protracted flow of carrier even over a frozen down solid can entrain away amounts which may not appear great in terms of partial pressure but may be large as a fraction of the total sample. This problem was encountered by Atkinson and Tuey (27) and was of sufficient magnitude to call for consideration. Thus, even in the simplest case it seems worthwhile to employ multiple series traps of large surface area and to direct flow through the trap only during the interval during which the sample emerges from a column. It is obviously a worthwhile precaution also to determine in advance the saturation vapour pressure of the sample at the trap temperature, and to evaluate its approximate partial pressure in the column effluent, since if the latter is the smaller, recovery is impossible.

One possible alternative approach to mere refrigeration of small samples has been explored by Jones and Ritchie (62). These workers mixed the sample vapour, as it left the column, with a large amount of vapour of some readily condensable liquid. This approach is basically similar to the use of short columns for trace component concentration (63, 64) and is an application of Henry's law. The effect of adding the excess vapour follows from equation 2.8, thus, in so far as the sample is concerned, we have

$$p = xp^0 = Np^0/N_a$$

where N_a is the number of moles of additive. The greater the amount of additive the smaller p becomes, and hence the greater the recovery of sample in the trap. For the best result, following the suggestions on p. 17, the added vapour should be of the lowest possible molecular weight. Recovery of sample from the frozen mixture is obviously of no great difficulty and for many purposes would be unnecessary, some concentration alone being sufficient. This method obviously has excellent prospects of providing a recovery technique suitable for use even with the smallest samples with which refrigeration alone would be useless. Another, and comparable, approach to the problem would be to pass sample into cold traps containing solid adsorbent. The recovery of infinitely small amounts in this way would seem possible when it is remembered that the highest vacua are achieved in a comparable way. Glueckauf (67) has described the recovery of 10^{-12} g. krypton in this way, while Ambrose (69) has used alumina to assist recovery of organic materials.

A final point of importance is that most detectors either destroy or modify the sample. Thus, in order to be safe in the matter of recovering an uncontaminated sample it should not have passed through the detector. One way out of this is to standardise column operation sufficiently well to make the time of emergence of components absolutely predictable. A simpler and probably more reliable method is to split the emergent stream so that a small fraction goes through the detector, and the residue goes straight to the recovery system.

REFERENCES

1. Ellis, J. F., *Gas Chromatography*, 1958, Butterworths, London (editor, D. H. Desty), p. 308.
2. James, A. T., and A. J. P. Martin, *Biochem. J.*, 1952, **50**, 679.
3. James, A. T., *Anal. Chem.*, 1956, **28**, 1564.
4. Orr, C. H., and J. E. Callen, *Annals N. Y. Acad. Sci.*, 1959, **72**, 649.
5. Kiselev, A. V., N. V. Kovaleva, A. Ya. Korolev and K. O. Shcherbakova, *Doklady*, 1959, **124**, 97; 1959, **129**, 131.
6. Perrett, R. H., and J. H. Purnell, *J. Chromatog.* (in press).
7. Iler, R. K., *The Colloid Chemistry of Silica and Silicates*, 1957, Cornell, New York, p. 257.
8. Runge, F., and W. Zimmerman, *J. prakt. Chem.*, 1955, **1**, 283.
9. Kohlschutter, H. W., P. Best and G. Wirzing, *Z. anorg. Chem.*, 1956, **285**, 336.
10. Martin, A. J. P., *Biochem. Soc. Symp.*, 1949, **3**, 12.
11. Howard, G. A., and A. J. P. Martin, *Biochem. J.*, 1950, **46**, 532.
12. Horning, E. C., E. A. Moscatelli and C. C. Sweeley, *Chem. and Ind.*, **1959**, 751.
13. Bohemen, J., S. H. Langer, R. H. Perrett and J. H. Purnell, *J. Chem. Soc.*, **1960**, 2444.
14. Langer S. H., Z. Connell, and I. Wender, *J. Org. Chem.*, 1956, **23**, 50.
15. Bohemen, J., and J. H. Purnell, *Gas Chromatography*, 1958, Butterworths, London (editor, D. H. Desty), p. 6.
16. McKenna, T. A., and J. A. Idleman, *Anal. Chem.*, 1959, **31**, 1021.
17. *Vapour Phase Chromatography*, 1957, Butterworths, London (editor, D. H. Desty), discussion, pp. 329-331.
18. Pratt, G. L. (Ph.D. Thesis, Cambridge, 1960).
19. Ormerod, E. C., and R. P. W. Scott, *J. Chromatog.*, 1959, **2**, 65.
20. Boehm, H. P., and M. Schneider, *Z. Anorg. u. allgem. Chem.*, 1959, **301**, 326.
21. Bohemen, J., and J. H. Purnell, *J. Chem. Soc.*, **1961**, 360; 2630.
22. Scott, R. P. W., *Gas Chromatography*, 1958, Butterworths, London (editor, D. H. Desty), p. 189.
23. Brennan, D., and C. Kemball, *Petroleum Refiner*, 1958, **37**, 258.
24. James, A. T., and A. J. P. Martin, *Analyst.*, 1952, **77**, 915.
25. Martin, A. J. P., *Gas Chromatography*, 1958, Butterworths, London (editor, D. H. Desty), p. 20.
26. Tuey, G. A. P. (see ref. 25), p. 21.
27. Atkinson, E. P., and G. A. P. Tuey (see ref. 25), p. 270.
28. Golay, M. (see ref. 25), p. 67.
29. Dijkstra, G., and J. de Goey, (see ref. 25), p. 56.
30. Scott, R. P. W., *4th Informal Symposium of Gas Chromatography Discussion Group*, London, April, 1959.
31. Desty, D. H., A. Goldup and B. H. F. Swanton *J. Inst. Petroleum*, 1959, **45**, 287.
32. Langer, S. H., and P. Pantages, *Anal. Chem.*, 1958, **30**, 1889,

33. Samsel, E. P., and J. C. Aldrich, *Anal. Chem.*, 1959, **31**, 1288.
34. Tenney, H. M., and R. J. Harris, *Anal. Chem.*, 1957, **29**, 317.
35. Ogilvie, J. L., M. C. Simmons and G. P. Hinds, *Anal. Chem.*, 1958, **30**, 25.
36. Dal Nogare, S., and L. W. Safranski, *Anal. Chem.*, 1958, **30**, 895.
37. Quin, L. D., and M. E. Hobbs, *Anal. Chem.*, 1958, **30**, 1400.
38. McCreadie, S. W. S., and A. F. Williams, *J. Appl. Chem.*, 1957, **7**, 47.
39. van de Craats, F., *Anal. Chim. Acta*, 1956, **14**, 136.
40. Glew, D. N., and D. M. Young, *Anal. Chem.*, 1958, **30**, 1890.
41. Dimbat, M., P. E. Porter and F. H. Stross, *Anal. Chem.*, 1956, **28**, 290.
42. Porter, K. (Ph.D. Thesis, Cambridge, 1960).
43. Pratt, G. L., and J. H. Purnell, *Anal. Chem.*, 1960, **32**, 1213.
44. Janak, J., and R. Komers, *Gas Chromatography*, 1958, Butterworths, London (editor, D. H. Desty), p. 343.
45. Hooijmeijer, J., A. Kwantes and F. van de Craats, *ibid.*, p. 288.
46. Pitkethly, R. C., *Anal. Chem.*, 1958, **30**, 1309.
47. Purnell, J. H., and C. P. Quinn, *Nature*, 1961, **187**, 656.
48. Pratt, G. L., and J. H. Purnell, *Proc. Roy. Soc.*, 1961, **A260**, 317.
49. Glueckauf, E., *Gas Chromatography*, 1958, Butterworths, London (editor, D. H. Desty), p. 22.
50. Kwantes, A., and G. W. A. Rijnders, (see ref. 49), p. 125.
51. Adlard, E. R., and B. T. Whitham, (see ref. 49), p. 351.
52. James, D. H., and C. S. G. Phillips, *J. Sci. Instr.*, 1952, **29**, 362.
53. van de Craats, F., *Gas Chromatography*, 1958, Butterworths, London (editor, D. H. Desty), p. 248.
54. Hawkes, J. C., *Vapour Phase Chromatography*, 1957, Butterworths, London (editor, D. H. Desty), p. 266.
55. Ashbury, G. K., A. J. Davies and J. W. Drinkwater, *Anal. Chem.*, 1957, **29**, 918.
56. Felton, H. R., *Gas Chromatography*, 1958, Academic Press, New York (editor, V. J. Coates, et al.) p. 131.
57. Lewis, J. S., and H. W. Patton, (see ref. 56), p. 145.
58. Condon, R. D., *Anal. Chem.*, 1959, **31**, 1717.
59. Stanford, F. G., *Analyst*, 1959, **84**, 321.
60. Craig, B. M., T. M. Mallard and L. L. Hoffman, *Anal. Chem.*, 1959, **31**, 319.
61. Norrish, R. G. W., and J. H. Purnell, *Proc. Roy. Soc.*, 1958, **A243**, 435.
62. Jones, J. H., and C. D. Ritchie, *J. Assoc. Offic. Agr. Chemists*, 1958, **41**, 749.
63. West, P. W., B. Sen and N. A. Gibson, *Anal. Chem.*, 1958, **30**, 1390.
64. Boggus, J. D., and N. G. Adams, *Anal. Chem.*, 1958, **30**, 1471.
65. Kronmueller, G., *2nd International Symposium, I.S.A.*, Lansing, Mich., 1959. Preprints, p. 79.
66. Decora, A. W., and G. U. Dinneen (see ref. 65), p. 12.
67. Glueckauf, E., *Vapour Phase Chromatography*, 1957, Butterworths, London (editor, D. H. Desty), p. 210.
68. Norrish, R. G. W., and G. W. Taylor, *Proc. Roy. Soc.*, 1956, **A234**, 160.
69. Ambrose, D. A., *Vapour Phase Chromatography*, 1957, Butterworths, London (editor, D. H. Desty), p. 210.
70. Desty, D. H., *5th Informal Symposium of Gas Chromatography Discussion Group*, Brunel College, London, April 1960.
71. Boer, H. (see ref. 70).
72. Purnell, J. H. (see ref. 70).
73. Girling, J. (see ref. 70).
74. White, D., and C. T. Cowan, *Gas Chromatography*, 1958, Butterworths, London (editor, D. H. Desty), p. 116.

The demands made of a gas chromatographic detector are so great that in the earliest days of development in the field it looked very much as though few, if any, devices would prove satisfactory. This view proved to be completely erroneous, as is shown by the fact that, today, more than twenty instruments, each operating on a different principle, have been used with some success or other. The major requirements of a detector are high sensitivity and stability, combined with the maximum speed of response to change in the chromatographic effluent composition. The highest sensitivity is likely to be realised if the property to which the detector responds is characteristic only of the eluted solutes and not of the carrier gas. However, there are few physical properties which are not common to all substances, and so the most that can be hoped for is an approximation to this ideal. A few present-day devices virtually fulfil the ideal condition and so constitute a group of "supersensitive" detectors. The majority of instruments, however, fall into a class which we may designate as "of conventional sensitivity" and so, in the following pages, only the more successful of these are described in any detail.

Before we discuss individual detectors it is well to consider what may be meant by sensitivity. Glueckauf's equation (7.32) can be used to calculate the maximum concentration of a solute emerging in a column effluent if the theoretical plate equivalent of the column and the initial concentration of sample are known.

In a simple case such as when the column is of 1000 theoretical plates and sample injection is as a pure plug, the

12
DETECTORS

sample occurs in the effluent at a maximum concentration near 1 per cent by volume. This then would represent about the upper limit of concentration met with in gas chromatography and the lowest detector sensitivity level of any value would be an easily measurable response to a solute concentration of 1 part per 100 of carrier. If allowance were made for sample dilution during injection, say by a factor of ten, and a component constituting only 1 per cent of the sample analysed was of interest, it would be necessary for the detector to give a reasonable response to a solute concentration of between 1 part in 10^4 and 1 part in 10^5 of carrier gas. This is quite a low level of impurity in the carrier which before the advent of gas chromatography might have been considered impossible to detect.

This kind of detector performance represents a reasonable estimate of the sensitivity of a "conventional" detector. If a very efficient column were used for an analysis, a 100,000 plate capillary, for example, the detector would need to be able to respond to solute concentrations of at least the order of 1 p.p.m. Such sensitivity is indeed very high, and the maintenance of stability, that is, the absence of significant noise, is then not only a matter of high priority but also relatively difficult to achieve. Some idea of the magnitude of the problem can be gained if we assume, not unreasonably, that a full scale electrical signal for 1 p.p.m. of solute in carrier gas is 1 mv., then, if noise is to be no more than 1 per cent it corresponds to only 10 μv. High quality electrical components are clearly a first essential in such conditions. The stability demanded when the extreme limits of some detectors are reached may be quite remarkable, as can be gauged from McWilliam's claim (71) that the flame ionisation detector is capable of responding to the presence of organic substances diluted to nearly 1 part in 10^{11} in carrier gas.

DETECTORS OF CONVENTIONAL SENSITIVITY

INTEGRAL METHODS

Gas chromatographic detectors are frequently classed either as "integral" or "differential" in type, although this classification is somewhat arbitrary, since methods are available to convert one to the other. Those which are normally regarded as integral detectors have never proved popular and are only occasionally used. They are all of conventional sensitivity or less. Predominant among them are automatic titration (1) as employed in the original work of James and Martin, which is suitable only for acids and bases; measurement of conductance of a solution (2); coulometric titration (3); and volume or pressure increment devices such as the Janak nitrometer (4).

Automatic titration has been used by some workers because of the relative simplicity of the apparatus, but its sensitivity is not very high and it lacks generality of application. Conductance and coulometric devices are also relatively limited in application, and although less so than direct titration, their sensitivity is again low. The only integral technique which has been at all widely employed is the nitrometer method. In this, carbon dioxide used as carrier gas is completely absorbed during passage through a caustic potash solution at the column outlet, the residual gases being passed into small graduated volumes. Recording of volume can be visual or made automatic by appropriate modification (5, 6, 7, 8). A visual arrangement has been consistently used with success in gas kinetic studies by Knox and his co-workers (9) and several versions of the automatic device are available commercially. The detector is useful only for solutes which do not condense at room temperature or react with the alkali, and its sensitivity is limited by the difficulty of measuring volumes smaller than about 10^{-2} ml. with any accuracy, although van de Craats (7) has improved the design in this respect by measuring pressure instead. Even so, except for its constructional simplicity, the detector is hardly to be recommended nowadays.

A detector which is of interest because of its simplicity, but more so because of its ingenuity, is the limit of inflammability device described by Behrendt (57). A mixture of fuel gas (propane for example) and oxygen which is just below the inflammability limit is fed into the column effluent. This mixture is then directed at a small pilot flame. Addition of carbon containing compounds from the column raises the fuel content above the inflammability limit, and so causes the effluent to explode and a flame to back flash into the effluent flow line. The gas expansion, which is quantitative, causes a mercury relay to actuate an electrolysis cell and an exactly correct volume of oxygen is fed back into the effluent. The hydrogen generated is collected in a nitrometer and measured as in the Janak method. The device is claimed to work well.

DIFFERENTIAL DETECTORS

A very large number of detectors of this type have been developed and tested. While almost all have proved suitable for some purpose or another, the exceptional merit of a few has led to their adoption almost to the exclusion of the others. Understandably, therefore, the space devoted to individual detectors in the succeeding discussion varies markedly, those described first being, on the whole, those which have excited least interest or appear to have little prospect of attaining popularity. This cannot be taken to mean, however, that they may not be capable of further development.

GAS FLOW IMPEDANCE

The rate of gas flow through a capillary restriction depends upon the viscosity of the gas (equation 5.2) but that through an orifice depends upon the density. As was pointed out on p. 52 there should, in theory, be a definite numerical relationship between these quantities and so, at a fixed pressure, it should matter little which type of restriction is used as the basis of a detector system. In fact, an orifice is the preferred choice, since flow through this is rather more sensitive to composition change. Griffiths, James and Phillips (10) used an orifice detector in which flow was held constant and the pressure developed across the orifice was used as a measure of composition change in the gas stream. It appears that the response was close to linear in terms of solute concentration, but sensitivity was low. It is, no doubt, possible that improvement might be effected by modification of design, but it is not likely to be worthwhile. One aspect of the device which might be worth exploring is that, as a density measuring instrument, it could be useful for identification purposes.

SURFACE POTENTIAL CHANGE

The earliest work on the detection of vapours by measurement of surface potential change was that of Phillips (23); so far as is known, its only application in gas chromatography is that by Griffiths and Phillips (11). The underlying principle of the method is that since two plates of dissimilar metals have different potentials when they are held closely together and connected by a conductor, vibration of one sets up an alternating current. Adsorption of vapours out of a gas stream alters the surface potentials and so, after the e.m.f. corresponding to the pure gas flow is biased off, any signal is a measure of the vapour concentration. Griffiths and Phillips found that instead of plates of different metals, it was more effective to use a pair of steel plates, one of which carried a layer of stearic acid or octadecanol. The sensitivity attained was worthwhile only with polar substances, but then serious problems of sluggishness, irreversibility of adsorption and non-linearity of response were encountered.

DIELECTRIC CHANGE

Simple calculation shows that the most sensitive detector one can design to operate on the basis of changes of dielectric constant will only be of comparable sensitivity to most other conventional detectors, and then only towards highly polar substances. Griffiths et al. (10) have used such a device but with little success, while more recently Turner (12) has returned to the problem and introduced some improvements. Even so, there is little doubt that the detector is of no value to gas chromatography on the analytical scale, although it might be useful for preparative work. Its main utility, however, would seem to lie in liquid chromatography, where the greater dielectric constants met with would favour its performance.

SPECTROSCOPIC ANALYSERS

Martin and Smart (13) first used an infra-red analyser to study gas chromatographic column effluent composition. Evidently, it would be a complication to alter throughout a single analysis the frequency at which absorption was measured, and so the most practicable approach is to combust component vapours to CO_2 as they emerge from the column and to set the analyser to work at a single CO_2 absorption wavelength. This approach is claimed to be effective. The detector has been used with some success by Franc and Jokl (14) and for hydrocarbons, without combustion, by Liberti, Costa and Pauluzzi (15). The use of this instrument as a detector is of doubtful value if only on the grounds of expense, but in any case it does not offer particularly high sensitivity and has a very large dead volume. Obviously, ultra-violet absorption can be used in a manner analogous to infrared, but suffers the same drawbacks. Johnstone and Douglas (16) have used it in the analysis of aromatic hydrocarbons, but the method is unlikely to be of more than restricted utility.

HEAT OF ADSORPTION MEASUREMENT

Dudenbostel and Priestley (17) have described a very simple detector in which thermocouples were buried in a short plug of solid adsorbent situated at the end of a column. A second column/thermocouple pair acted as a dummy and the heat liberated on adsorption of vapours emerging from the analytical column was recorded as an oscillating temperature change by the thermocouples. The method offers quite reasonable sensitivity, since the heats of adsorption involved are of reasonable magnitude, and the method was, in fact, sufficiently successful to have been used in a process monitoring unit. Heats of solution could undoubtedly be used in an analogous fashion, and an elegant approach, which was adopted by Priestley (18), was to dispense with the extra sorbent plug and merely to utilise the last few centimetres of column. It was reported that the signal obtained in this way was proportional to the amount of sorbed vapour. However, there seems no doubt that devices of this sort may be subject to trouble, first through hysteresis, and secondly through the variation with concentration of heats of adsorption or solution. These drawbacks are likely to be least important with heats of solution, and so the latter version seems to have the better prospects. This detector is probably the simplest of all to construct, since it requires only a thermocouple and a recorder, and might well repay further study, since its apparent simplicity is very attractive.

POLAROGRAPHIC DETECTION

Polarographic detection and estimation of the constituents of the effluent from liquid chromatographic columns has been used to a considerable extent, in particular by Kemula and his associates (109). It has only occasionally been used in gas chromatography. Janak, Nedorost and

Bubenikova (19) employed a polarograph in connexion with the chromatography of halogens. These, after elution, were passed into a solution of Ti(III) ions and determination was made by measuring the increase in the Ti(IV) wave height. The cell used for the study has been described in some detail by Nedorost (22). The approach is obviously limited in many ways, and is unlikely to be of great value. As originally described, an integral result was obtained, but it could very simply and more satisfactorily be used differentially.

INTERFEROMETRY

Gas interferometers have been used with limited success in gas chromatography by Turkeltaub (20) and by Zderic, Bonner and Greenlee (105). It is doubtful whether they offer advantages in any respect.

RADIOACTIVE DETECTION

The detection of radioactive materials as they are eluted from gas chromatographic columns has been reported several times (58, 59, 60, 95). Any radiation counter can be used, but response is generally slow (95). Behrendt (61), has recently developed a method in which non-radioactive substances are, after chromatography, subjected to exchange reactions. Organic vapours were burned over CuO and the CO_2 formed was labelled by exchange with hot $Na_2^{14}CO_3$. Comparative chromatograms suggest a sensitivity to propane in nitrogen about 100 times that of a katharometer and Behrendt claims that with development a further 10^4-fold improvement should be possible. Other radioactive species used were ^{18}F, ^3H, ^{31}Si, ^{35}S and ^{221}Fr. If it is established that the response is fast enough and the volume small enough, both of which seem doubtful this detector must have considerable potential.

THE GAS DENSITY METER

The comparison of gaseous densities for molecular weight or composition measurement is a technique of long standing. However, the first practicable density meter for use in chromatography appears to have been constructed relatively recently by Claesson in connexion with his studies of the displacement method (101). The apparatus consisted basically of a liquid manometer connected across two columns of gas, one being a pure reference gas. Any difference in mass of the two columns set up a measurable pressure differential in direct proportion. The columns were as much as six feet long and of considerable diameter, a feature of no consequence in Claesson's work, but obviously reducing the generality of the method very considerably. Martin and James (102) devised means not only to miniaturise the device, but also to convert the pressure differential to a substantial electrical signal. Another important point in their design was that the chromatographic column effluent never came into contact with the signal generating element. These advantages combined with the fundamental and desirable fact that the response at reasonable flow rates is strictly a function of molecular weight, make the detector one of considerable attractiveness.

Figure 1 shows schematically the network of gas flow paths which are drilled out of a solid metal block. Column effluent enters at A and splits

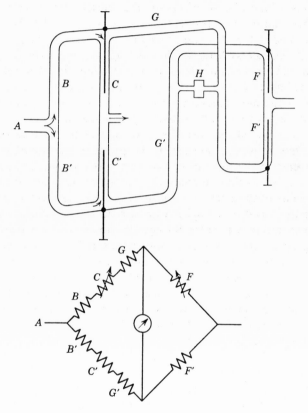

FIG. 1. Schematic view of the gas density balance detector showing also its electrical analogue. *By courtesy of the Biochemical Journal and Butterworths.*

approximately equally along B and B'. It then passes through the two arms C and C' to recombine and leave the apparatus at D. The rate of flow through C and C' can be controlled with the choke rods shown, only one of which needs to be adjustable. A reference stream of pure carrier gas enters at E, divides to flow through F and F', and on through G and G' to emerge, combined with column effluent at D. Adjustable chokes are again provided in F and F'. An added connexion tube across F and F' contains a small spiral electrical heater located beneath two thermocouple junctions. At zero gas flow through the thermocouple chamber, the temperatures recorded by the thermocouple junctions should be identical and the siting of these is thus important. Means to adjust their position from outside are provided. With a flow of pure carrier gas entering at both A and E, the chokes are adjusted to give zero flow across the detector element H. When this is achieved there is flow balance at the junctions of C with G and C' with G'.

If, because of the addition of vapour, the density of the gas entering A is greater than that of the carrier entering E, flow in B and B' becomes unbalanced, those in G and G' are equally affected, and so the pressure gradient developed across H causes flow through it from right to left. The convected heat stream is displaced by the resultant flow and the thermocouple junction at the entrance side is cooled while the other is heated. The output of the thermocouples thus provides a measure of the direction and velocity of the gas flow. A "negative" signal would be obtained if the density of the column effluent were less than that of the pure carrier. Provided all flow resistances are equal, the pressures developed across the various points in the instrument and across H are independent of flow rate and the flow is thus determined only by density difference.

The stability of the detector is greatest when hydrogen is the carrier, but its sensitivity is said to be higher with nitrogen, as a result of the higher heater temperature attainable through the lower thermal conductivity. Of very great significance in determining the stability is the uniformity of block temperature. The maximum difference of temperature between channels which can be tolerated is only about $0.001°$, and so very effective thermostatting is essential. The onset of turbulence in the flow lines, especially at the choke rod orifices, limits the flow rates at which the detector can be used. At very high flows, therefore, it is necessary to bleed off a portion of the column effluent.

Munday and Primavesi (103) have carried out a detailed study of the performance of the density meter and have illustrated its design and mode of operation by comparison with a Wheatstone network. This is shown in approximate analogy in Figure 1. They constructed an ingenious electrical equivalent to the detector and carried out a number of measurements with this. They found that the electrical output of their instrument was a linear function of flow through H up to 15 ml. per min. This flow represents a very considerable range of concentration in the effluent as is seen from their estimate that 0.5 ml. per hour through H represented a concentration of 1 part of amyl alcohol in 5×10^5 of nitrogen. In their instrument, which in contrast to the original, was constructed in tubes. the noise at zero flow was about 1 μv. and under operating conditions no more than 2 μv. The block design was found to be rather less noisy than this, presumably because of better thermal characteristics. On the other hand, its response was found to be linear only up to about 3 per cent change of density, in comparison with the 10 per cent quoted above for the skeletal design. In either case the region of linearity almost certainly covers anything likely to be met with in gas chromatography.

Liberti, Conti and Crescenzi (104) have used the density meter to determine gaseous molecular weights with some success. This aspect of the potential of the instrument is, in the author's view, a very important one since the considerable difficulty of its construction and the great expense involved have proved a deterrent to its wide adoption. Those who have used it find it an excellent device and it probably represents the best conventional detector. It is clear that it offers a valuable aid to the identification of unknowns since in the right circumstances it gives a more or less unequivocal value of molecular weight. It is an interesting prospect that this device, which performs much the same function as a mass spectrometer, might be operated in series with another detector, and thus give a result which would first classify and then identify almost certainly anything which can be resolved by gas chromatography. This prospect is discussed later at great length.

THE HYDROGEN FLAME TEMPERATURE DETECTOR

The study of reactions in flames by the use of temperature sensitive probes has been practised for some time. Scott, however, applied the technique to the determination of the composition of column effluent and in so doing developed a detector of considerable elegance, simplicity of design and reasonably high sensitivity (106, 107). Although it is undoubtedly, a very successful detector it has not been extensively used, probably because its emergence directed interest to other properties of flames, an interest which culminated in the development of the flame ionisation detector (69–72). Even so, for work at conventional sensitivities, particularly when extensive electronic or mechanical facilities are not available, it still represents a very useful tool.

In its original form, hydrogen used as carrier gas left the column and passed immediately into a short length of hypodermic tube at the tip of which it was burnt. Centrally situated above the flame was one junction of a thermocouple, the other being immersed in a constant temperature bath. The standing e.m.f. was biased off by use of a dry cell and resistor. When carbon containing compounds entered the flame the temperature increased and the e.m.f. generated was fed directly through a simple potential divider to a recorder or galvanometer. The jet and thermocouple were contained in a metal box fitted with a number of baffles, glass beads etc. to break up the air flow. It was found beneficial to have a forced air flow into the container since a diffusion flame is unable readily to draw in sufficient air for complete combustion without aid and thus tends to change both shape and size when its composition alters. Scott found that in appropriate circumstances there was a linear relationship between chromatographic peak height and sample size and a common calibration plot was obtained for a number of similar hydrocarbons when peak area was plotted against weight of sample.

An improved sensitivity and stability is obtained if, instead of pure hydrogen, a mixture of roughly equal parts of nitrogen and hydrogen is used. In this case it is best to use nitrogen and not the mixture as carrier gas, thus often improving column efficiency with conventional columns, and to mix in the hydrogen after the column (53). This result has been confirmed several times (77, 98). Wirth (53) found that the relative response to a variety of organic types was very close to their relative calorific values.

This aspect was studied in more detail by Henderson and Knox (98), who found that the temperature rise in the flame is directly proportional to the rate of heat release and obtained excellent agreement between relative response values and those calculated from the relative heats of combustion of a wide range of compounds. This result implies that calibration of the device for one compound only is sufficient since data for other substances can be computed from this. Alternatively, observed responses may be used to assist in the identification of unknowns by reference to tables of heats of combustion. However, Bullock (99) and Primavesi (100) state that the relative response is not exactly that to be expected from the heats of combustion. These workers used fairly large liquid samples and it is possible that in their flames there was incomplete combustion, even though they used a forced draught. Scott (110) has stated that the use of oxygen instead of air improves the linearity of response very considerably and its use, possibly in a pre-mixed flame, may be advantageous.

Primavesi, Oldham and Thompson (108) made a detailed study of temperature contours with a hydrogen/nitrogen flame. They found that in a normal sized flame the temperature immediately above the burner tip was about 800°C. and fell progressively up the flame to about 200° at a height of 8 cm. The introduction of probes, of course, very markedly alters conditions within a flame, and so these values are probably very much lower than the true ones. However, the general form of the contours is probably correct. The addition of a small quantity of toluene, about 0.1 moles per cent of the total flame gas before burning, led to a temperature increase of about 100°C. at all points in the flame. This corresponds to a signal of approximately 3 mv. with chromel/alumel thermocouples. They suggested that with more or less conventional gas flow rates and burner size, the thermocouple is best sited about 1.5 cm. above the burner tip for liquid samples bigger than about 1 μl. Scott (110), however, using oxygen for combustion, and limiting the sample size to about 0.5 μl, found that a 3 mm. separation gave the best results.

Obviously, the exact dimensions are a matter of some flexibility and depend to a large extent on the geometry, mode of operation of the system and the size of sample analysed. The utility of the detector is obvious since it can deal adequately with sub-milligram samples with a repeatability agreed by the authors cited above to be better than 1 per cent. The only drawbacks to be reckoned with are the relative insensitivity to inorganic substances, the occasional dousing of the flame by halogen containing solutes and the total destruction of the sample. The first of these is common to a number of the popular detectors and is not insuperable. The second can be eliminated by the use of small samples, while the last is not really significant, since the column effluent can readily be split. On the whole, therefore, this detector has much to recommend it.

FLAME EMISSIVITY

A detector which has a number of desirable characteristics has been described by Grant (21). Basically, it is one of the several modifications of the hydrogen flame detector originally described by Scott (106, 107). Effluent from a column is mixed in constant proportions with a stream of coal gas, the mixture then being burnt at a wide stainless steel jet. The light emission from the flame is measured with the aid of a reflector, an optical condenser lens and a selenium photocell. As the carbon content of the flame changes, so does the emission. The linearity of response depends primarily upon the level of background emissivity, hence the need to add coal gas, and improves up to a point as the background increases. With the apparatus used by Grant, a background emission corresponding to a signal in the range 0.5 to 1 mv., gave good linearity. It is evident that reasonably close control of all gas flows is needed.

In practice the emissivity can readily be adjusted by variation of the coal gas flow, and Grant found that operation with a background of 0.8 mv. permitted quantitative work in the linear region of response over a wide range of column temperature. Grant has obtained excellent quantitative data with this detector and the sensitivities achieved were comparable with the best conventional detectors. However, it is not a particularly simple device to construct, despite the claims made for it; it is certainly no simpler than other flame systems and, further, much of the inherent sensitivity of a flame system is thrown away through the need to provide an emissive background. On these grounds the detector is unlikely to prove popular.

One very interesting property of the device, which has been exploited by Grant, however, is the close similarity in response of homologues and the widely differing response of different homologous series. This permits class identification of unknowns provided only that their initial sample size is known. For example, methylated benzenes all gave a molar response relative to benzene of about 1.3, in comparison with *n*-alkanes whose relative response was about 0.15. This order of magnitude difference would leave no doubt as to what was what in a complex alkane/aromatic mixture. Obviously, as Grant points out, this distinction may extend to many classes of compounds and further study might well be very profitable. The need to know the sample size can be overcome by use of a katharometer in series with the flame. Then the relative response from the two detectors can be used for identification. In the author's view it is this aspect which will determine the extent of further use and development of this detector.

THERMAL CONDUCTIVITY DETECTORS

According to the kinetic theory of gases the coefficient of thermal conductance $\tilde{K}$ of a pure gas is given by

$$\tilde{K} = \tfrac{1}{2}\rho\bar{c}\lambda c_v$$

where ρ is the density, $\bar{c}$ is the average molecular velocity, λ is the mean free path and c_v is the specific heat per gram at constant volume. Comparison with the equations of p. 52 shows that, ideally, $\tilde{K}$ is related to the coefficients of self-diffusion and viscosity by

$$\tilde{K} = D\rho c_v = \eta c_v$$

Since the product $D\rho$ is, in principle, independent of pressure, so also is $\tilde{K}$. This is true, however, only at pressures greater than about 10^{-1} mm. Hg, since below this value, molecular collisions are less frequent than is assumed in the derivation of the above equations. Thus, at very low pressures, thermal conductivity devices act as Pirani pressure gauges, while at high pressures they are predominantly sensitive to composition change.

Many gases have a very simple temperature dependence of heat conductance of the type

$$\tilde{K}_t = \tilde{K}_0(1 + \beta t)$$

where $\tilde{K}_0$ is the thermal conductivity coefficient at some standard temperature, usually taken as 0°C. when t becomes the Centigrade mean temperature of the gas. β is a coefficient which differs from gas to gas. The temperature dependence of thermal conductivity of the majority of organic vapours, however, is more complex and it is necessary to use more elaborate equations. One which is fairly generally used, but is only one of many, is of the form

$$\tilde{K}_t = \tilde{K}_0(1 + \beta t + \gamma t^2 \cdots)$$

The experimental determination of $\tilde{K}$ for gases was highly developed towards the end of the last century, in particular in the work of Callendar.

The most widely used method was that in which the rate of heat loss from an electrically heated metal filament, coaxially situated within a metal cylinder, was measured. The theory of this approach yields an expression for the rate of heat loss from a filament of length L,

$$\frac{i^2 R}{J} = \frac{2\pi \tilde{K} L(T_f - T_c)}{\ln r_c/r_f} + S' \tag{12.1}$$

where J is the mechanical equivalent of heat, T_f and r_f are the temperature and radius of the filament while T_c and r_c are the corresponding quantities for the containing cylinder. The term S' represents the sum of heat losses by conduction through the electrodes, radiation, free convection and, when a gas flow is imposed, forced convection. These are often taken to be negligible although this approximation may be far from justifiable in most situations.

Evidently, if $\tilde{K}$ varies, so too does $i^2 R$ and, at constant i, the filament resistance therefore changes in proportion to the thermal conductivity change. If the filament forms part of a resistance bridge, changes of thermal conductance are therefore converted into proportional electrical signals. In an ideal gas mixture the net conductance should be calculable from a simple mixture law, from which, if x represents a mole fraction, for a binary mixture,

$$\tilde{K}_{\text{net}} = x_1 \tilde{K}_1 + x_2 \tilde{K}_2$$

whence,

$$\Delta \tilde{K} = \tilde{K}_1 - \tilde{K}_{\text{net}} = x_2(\tilde{K}_1 - \tilde{K}_2) \tag{12.2}$$

Thus, ΔK should be proportional to the difference in conductivities of the carrier and contaminant gas and to the mole fraction of contaminant. However, very few gas mixtures obey this rule and the thermal conductivity/concentration isotherm may not only be curved but, in addition, exhibit maxima or minima. Many mixture laws for thermal conductivity have been proposed, but the subject is one of great complexity and is not well understood. At very low concentrations of one component, nevertheless, the relationship of $\Delta \tilde{K}$ with concentration may be close to linear, although not ideal. This state of affairs is comparable to that illustrated on p. 19 in the discussion of Raoult and Henry's laws.

In order to minimise the temperature dependence of $\Delta \tilde{K}$ and to achieve linearity of this quantity as a function of composition, it is obviously prudent to choose to use thermal conductivity in the analysis of mixtures of two components of greatly different $\tilde{K}$ since, then, variations in $\Delta \tilde{K}$ are small in comparison with $\Delta \tilde{K}$ itself.

Table 1 lists values at 0°C. of $\tilde{K}$ for some common gases. Included also are values of $\tilde{K}_1 - \tilde{K}_2$ where $\tilde{K}_1$ is either hydrogen, helium or nitrogen. These indicate the order of magnitude of $\Delta \tilde{K}$ to be expected.

Clearly, the greatest differences are those observed when hydrogen or helium are the diluting gases and further, the differences for most things are roughly equal and have the same sign. The only significant exception is when hydrogen is diluted in helium. When nitrogen is the diluting gas, because of its low $\tilde{K}$, there are changes of sign of $\Delta\tilde{K}$ from substance to substance, and, more important, the differences are relatively small and vary greatly in relation to each other. Thus, ideally at a mean temperature of 0°C., acetone would be more than twice as readily detected in nitrogen as

TABLE 1

THERMAL CONDUCTIVITY COEFFICIENTS OF GASES AT
0°C. ($\times 10^6$).

x	$\tilde{K}_x$	$(\tilde{K}_{N_2} - \tilde{K}_x)$	Relative Sensitivity	$(\tilde{K}_{H_2} - \tilde{K}_x)$	$(\tilde{K}_{He} - \tilde{K}_x)$
N_2	58	0	0	358	290
H_2	416	−358	−25.5	0	−68
He	348	−290	−20.7	68	0
CH_4	72	−14	−1.00	344	276
C_2H_6	44	14	1.00	372	304
C_3H_8	36	22	1.57	380	312
C_4H_{10}	32	26	1.85	384	316
$CHCl_3$	16	42	3.00	400	332
CH_3OH	34	24	1.71	382	314
$(CH_3)_2CO$	24	34	2.43	392	324

would ethane and, while methane and ethane would be equally readily detectable, the addition of methane to nitrogen would lead to an increase in conductance, while that of ethane would lead to a decrease. Obviously, in the case of dilution by nitrogen, small operating temperature changes might affect $\tilde{K}_1$ and $\tilde{K}_2$ so differently as to change greatly the magnitude and possibly the sign of $\Delta\tilde{K}$ for a given substance. So radical an effect is evidently unlikely in hydrogen or helium because of the large value of $\Delta\tilde{K}$.

Notwithstanding the possible complications outlined, the measurement of $\Delta\tilde{K}$ is clearly an acceptable basis for gas analysis. The first worthwhile device specifically designed for the purpose was patented in 1915 by Shakespear and called a "katharometer" (purity meter). In the following decade gas analysis by this means was both intensively studied, particularly by Daynes (29), and widely used; a notable example being in the analysis of mixtures of *ortho* and *para* hydrogen (see, for example, 25, 28). The work, however, was almost always carried out in static systems. The first application of a katharometer in gas chromatography appears to be that by

Claesson (101) but it was with the coming of gas-liquid elution chromatography that it became really widely adopted, its eminent suitability being established early by Ray (30) and Griffiths et al. (10).

Design Features. Basically, all katharometers are of similar design. The heated element may be a straight wire, a coil or a semi-conductor bead or flake. The cavity is almost always cylindrical for constructional reasons. The main difference in design lies in the gas flow pattern. Figure 2 illustrates the four common configurations. In (*a*) the gas flows directly over

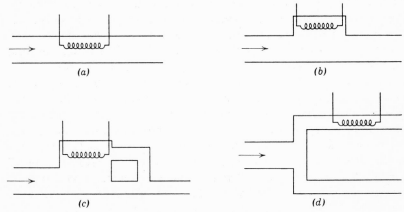

FIG. 2. Common configurations in katharometer design; (*a*) direct flow, (*b*) side chamber diffusion, (*c*) side chamber diffusion split flow and (*d*) split direct flow.

the heated element and this pattern therefore offers the most rapid response to concentration change. It is, however, flow sensitive, that is, the term S' in equation 12.1 is not negligible. Conformation (*b*) is designed to eliminate this by having the heated element located in a side chamber, gas entering and leaving the chamber by diffusion. Even in the most favourable cases, diffusion is so slow that response to change of composition may take 20 sec. or so, in contrast to the 0.1 to 1.0 sec. response of type (*a*) (44, 49). This sluggishness may often lead to grave distortion of the concentration profile in the gas, thus giving a false impression of the performance of the chromatographic part of the apparatus. This drawback is so significant that, in the author's view, it renders the design virtually useless for most purposes, although it is, in fact, very widely used.

The configuration shown in (*c*) is an attempt to reconcile (*a*) and (*b*) in that the side chamber is connected to the main flow path on either side of the heated element. Thus, it is possible for gas actually to flow into the side chamber. However, since the ratio of flow splitting between the main and side channels is fixed, the total flow through the side chamber at high column flow rates may become comparable with that in design (*a*) at lower column flows. Thus (c) achieves little, in particular since it seems that at low column rates it is still mainly a diffusion device, as is shown by the fact that its time constant in these conditions is about 10 sec. (44).

The most suitable design, in the author's view, is that shown in (d) in which there is adjustable flow splitting before entry into the heated element chamber. Thus, the total flow through the latter can be maintained constant, irrespective of the column flow rate, and so analytical calibrations are flow insensitive, since the term S' of equation 12.1 is constant. The flow through the element chamber can readily be adjusted at almost any reasonable column flow so that response time is less than 1 sec. and so is faster than most electronic chart recorders with which the detector may be used.

The heated element is almost always used in a Wheatstone network, although a potentiometric system could be used. In the simplest case, a single unit can be operated with three external resistors. Bohemen and the author have for several years used such a katharometer with success, although it demands excellent thermostatting. In order to reduce the demands on the thermostat arrangement it is most common to use a pair of heated elements situated close together and subject to gas flow from the same source. The gas flow over one element (the reference) is always "pure" carrier. It is often the case that the reference channel is incorporated between the carrier gas supply and the point of sample injection at the column head, but this is bad practice on two counts. First, small pressure or flow variations at the column inlet are retarded by the column and may take several seconds to reach the detector reference channel situation at the column outlet. Secondly, although $\tilde{K}$ should be pressure independent above a few mm. Hg, this is only approximately true, and, in fact, $\tilde{K}$ increases somewhat with increasing pressure. Thus, at the inlet end, the heated element is more affected by small pressure and flow changes than it would be at the outlet end of the column. The net result is an assymetric saw tooth contribution to the noise. It is undoubtedly best to have both the reference and detector channels fed by gas at the same pressure and derived from a pair of columns operating, as nearly as possible, under the same pressure and flow conditions. In order to achieve this, and it amounts to equalising S' of equation 12.1, it is best to make the two columns as nearly identical as possible. The columns, of course, can contain different stationary phases and so, as required, can become either the analytical or reference column.

There are a number of possible Wheatstone bridge arrangements for double channel katharometers. The more common of these are illustrated in Figure 3, a and b. In the former, the detector D and reference R are in series with each other and in parallel with two external resistors. It is common practice to make the latter quite large, 100 Ω or even more. In the latter arrangement the detector and reference are in parallel. The latter system is most widely recommended on the basis that small changes in resistance of the detector give rise to smaller changes in current. This is certainly an advantage since it helps to maintain linearity of response. However, for a given voltage, more power is dissipated and higher element temperatures are achieved in arrangement (*a*), and so the bridge is more sensitive. Thus, if network (*b*) is used, it is necessary to use greater voltages

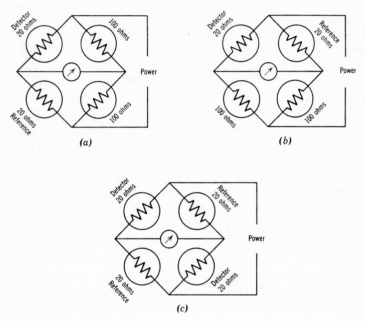

(a)   *(b)*

(c)

FIG. 3. Conventional bridge circuits for multi-channel katharometers. Resistances quoted are illustrative only.

for a given sensitivity than when (*a*) is employed. Some gain in sensitivity results if all the resistors are of comparable magnitude, as can be shown by application of Kirchhoff's laws. The maximum gain attainable is only a factor of two, but this may, of course, be worthwhile. However, small resistance changes then lead to relatively large current changes and so there is a greater tendency to non-linearity of response.

An elaboration of the two-channel katharometer is the four element type which is shown in Figure 3*c*. There are no external resistors, other than one for fine adjustments, and diametrically opposite pairs of resistors are contained in the same gas flow channel. Any composition change in the gas, therefore, upsets the bridge on both sides and in opposite directions, thus doubling sensitivity by doubling the off-balance current in the bridge.

This gain is to some extent offset by the fact that, for constructional reasons, it is usually necessary to use coiled filaments which undoubtedly confer less sensitivity than straight ones of the same resistance.

In order to provide, as nearly as possible, identical thermal conditions in both channels of a katharometer these are generally contained within a metal block. This construction also helps thermostatting for a single channel instrument. In a design due to Brooks, Murray and Williams (54) the filaments are first mounted within narrow glass tubes, the electrodes being sealed directly into the glass. The tubes are enclosed in a brass block prepared by halving after drilling out the appropriate depressions; the two halves are then bolted together. This design has been used with satisfactory results in the author's laboratory for some time and is extremely simple to construct. Most workers, however, simply drill out cavities within a solid metal block (see, for example, 35, 36, 41, 42). Since, in this design, the carrier gas comes into contact with the block metal, brass and copper are not always satisfactory for the purpose despite their excellent thermal properties (p. 170). Stainless steel, or, perhaps, some aluminium alloy, would seem to be the best metals to employ, although the use of the former introduces difficulties in the drilling of long holes.

Thermistor Elements. The relative merits of metal filaments or spirals and thermistors have never been explicitly discussed. In principle the latter ought to be much more effective, since although the temperature dependence of their resistance is negative and non-ohmic, it may be a hundred or more times as great as that of any metal. The drawback, however, is that the temperature differential between the element and its surroundings which can be obtained is often only a few degrees, in contrast to the hundreds of degrees attainable with filaments, while when heated to high temperatures, thermistor response falls off rapidly. Further, while filaments can fairly readily be exactly matched for resistance and temperature dependence of resistance, the same is not true of thermistors. However, thermistor cells have been used with considerable success and form the basis of at least one very widely used commercial chromatograph.

The earliest published work appears to be that of Ambrose and Collerson (24), but their design, while reasonably sensitive, appeared to be noisy and rather inflexible. Davies and Howard (47) have recently discussed bead thermistor cells with particular reference to the noise problem. They found that the best results were obtained if the detector unit was never switched off and that, further, it was unwise to use hydrogen as carrier gas, since this led to breakdown of the thermistor, even when the bead was glass coated. Musgrave (48) has claimed, however, that thermistors are less noisy than hot wire katharometers and operate well even at 200°C. if they are of very high resistance in the cold (>2000 ohms).

By far the most comprehensive study is that of Cowan and Stirling (49). They, like Musgrave, found greater sensitivity with higher resistance beads and, most of all, if the beads were bare and not glass coated. Increased physical size and resistance both led to more noise which was found to depend upon bridge current as i^h where $h = 1.2$ to 1.8. Aging by excessive heating (over-running) was found to be essential for stability and they substantiated the suggestions of Davies and Howard about continuous running and attack by hydrogen. If the detector was switched off for 1 min. and then on again the noise increased tenfold and it required at least four minutes to settle to the original level. They concluded that the best thermistor katharometer performance was consistent with the use of both the minimum current and the minimum temperature difference between the thermistor and surroundings. Clearly, these conditions militate against the best sensitivity.

In so far as matching criteria were concerned, they decided that for use in a double channel detector matching of thermistor resistance to 1.5 per cent and temperature dependence of resistances to 2 per cent per °C. is essential, and even then ambient temperature must be controlled to 0.4°C. and bridge voltage to 0.001 per cent. These requirements are so exacting that it is surprising that they can be met without excessive instrumentation. However, it is evident that it is possible. The sensitivity claimed for bead thermistor katharometers is comparable with that of most hot wire detectors, although less than has been occasionally claimed for the latter. However, flake thermistors of high dissipation constant and low thermal response time have recently been employed in a commercial instrument and have been claimed to be capable of detecting as little as one part of vapour in 10^7 of carrier gas. This is a level of sensitivity well beyond that attainable by the best hot wire cell yet designed, and developments in this direction will, therefore, be awaited with interest.

Metal Filament Elements. The metals most commonly used as hot filaments are platinum and tungsten. The latter has slightly the greater temperature coefficient of resistance but the former has the greater specific resistance. Since tungsten is much stronger and more easily worked it is, therefore, the more convenient, particularly since pre-formed coiled coils are readily available. For use with corrosive materials, nickel, despite its softness and unfavourable electrical characteristics, has been recommended in virtue of its chemically resistant qualities (32).

The filaments most commonly used have a diameter in the range 0.001 to 0.002 in. They must be mounted under tension to allow both for expansion at high temperature and to avoid vibration. In some very elaborate designs, small copper/beryllium or platinum/iridium springs are used (27, 35, 36). The author feels that such refinement is only necessary in extreme cases when, in any case, other detectors are probably more suitable. The stressing, however achieved, must be no greater than is consistent with the elimination of sag and microphony, and in the author's experience a 5 g. weight attached before the final sealing of electrodes gives adequate stress for a 0.002 in. tungsten filament. It is important in this connexion to match, so far as possible, the coefficients of expansion of the various materials used. Kovar metal/glass insulator seals have been found to be excellent in this respect to as high as 300°C., while tungsten/Pyrex or platinum/soda glass seals are equally good. Concentricity of mounting of the filament or coil is also important and Davies and Johnson suggest that in matching pairs, neither should be more than 25 microns out of line. This would appear to be a very stringent requirement, but is more readily achieved in practice than might be expected if simple plumb lines are used during construction. The electrodes used for electrical connection to the filaments should be of as small a diameter as possible in order to reduce end thermal losses.

In many modifications in which spirals or coiled coils are used, these are not mounted along the length of the cylinder, but bunched up at some central point. The theory attending this configuration is not easy to evaluate, as also is true of thermistor cells, since their geometry is ill defined. However, they work well but, in the author's experience, are always more prone to non-linear or anomalous response than are concentric designs. This view has been substantiated several times (38, 55, 56). However, Felton and Buehler (33), for example, have described a very neat design in which the filaments used are part of a model aeroplane glow plug, which, being small and threaded, means that it can readily be inserted or replaced in the katharometer block and is, of course, cheap. This model was operated very successfully at an ambient temperature of 400°C. A comparable approach is that of Stuve (43), who removed the glass capsules from miniature 2-w. electric light bulbs and used the thread mounted spirals as the heated elements. A double channel katharometer incorporating these was claimed to give no perceptible noise with a 5 mv. recorder and a steady drift of only 0.025 mv. per hour. Operated in a bridge at 4 volts, Stuve claimed that 1 p.p.m. of methyl caproate in nitrogen gave an off-balance signal of 0.1 mv. This is quite a high sensitivity for a katharometer.

A further alternative form of heated element to the concentric filament is a metal tape. Kaiser (51) has given details of their performance in a katharometer. The tapes used were of platinum/nickel alloy being 4 μ thick and 50 μ wide. The resistance of such tapes was about 1 ohm per mm. length, roughly ten times that of a 0.002 in. diameter tungsten filament. This increased resistance is advantageous since the Wheatstone bridge sensitivity is proportionately greater at the same element temperature.

Further, since the tapes are much more robust than filaments, construction is simplified. The sensitivity claimed by Kaiser is comparable to the best reported for katharometers.

Katharometer Response. In theory, the response of a katharometer to the introduction of a sample of one gas into another should be calculable from the individual values of $\tilde{K}$ on application of the simple mixture law. In practice, the problem of reconciling the calculated and experimental thermal conductivity of mixtures is as yet unsolved, and is so complex that Littlewood (52), for example, considers that katharometer responses will never be theoretically calculable, an opinion with which the author concurs although it conflicts with views expressed by van de Craats (39). Thus, katharometer responses are likely always to have to be determined empirically, in particular, when the carrier gas is of low thermal conductivity.

Even in the most favourable situations in gas chromatography, such as when helium is used as carrier gas, the theoretical response, calculated through equation 12.2, for mixtures of known molarity has been found, on average, to be 11 per cent smaller than that found experimentally (40). An interesting, but as yet unexplained finding is that responses calculated from equation 12.2 by use of weight percentage composition instead of x, were in somewhat closer agreement with experiment, being only 6 per cent in error (62, 63, 64, 40).

Despite the lack of agreement between theoretical and experimental response, however, certain regularities have been noted. Rosie and Grob (40) and Messner, Rosie and Argabright (50) made a comprehensive study of helium/solute mixtures and found that the katharometer response per mole of solute relative to that per mole of benzene (R_b) could, for a number of homologous series, be represented by an equation of the type

$$R_b = X_1' + X_2'\text{M} \qquad (12.3)$$

where M is the molecular weight of the solute and X_1' and X_2' are series constants. Their derived values of X_1' and X_2' for a number of series are listed in Table 2.

The values of X_1' and X_2' listed, which were evaluated from peak areas were claimed to be independent of temperature over the range 30° to 160°C., of concentration over a tenfold range around 1 μl. of liquid sample and of helium flow rate between 30 and 120 ml. per min. Furthermore, exactly the same values were obtained with hot wire and thermistor instruments. Evidently, this behaviour can be expected to extend to other series and so may be very helpful in reducing the amount of calibration work necessary. No doubt, similar regularities exist for mixtures in which hydrogen is the diluting gas although no results have yet been reported. Mixtures containing nitrogen or carbon dioxide as carrier gas, however, are unlikely to show such regular properties, mainly because the thermal conductivity differences involved are relatively so small. This view is elaborated in the following section.

Anomalous Katharometer Response. At a fixed current, the element of a katharometer is hotter in an atmosphere of nitrogen, argon or carbon dioxide than in one of hydrogen or helium because of the lower thermal conductivities of the members of the former group. Thus, at any given

TABLE 2

INCREMENTAL KATHAROMETER RESPONSE TO HOMOLOGUES IN HELIUM EXPRESSED AS $R_b = X_1' + X_2'$ M. R_b IS RELATIVE TO BENZENE = 100, AND M IS MOLECULAR WEIGHT

Type	Carbon Content Range	X_1'	X_2'
n-Alkanes	1 to 3	20.6	1.04
	3 to 10	6.7	1.35
Me. Alkanes	4 to 7	10.8	1.25
1-Olefins	2 to 4	13.0	1.20
Tri Me. Alkanes	7 to 8	13.9	1.16
Me. Benzenes	7 to 9	9.7	1.16
Mono n-alkyl benzenes	7 to 9	17.9	1.06
Mono sec-alkyl benzenes	9 to 10	18.1	1.04
n-Ketones	3 to 8	35.9	0.86
Primary alcohols	2 to 7	34.9	0.81
sec-Alcohols	3 to 5	33.6	0.86
tert-Alcohols	4 to 5	34.9	0.81
n-Acetates	2 to 7	37.1	0.84
n-Ethers	4 to 10	43.3	0.89

bridge current, the ratio of the detector's sensitivity for substances diluted in nitrogen to that for the same substances diluted in hydrogen is greater than would be anticipated from data such as are contained in Table 1. However, it would be unreasonable to operate an instrument at constant current for all carrier gases, and for comparative purposes equal element temperatures should be employed. In this situation, the light gases offer the added advantage that the greater value of $\Delta \tilde{K}$ is accompanied by a greater bridge current which itself confers extra sensitivity.

Response in nitrogen is not only smaller than in the lighter gases but is often very markedly non-linear with mixture composition. In the extreme case, grave peak distortion is observed which may culminate in partially inverted (W-shaped) or completely inverted peaks. Attention was first directed to these phenomena by Mellor (38) and by Keppler, Dijkstra and

Schols (35). The latter postulated that decomposition of solutes on the hot element was responsible for the inversions and reported the formation of aldehydes from alcohols passed through a hot wire cell. However, peak inversion effects have been shown (56) to be more readily induced at high gas flows through the katharometer, that is, with reduced time in the locality of the hot element, and so this seems very unlikely to be a generally applicable explanation. Furthermore, while chemical reaction in the katharometer would have been expected to be as rapid, if not more so, if hydrogen were the carrier gas, the only known inversion in hydrogen is that of helium peaks (39), a result predicted by the theory of the flow sensitivity of katharometers discussed later (56).

An alternative explanation of peak inversion was advanced by Harvey and Morgan (34), who pointed out that due to differences in the form of the temperature dependence of $\tilde{K}$ for mixture components, thermal conductivity isotherms might change slope. With change of ambient or element temperature, katharometrically recorded peaks might then change sign. They determined the isotherms for some methanol/nitrogen mixtures and found a change of slope in the region of 100°C. They also found maxima in the isotherms in the region of 10 per cent v/v methanol. One drawback to the latter experiments was that they were carried out with very large flow rates and so cannot be true conductivity isotherms. This view is substantiated by the fact that the most extreme precautions are taken in thermal studies to eliminate even free convection and, further, the determination of gaseous heat capacities is conventionally carried out by measuring heat losses from hot elements to fast flowing gas streams.

Keulemans, Kwantes and Rijnders (36) took the view that peak inversion resulted from the occurrence of maxima or minima in conductivity isotherms. This approach has been further developed by Littlewood (52) and Schmauch (44) and was also mentioned as a possibility by Keppler, Dijkstra and Schols (35). However, it should be pointed out that the maxima and minima described in the literature are usually located at moderately high concentrations, in excess of those to be anticipated at the outlet of gas chromatographic columns. Furthermore, peak inversion occurs almost exclusively in carrier gases of low thermal conductivity and for almost all types of solutes. It would be surprising if all substances exhibited maxima or minima in nitrogen, always in the region below about 1 per cent concentration, but never in lighter gases in any conditions. Another argument against this hypothesis lies in the peak shapes obtained.

Figure 4a shows a hypothetical isotherm with a maximum and the series of peaks which would be obtained as the sample size increased. If the sample were sufficiently big to reach concentration A, a normal peak would be obtained. The larger sample B would give again a normal peak but its height would not be in proportion, a situation even more marked for the sample C, which corresponds to the concentration at the isotherm maximum. A larger sample D would obviously go through A, B and C but then the peak would start to invert. The inversion would be greater for E, the peak shape obtained might well, in fact, be mistaken for a pair of peaks. At F, a negative dip would occur. In fact, this sequence of peak inversions,

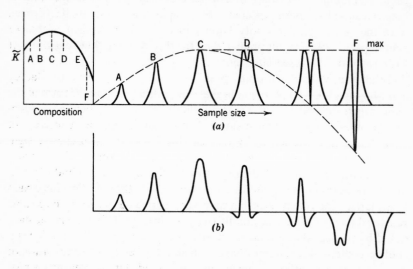

FIG. 4. Illustration of katharometric peak distortion increasing with sample size (a) as expected from the hypothetical thermal conductivity isotherm shown and (b) as most frequently observed.

from the top, with constant height on the "positive" side of the base line, is rarely observed, and the common sequence is as shown in Figure 4b with inversion *from the bottom.* It has been suggested that this sequence would result from an isotherm with a minimum (65) but this is, of course, incorrect since the sequence then would be exactly as in 4a with reversed polarity. The arguments outlined assume that the filament or thermistor temperature do not vary during passage of solute through the detector, but, even if they did, the basic viewpoint would be unchanged.

In order to study further the causes of peak inversion Bohemen and the author (56) carried out a comprehensive study of the phenomena. The most striking fact elucidated was that the inversion temperatures were highly flow rate dependent and since thermal conductivity is, supposedly, both flow and pressure independent, this implies a mass effect. Combined with the knowledge that, at very high flows, what are effectively katharometers are used for heat capacity measurements, this seems reasonable evidence that peak inversion is, at least to some extent, connected with the S' term in equation 12.1. Extending the latter by introducing a term for forced convection gives, for a filament of length L,

$$\frac{i^2 R}{J} = \frac{2\pi \tilde{K}(T_f - T_c)L}{\ln r_c/r_f} + \frac{mC_p(T_f - T_c)}{2 \ln r_c/r_f} + S'' \qquad (12.4)$$

where m is the mass flow of gas in moles per second and C_p is the gaseous molar heat capacity at constant pressure. The sensitivity of the detector, if i and T_f are regarded as approximately constant, is then given by

$$\frac{i^2 \Delta R}{J} = \frac{2\pi \Delta \tilde{K}(T_f - T_c)L}{\ln r_c/r_f} + \frac{m \Delta C_p(T_f - T_c)}{2 \ln r_c/r_f} \qquad (12.5)$$

where ΔC_p represents the difference between the heat capacity of the pure carrier gas and the mixture. When nitrogen is the carrier gas, $\Delta \tilde{K}$ and ΔC_p

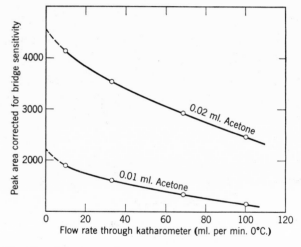

FIG. 5. The effect of carrier gas flow rate through a katharometer on the recorded peak area at constant solute concentration in nitrogen. *By courtesy of Chemistry and Industry.*

virtually always have opposite signs, and so, increasing flow rate (m) reduces sensitivity as seen from the experimental data shown in Figure 5. Further $\Delta \tilde{K}$ for most mixtures decreases more rapidly with temperature than does ΔC_p, and hence, at elevated temperatures, the convection term becomes more important. In appropriate conditions it may become equal to or exceed the conduction term.

Figure 6 shows peak area/filament temperature plots for several organic types eluted in nitrogen, the areas having been corrected for bridge current differences. Sensitivity, in each case, goes through a maximum and then, eventually, through zero to negative values. It is around this zero (cross-over temperature) that W-shaped peaks occur. As seen from Figure 7, increasing the katharometer body temperature narrows the temperature range of "positive" response and widens the region in which anomalies are observed. Above some temperature all peaks would be "negative". The

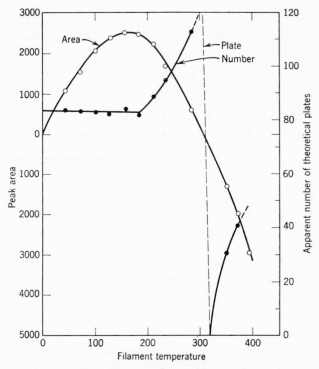

FIG. 6. The effect of katharometer filament temperature change on the recorded peak area at constant solute concentration in nitrogen, nitrogen flow rate and detector ambient temperature. Plotted also are the apparent theoretical plate heights measured from the peaks; variations reflect detector inadequacy. *By courtesy of the Journal of Applied Chemistry.*

theory based on equation 12.4 predicts the symmetry seen in Figure 7. Figure 8 shows a series of corrected peak area/gas flow rate isotherms. With increasing filament temperature, cross-over temperatures move to lower flow rates, and at the highest filament temperature all peaks are always "negative". Such negative peaks, incidentally, are always highly distorted.

The explanation offered by Bohemen and the author is, in effect, that inversions arise when convection and conduction become of comparable magnitude, when small changes in either then lead to big changes of both magnitude and sign of their difference. It is the view most in accord with the results, is based on detailed experiments, and gives a quantitative account of the findings. Further, the means deduced to avert inversions, without considerable sensitivity loss, are usually correct. Finally, the

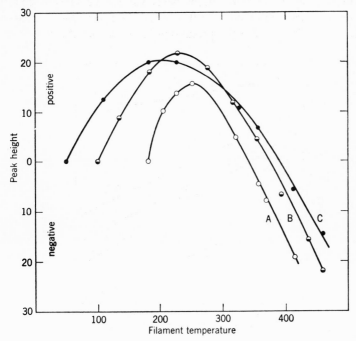

FIG. 7. The effect of change of ambient temperature on recorded peak area at constant nitrogen flow rate, filament temperature and concentration of solute in the carrier gas. Ambient temperatures: A, 184°C.; B, 100°C.; C, 54°C. *By courtesy of the Journal of Applied Chemistry.*

theory predicted that only helium peaks would be inverted in hydrogen, a result now confirmed (39). The possibility that curved conductance isotherms are involved in inversion phenomena is not excluded and is the only possible explanation when gas flows are very small. On the whole, however, in conventional chromatographic conditions the heat capacity theory seems most appropriate.

The best means to deal with peak distortions are, therefore, in the first instance, to reduce the total flow rate through the katharometer as much as possible, hence the advocacy of the flow pattern illustrated in Figure 2d, and only then to lower the filament and/or the ambient temperature. Because of this need for flexibility of temperature control it is best that katharometers should not be contained within the column thermostat. Over quite a wide range of temperature or flow rate around a cross-over point, the detector gives anomalous signals even though this is often not evident without detailed study. Also included in Figure 6 are apparent theoretical plate values deduced from the results plotted which illustrate this point. Since column conditions never varied, the marked changes reflect katharometer anomalies. In theoretical studies in which katharometers are used it is a worthwhile precaution to check that the chosen flow

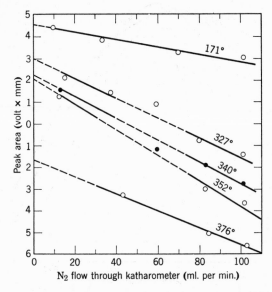

FIG. 8. Peak area/carrier gas flow rate through detector, isotherms for fixed acetone-nitrogen mixture. This shows the experimental conditions corresponding to the observation of positive and negative signals. In the region close on either side of the area zero W-shaped peaks are common. *By courtesy of the Journal of Applied Chemistry.*

and katharometer temperatures contributed nothing to apparent column performance (55). This is particularly appropriate too, to preparative column arrangements where often litres of gas pass rapidly through the detector. It seems possible that preparative column results may, in some instances, have been much better than authors believed, and would have been seen to be so if flow splitting had been practised.

Peak inversions in carrier gases such as nitrogen and carbon dioxide are observed not only with hot filaments and spirals, but also with thermistors. They are less easily dealt with in the latter case because it is not possible to vary bridge currents widely, owing to the rapid changes in their characteristics. There is, thus, something to be said for the development of specific heat detectors for use particularly at high temperatures. A specific heat detector would have the very desirable characteristics of equal sensitivity in nitrogen and hydrogen since ΔC_p would be much the same for both, and that inversions would be much more difficult to induce. Presumably the general design features would be the reverse of those for katharometers, in that construction would require a good insulating material for the body and indirect heating of the resistance element.

Ancillary Equipment and Methods. Katharometers are normally operated in d.c. bridges since lead accumulators conveniently provide highly stable low voltages and resistive balance is simply achieved. The leads should all

TABLE 3

A.C. BRIDGE NOISE FOR KATHAROMETER

Bridge Volts	Katharometer Total Noise, μv	+ Filter	+ Capacity	+ Filter + Capacity
7	810	540	720	15
5	300	213	258	7
3	72	63	64	0

be screened, however, to avoid a.c. pick-up problems. One drawback to d.c. systems is that amplification is not as readily possible as when a.c. is used. However, Bennett, dal Nogare, Safranski and Lewis (66) have described a neat unit which gives considerable amplification, as also have Ebeid and Minkoff (31) who used a commercially available instrument. The possibilities of a.c. katharometer arrangements were studied by Madden, Quigg and Kemball (37) who attempted to find means to achieve resistive balance, which is normally impossible to attain in a simple a.c. bridge. They found that the residual balance potential was a third harmonic component which could be eliminated by incorporation of a rejection filter. However, it was found necessary to use a capacity as well, as is seen from Table 3 which lists the noise observed at several applied voltages.

The marked improvement in performance is evident and clearly much amplification could be used, since the filter and capacity had no effect on the sensitivity. The theory advanced indicated that current of 1000 c.p.s. would have been even more successful, but the sensitivity achieved with 50 c.p.s. was considered adequate.

Chemical Convertors. Because of the relatively low sensitivity of katharometers operating in nitrogen they are particularly suitable for use in combination with chemical convertor units. Other detectors, too, often work more satisfactorily in combination with a convertor unit, but the most widespread use appears to have been with katharometers. Combustion tubes containing hot CuO were first used by Martin and Smart (13) and then by Green (67). A C_nH_{2n+2} hydrocarbon, for example, gives nCO_2 and $(n + 1)H_2O$ on combustion, thus effectively increasing the concentration $(2n + 1)$-fold. In addition, the detector may be more sensitive to CO_2 than to an equal molar quantity of the hydrocarbon. Sensitivity is undoubtedly gained in this way. Green went even further and passed the combustion products through a tube of hot iron. The $(n + 1)$ moles of H_2O yield $(n + 1)$ moles of hydrogen towards which katharometers show maximum sensitivity when operated in nitrogen. All in all, this double technique could increase sensitivity about twenty times. An additional advantage of chemical conversion is that katharometrically recorded peaks generally diminish in height along a chromatogram, an effect which is very largely redressed by the convertor, since increased molecular size and retention time generally go hand in hand. Thus, they are very useful, especially when trace analysis for peaks appearing late is attempted. Their deficiencies lie in the need for complete reproducibility of reaction in the convertor, the reaction time lag and the large volume they introduce, which may apparently affect the performance of the chromatographic unit. Even so, they are sufficiently successful as to be standard items in a number of commercial gas chromatographs.

DETECTORS OF HIGH SENSITIVITY

THE THERMAL IONISATION DETECTOR

The concentration of ions in a clean hydrogen/oxygen flame is so extremely low that, in comparison, the concentration when carbon compounds are added is very considerable and the electrical resistance of the flame changes by many orders of magnitude. The process is reputedly not simply one of ionisation of the organic fuel since it is suggested that the ion concentrations are far too high to be compatible with the known ionisation potentials. According to Stern (68) there is stripping of the molecular skeleton until the flame contains particular aggregates of carbon of about 10^{-6} cm. diameter, each singly positively charged. The work function of carbon is low enough (ca. 4.7 e.v.) to account for the high ion concentrations observed. A second charge would be unlikely since the removal of the first electron would raise the work function to about 6 e.v. The recent work of Sugden and his collaborators (111), however, casts doubt on this view. Using a mass spectrometer, they showed that the total ion yield in a hydrogen/oxygen/hydrocarbon flame could be completely accounted for by ionised, hydrogen deficient polymers of the fuel. With acetylene, for example, polymeric ions as high as C_{20} were found. The ions formed represented about 1 p.p.m. of the fuel burnt and the extent of ionisation was linearly related to fuel concentration if the latter did not exceed 1 per cent of the total flame gas.

The temperature and emissivity modifications of the flame detector suffer from the fact that they measure small differences in large quantities. Even so, they are quite highly sensitive to the presence of organic vapours. McWilliam (69) and Harley and Pretorius (72) first explored the possibility of using the electrical properties of the hydrogen/oxygen flame as the basis of detection. Their work met with immediate success which was later substantiated and amplified by McWilliam and Dewar (70, 71). Not the least remarkable feature of the detector is its simplicity of design and construction. The original arrangement differed little from that of Scott (p. 273) utilising a brass electrode in place of the thermocouple, the jet itself acting as the other electrode. The electrodes were connected in series with a 10^5-ohm resistor and a 300-v. d.c. supply; the current developed across the resistor was fed to a suitable 10 mv recorder. McWilliam and Dewar (71) used nitrogen as the column carrier and mixed in an equal flow of hydrogen between the column and the burner. They showed that, in these circumstances, the detector response in terms of area was linear with concentration over the sample size range, 0.2 to 2 mg. of diethylether, hexane, ethanol and methanol. The steady background current was about 0.3 mv, that is, 3 per cent of the recorder scale, with noise equivalent to about 10 μv. This very elementary design was roughly ten times as sensitive as a good katharometer and had a noise level within the limits discussed on p. 322. With a more refined and more sensitive dual jet arrangement designed to eliminate background, but not, of course, any noise, even better results were claimed. Thus, with background of 70 μv., drift was less than 0.2 mv./hr. and it was possible to obtain a signal of 9 mv. for 10^{-10} g. of diethylether distributed as a peak in 20 ml. of carrier gas.

Preliminary experiments indicated that not only was response a linear function of sample size, but also of carbon content for related compounds, although the absolute response was somewhat variable from class to class (73). In later work (74), McWilliam replaced the series resistor by one of 10^{10} ohms and included an impedance convertor device. With this arrangement, quite remarkable sensitivities were observed. For example, 10^{-12} g. of benzene gave distinct and measurable peaks on a chromatogram while a wide boiling petroleum ether sample of 10^{-11} g. was adequate to show all the component peaks. The stability of the instrument in these conditions was described as equivalent to the presence of 1 part of benzene in 10^{12} of carrier. Results of this sort were sufficient to catalyse the interest of many people and there have since been several detailed studies of the performance of this detector, the most comprehensive being that of Onkiehong (75, 76), which has been complemented by the work of Condon, Scholly and Averill (77).

Circuitry. Onkiehong has studied numerous possible circuits and concludes that the best arrangements are as shown diagrammatically in Figure 9, *a* and *b*. Happily these are the simplest. The double flame arrangement is not now considered worthwhile; the author, for example, has found that it is of little benefit, a view also held by Condon et al. and by Onkiehong. For practical chromatography, therefore, a single jet system is all that is

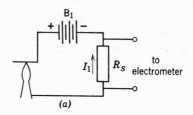

(a)

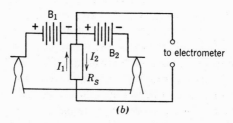

(b)

FIG. 9. Basic circuits for use with the flame ionisation detector; (*a*) single flame system, (*b*) double flame system. *By courtesy of Butterworths.*

required. The series resistor R_p should not be greater than about 10^{10} ohms, because then it becomes comparable in magnitude with the flame itself (estimated at $\gtrsim 10^{12}$ ohms) and the voltage across R_p is no longer a linear measure of circuit current. In addition, higher resistors tend to instability and leakage and also, in combination with the cable capacitance, cause the time constant of the assembly to increase to an undesirable level. Thus, the worthwhile range of R_p values is $10^5 - 10^{10}$ ohms with $10^7 - 10^{10}$ ohms as a reasonable group for a single instrument. This gives a sensitivity range of 1000 : 1 which is more than adequate for most purposes. Recorders are now available with input impedances as high as 10^8 ohms but the input impedance of most millivolt recorders is only about 1000 ohms or less. With these, therefore, an impedance convertor circuit is always required. This is not a serious problem; Onkiehong and many others use a vibrating reed type electrometer while chopper amplifiers have also been used.

A very useful circuit, designed specifically for use with high impedance detectors, has been described by Thompson (78) and a similar but slightly simpler and more stable arrangement used in the author's laboratory is shown in Figure 10. This circuit can be readily constructed, and if R_p is no greater than 10^8 ohms it is not even necessary to match the electrometer valves. In the circuit described by Condon et al., the effect of cable capacitance on the detector time constant is effectively eliminated. This has some advantage if the detector is operated at maximum sensitivity. Onkie-hong (76) has pointed out that it would be best if the electrometer is operated with the low terminal earthed. Since one detector terminal is earthed this means that a junction of detector and resistor is also, and so the d.c. supply floats on high impedance. This condition is difficult to achieve with mains supplied d.c. sources and so he uses a guarded hearing aid battery in a Teflon box. This is a very convenient system and the current drain is so small that the battery life is effectively its shelf life.

Applied Voltage and Electrode Spacing. The effect of applied voltage on the sensitivity has been studied by Onkiehong (75, 76). Below a certain voltage the flame is more or less ohmic in behaviour, the precise voltage depending somewhat on the electrode separation. Above this voltage the detector output is independent of applied voltage. With a constant sample of about 5 p.p.m. of n-butane in nitrogen, Onkiehong found that the critical voltage for his detector was about 30 v. for electrode spacings between 1 and 2 cm. although the detailed sensitivity/voltage curves below the critical value were dependent upon spacing. With a butane feed of 0.1 per cent the data were very different, the limiting voltage for a 1-cm. electrode spacing being 40 v., but 180 v. for a 2-cm. separation. For operation over this concentration range, therefore, a 200-v. supply would ensure that no matter what the spacing the detector would always operate in saturation conditions. Undoubtedly, lower voltages could be used satisfactorily, but since Onkie-hong's data refer to a particular flow rate and gas mixture there seems little point in working nearer the limit. All workers seem agreed that 200 v. represents a saturation condition even though their detector design and operating conditions may have varied quite widely.

It appears that the electrode spacing should be as small as is consistent with stability. In practice it is found that as the electrode spacing is reduced there is a point when very considerable noise appears. The distance is undoubtedly related to the height of the flame reaction zone and hence the jet size and gas flow. Condon et al. have found that by use of a very heavy walled jet, noise is significantly reduced, possibly because the metal acts as a heat sink and reduces the flame temperature. This is consistent with calculations (76) which predict that this should be the case and also with the improvement observed when nitrogen dilutes the flame, since there is no

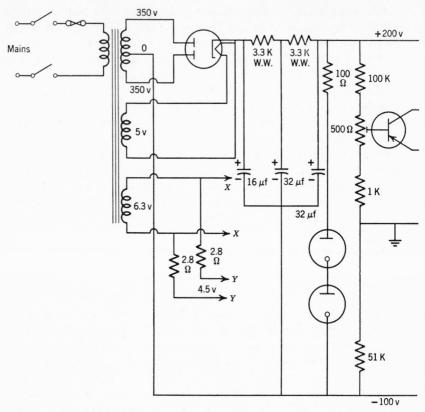

FIG. 10. Inexpensive impedance convertor circuit suitable for use with high impedance devices such as the flame ionisation detector.

doubt that diluted flames are cooler and more noise free, although perhaps less responsive to composition change.

Fuel Gas Composition. It is possible to burn hydrogen alone down to about 5 ml. per min. of flow at a jet of about 0.01 in. I.D., and Condon et al. report that a 1 : 1, N_2/H_2 mixture, which they recommend for general use, can be burnt down to 8 ml. per min. and up to 150 ml. per min. without trouble. The upper value quoted seems low but may relate to a specific electrode spacing. Quinn and the author (80) have worked continuously on occasion with pure hydrogen flows approaching 500 ml. per min. in which conditions, however, an electrode spacing of about 5 cm. is needed for stability. Onkiehong suggests that a N_2/H_2 ratio of 2 is the best choice since this not only reduces noise by a factor of two but confers added sensitivity. Obviously, the N_2/H_2 ratio is not very critical provided the hydrogen is between 40 and 50 per cent of the total burnt gas.

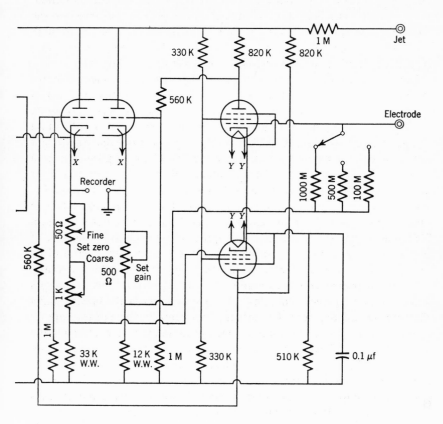

In common with other flame detectors the ionisation cell requires a forced air supply. Studies have shown that this should be at least ten times the hydrogen flow (76, 77), although excessive air flow induces flame instability. This point, however, can readily be determined experimentally. Another important reason for the need for a substantial air flow is to sweep water vapour out of the detector unit. If this process is inefficient not only does electrode insulation break down but water may actually collect at the bottom, and eventually, in the extreme case, extinguish the flame. To assist in the venting process it is worthwhile to have a small chimney over the flame although few workers use this. In the absence of a chimney it may be necessary to heat the upper part of the detector to eliminate condensation. The air supply is obviously a potential source of noise through the dust particles and vapours it may contain. Thus, it must be filtered through glass wool or sintered discs and, preferably, passed in addition through a copper oxide combustor at 800°C. and a column of silica gel or molecular sieve. This treatment is highly effective, even if the combustor is omitted. Occasionally, gases become contaminated by substances adsorbed on the walls of the equipment or in the column packing. Thus, a "conditioning" is usually necessary before stability is achieved. This simply means that a protracted cleaning gas flow should be used with new columns.

The possibility of using oxygen rather than air is of evident interest. McWilliam (74) has stated that this leads to great loss of sensitivity which he attributes to oxidation of ions. This result seems very surprising. Another interesting idea is to use air as column carrier and burn it in an atmosphere of hydrogen. Glueckauf (79) has pointed out that this might yield high column efficiency and reduce the gas mixing requirements and instrumentation somewhat. The possibility of using oxygen as carrier would seem to be precluded by McWilliam's statements. A final possibility which does not seem to have been studied is that of using a premixed flame which ought to be rather more stable than the diffusion type normally used.

Electrode Design and Location. The upper collector electrode may be of any metal but platinum would seem to be the best in consequence of its chemical inertness and high work function, the latter of which virtually eliminates thermal electron emission. The shape of the electrode appears to be of no consequence and loops, wires, gauze or plates all appear equally effective. Onkiehong considers that this is because electron or ion capture is complete in any circumstances, a view substantiated by the finding that a probe electrode above the collector gave no signal while, on the other hand, the collector give no signal when the probe was placed below it. Condon et al. are strongly of the opinion that the lateral placing of the electrode is important and that it should not in any circumstances enter the flame. It is difficult to know how to achieve this condition, since the extent of the flame is ill defined, but, in any event, it is probably only important at the very highest sensitivities. Evidence for this view is that even with a 10^9-ohm series resistor the author has experienced little trouble from this source when using a gauze electrode spread right through the flame.

McWilliam and Dewar (73) originally suggested that the upper electrode should be negative, but all subsequent workers have shown that it should be the anode, since this confers higher sensitivity and stability. Onkiehong explains this on the basis that loss of sensitivity is due to ion-electron re-combination. These, he postulates, are all formed very close to the burner tip and so, to minimise recombination, the slower moving particles should be attracted to the burner rather than have to traverse the whole flame. The large, slow moving positive ions should thus be made to move to the burner tip for maximum detector sensitivity. This explanation seems very reasonable and is consistent with the facts.

Sources of Background Current and Noise.   The main sources of noise in the flame system are:

1. Contamination of the gases at source.
2. Contaminants adsorbed inside the apparatus.
3. Inappropriate electrode location and spacing.
4. Solvent loss from the column.
5. The inherent ionisation of the clean flame.
6. Variations in flow rate of various gases.

The means to avoid trouble through (1) and (2) have been discussed, while (3) can be overcome in practice simply by adjustment. (4) and (5) contribute only to the background current and not to noise if there is a constant rate of solvent vaporisation, and so the most important problem is to maintain constancy of gas flow. This means that, at very high sensitivity, the best flow control valves are an essential, and, further, that they must be well thermostatted. According to Onkiehong, when flow variation is the only significant source of noise, the minimum detectable concentration (Δ) in parts per million of a sample mixed with hydrogen is approximately $20d$, where d is the mean flow fluctuation divided by the flow rate. Thus, we see that since even very coarse flow control will give $d = 0.01$, at worst the minimum detectable sample is about 0.2 p.p.m.   With very close flow control Onkiehong was able to detect 0.007 p.p.m. of n-butane in carrier gas, a figure little removed from that originally claimed by McWilliam.

The background current in a very stable and clean flame has been found to be 5 × 10^{-14} amp. (77), a value confirmed by Kieselbach (81) and which, in fact, approaches the Johnson noise level of the circuit resistors. Without adequate air filtration or when solvent bleeds from the column this value rises to about 10^{-12} amp.   In order to check on the extent to which circuiting contributes to the total noise the system can be operated without igniting the flame (both with and without flow). This is often a worthwhile precaution since inferior circuit components or condensation of atmospheric water vapour can be a serious problem.

Sensitivity and Response Regularities.   According to McWilliam a flame detector should be at least capable of responding to the presence of about 1 part of vapour per 5 × 10^8 of carrier, while giving a chromatographic peak recognisable above the noise. Onkiehong has more or less confirmed this value but points out (76) that since the detector response is proportional to the amount of material entering the flame per unit time the most reasonable way of expressing sensitivity is in terms of current/unit vapour flow rate, that is, in μa. sec. per mg. Condon et al. recommend this convention also. On this basis Onkiehong quotes as the maximum sensitivity he achieved for

n-butane the Figure 15 μa. sec. mg.$^{-1}$ which may be compared with Condon's value for propane of 30 μa. sec. mg.$^{-1}$ After allowance for the different carbon content and differences in design of the apparatus and its associated electronics this extent of agreement is obviously excellent.

The linearity of response with sample size which was shown to obtain at the milligram level (71) has now been proved (76, 77, 81) to extend over seven orders of magnitude, breaking down only at the point where the sample reaches about 0.5 to 1 per cent by volume of the total flame gas. This result is what would be expected on the basis of the work of Sugden described earlier. Linearity can be maintained to slightly higher concentrations by using the jet as the anode (74) and by using higher potentials in the flame circuit (77). However, neither of these expedients seems particularly worthwhile since it is only with gross samples eluted from inefficient columns that the linearity limit would be reached and, in any case, there would be so much sensitivity in hand that the column effluent could be split a hundredfold or more and then diluted. Thus, in effect, the detector is linear in response over its whole range of operation and calibration with fairly large and readily measurable samples can be extrapolated to zero with confidence. The range over which this detector is linear in response exceeds by several orders of magnitude that of any other detector known at this time.

Another desirable feature of the detector is that it shows a number of regularities in response towards related compounds. Onkiehong (75) made use of the so-called $\underline{C}$-factor to eliminate the need for calibration. This is defined by

$$\underline{C} = \frac{\text{molecular weight}}{12 \times \text{number of carbon atoms}}$$

in his investigations. This factor makes allowance for the fact that equal weights of organic substances do not contain equal weights of carbon, and effectively converts response per gram of sample to response per gram of carbon. Table 4 shows some analytical data for a mixture of n-alkanes.

TABLE 4

PEAK AREAS OF n-ALKANES (75)

	Known Composition % by Weight	Peak Area as % of Total for All Peaks
C_{12}	8.8	8.8
C_{13}	20.8	20.6
C_{14}	30.0	30.1
C_{15}	40.4	40.5

TABLE 5

**C-FACTOR CORRECTION OF PEAK AREAS OF ALKANES
AND AROMATICS.**

	Known Composition % by Weight	Recorder Peak Area % of Total	C	Corrected Area/C Atom
n-Hexane	10	8.8	1.19	9.5
Benzene	20	20.3	1.08	20.0
n-Heptane	10	9.0	1.19	9.7
Toluene	60	61.7	1.09	60.8

Since the C-factor is virtually the same for all, the peak areas should be in proportion to the individual weights if it is the case that the origin of the carbon atoms is immaterial.

The agreement is obviously excellent and establishes that up to C_{15}, at least, response is a linear function of carbon content for the alkanes. The successful use of the C-factor response correction is shown in Table 5.

When solutes contain oxygen the C-factor correction is less satisfactory but, it is suggested, a good approximation is to split off as many CO_2 groups as possible from the parent molecule and to use only the residual carbons for calculation purposes. Table 6 illustrates some corrections carried out in this way with some success.

On introducing chlorine into the molecule, however, the C-factor method is rather less successful, as seen from Table 7.

That the CO_2 splitting approximation may not be generally applicable and that structural differences are important appears to be shown by the

TABLE 6

C-FACTOR CORRECTIONS FOR MIXED SOLUTE TYPES (75)

	Known Composition % by Weight	Recorded Peak Area % of Total	C	Corrected Areas
n-C_{16} alkane	10.1	13.3	1.18	10.0
α-Methylnaphthalene	29.9	43.2	1.08	29.8
Dimethylterephthalate	60.0	43.6	2.15	60.2
n-Nonane	9.4	18.1	1.18	8.2
Ethanol	90.6	81.9	3.07	91.8
Benzene	48.6	55.8	1.08	50.0
Diethylether	20.1	14.1	1.71	19.9
n-Butane	31.3	30.1	1.21	30.1

TABLE 7

C-FACTOR CORRECTIONS FOR MIXTURES CONTAINING
HALOGENATED COMPOUNDS (75)

	Actual Composition % by Weight	Recorded Peak Area % of Total	C	Corrected Areas
CH_3Cl	37.9	21.1	4.2	37.2
$n-C_4H_{10}$	30.6	74.2	1.2	37.7
CCl_4	31.5	4.7	12.8	25.2

data presented by Condon et al. Table 8 lists some of their data for the relative response of a number of oxygenated compounds, all containing four carbon atoms.

The variation in response with alcohol structure is small but appears real, and is in accord with what might be expected from combustion studies. Much greater divergence is seen in the lower group of compounds, although some improvement is effected by making allowance for differences in oxygen content. In the original paper, a C-factor correction was applied to the molar response, but this is incorrect since the factor is itself a means to convert weight to molar response or vice versa. Even though the divergences listed appear considerable they are not really very significant when the range of chemical types detected is considered. They may not, in fact, be as great as is suggested since it is seen from Table 6 that Onkiehong did not find any significant difference in response per carbon atom. Evidently further studies of the type discussed here would be very worthwhile in order to clarify matters and to help reduce the amount of detector

TABLE 8

MOLAR RESPONSE OF SOME C_4 OXYGENATED COMPOUNDS;
RESPONSE OF n-BUTANOL = 1 (77)

	Molar Response	Corrected by CO_2 Split-Off Method
n-Butanol	1.00	1.00
Isobutanol	0.98	0.98
sec-Butanol	0.95	0.95
tert-Butanol	1.09	1.09
Ethyl acetate	0.78	0.91
Diethyl ether	0.84	0.84
1,4-Dioxan	0.62	0.72
n-Butyraldehyde	0.85	0.85

calibration necessary. However, at the present time it would seem safest to carry out individual calibration experiments for most substances. **Conclusions.** From what has been said it is clear that the actual design features of the flame unit are of little significance, and dimensions and tolerances can vary between wide limits without significantly affecting performance. A simple design used in the author's laboratory is illustrated in

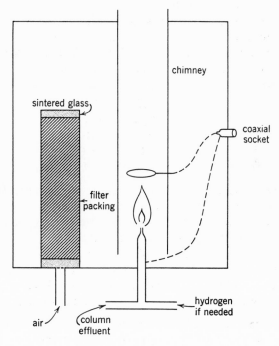

FIG. 11. Illustration of the basic construction details of a flame ionisation detector. The design shown is the simplest but works very satisfactorily.

Figure 11, and operates with complete satisfaction. The containing box is about 3 × 3 × 2 in. and, on occasion, a small heater winding or spark coil is built in for ignition of the flame. Many design modifications can be envisaged, and considerable miniaturisation is possible. The main bulk determining feature is the size of the air filter. If this were taken outside the flame assembly there is no reason why the latter could not be reduced to a volume of 10 ml. or less.

The considerable advantages of the detector are worth listing. (*a*) It is extraordinarily sensitive and stable. (*b*) It is linear in response over a vast concentration range. (*c*) Heating to prevent vapour condensation and hence thermostatting, is not required. (*d*) The effective volume of only a few microlitres and the rapidity of combustion mean that it is very much faster in response than any other detector, or its associated equipment. (*e*) Construction is simple and the necessary electronic equipment is not complicated or expensive. (*f*) Its high sensitivity permits the use of recording milliameters or voltmeters of low cost. (*g*) The detector background current is only very slightly sensitive to burner gas composition and flow rate, as also is its sensitivity.

The disadvantage which must be emphasised lies in the utter lack of response towards many substances, all, so far as is known, however, inorganic. Condon et al. have given a list of substances which evoke little or no response. These are tabulated below, since their identification here may be of value.

All rare gases	$SiCl_4$	SO_2	NO	CO_2
H_2	CH_3SiCl_3	CS_2	NO_2	
O_2	SiF_4	NH_3	N_2O	
N_2	H_2S	H_2O	CO	

This list is short in comparison with the whole range of organic compounds but often, of course, some of these compounds occur admixed with organic substances. In this situation there is no reason why a double detector system could not be used, a katharometer, for example, run in series with a flame would probably suffice for most purposes. An alternative possibility is to use a hotter flame in order to procure ionisation of inorganic substances. Cyanogen flames are extremely hot, and it might possibly be worthwhile to study their possibilities in this direction.

LOW PRESSURE GLOW DISCHARGE

The possibilities of a simple gas discharge system as a chromatographic detection device were first investigated by Harley and Pretorius (82). The properties of a discharge are determined to a large extent by the nature of the gas present, and since the discharge running or striking voltages involved are large, high sensitivities to impurity might be expected. Harley and Pretorius used a diode as one arm of a Wheatstone bridge operated with 900 v. d.c. With this very simple system they were able to detect the presence of only 10^{-12} moles of hydrocarbon in nitrogen. The results were so striking that Pitkethly (83) carried out a very comprehensive study of the characteristics of this detector. He first studied various electrode configurations and materials and found that a relatively small spacing, a large cathode area and a cathode of material of low work function all contributed to enhanced stability and sensitivity. The necessary conditions are, in fact, well met by commercial neon indicator lamps designed to run at 260 v. The best for use should have iron electrodes and they require only to be modified by puncturing the glass capsule and attaching glass inlet and outlet tubes.

Cells of this type were found to be virtually current and pressure independent in the ranges of 1 to 1.5 ma. and 3 to 5 mm. Hg when operated at 200 to 300 v. in a bridge system containing paired cells. In this, the most favoured arrangement, the running voltage changes were fed through an electrometer amplifier to a recorder. The response of the detector, operated in the above conditions, was found to be linear with concentration of hydrocarbons in nitrogen for gas samples between 10^{-7} ml. to 10^{-3} ml. originally injected into a column. Experiments outside these limits were not carried out but it is likely that the linearity might be maintained over a much wider range. Some idea of the sensitivity attained in Pitkethly's arrangement can be gained from the fact that 10^{-3} ml. of propane eluted from a column gave a peak height corresponding to 40 v. The detector is thus as sensitive as any other known.

Apart from the work described here the detector's potentialities do not seem to have excited interest. This may be because the need to pump and maintain, even roughly, some low pressure is not an attractive proposition. In addition, it seems to be widely assumed that trouble is experienced through adsorption or decomposition on the electrodes, although Pitkethly states that this is not the case provided the electrodes are not at all oxidised. Whatever the explanation, the glow discharge has not been widely adopted but it should be borne in mind that it has one great advantage, which has apparently been entirely overlooked, that it responds to everything and not just to carbonaceous matter. It may be that in the chromatography of inorganic materials, in particular, this detector may eventually find use.

RADIO-FREQUENCY DISCHARGE

It was pointed out by Pitkethly (83) that a glow discharge detector might be constructed in which the discharge was excited at microwave or radio-frequencies. These methods are widely used in the production of atomic or excited species for kinetic studies and have the attractive feature of functioning at relatively high gas pressures; radio-frequency discharges can be maintained even at atmospheric pressure. Further, it is possible to work with the exciting electrode outside the vessel containing the gas. These two features might go far in overcoming some of the objections to the Pitkethly type detector.

Karmen and Bowman (86, 87, 88) constructed a R.F. detector which appears to have been very successful. Their design employed a filament electrode, 0.02 in. in diameter and about 1 in. long, mounted along the axis of a metal cylinder 0.15 in. in diameter. R.F. power derived from a crystal oscillator and power amplifier supplied with a regulated high voltage, was conducted to the central wire via a coaxial cable followed by a step-up R.F. transformer. The latter required a matching network. Stainless steel, tungsten or platinum wires were found to function equally well and brass or stainless steel cylinders were used with equal effect. The central wire was connected to the cylinder wall by a 500-ohm resistor, the voltage drop across which was fed directly, without amplification, to a conventional millivolt recorder.

When operated with helium as carrier gas the discharge was self starting at low R.F. voltages and appeared to be uniformly around and close to the central wire. Increased voltage caused the discharge to expand and eventually to become erratic. For analytical work, therefore, some voltage in the uniform discharge region was used. The power which can be supplied without arc-ing was found to increase with frequency and Bowman and Karmen (88) recommended the use of 27 mc. per s. Addition of impurity to the helium caused a reduction in the glow diameter, and the R.F. voltage. The glow, although itself induced by an a.c. field, results in a d.c. gradient across the field and it is this which was used as the detection signal. The measurement of the d.c. current, of course, requires filtering of the R.F. currents. The electrical conditions used by Bowman and Karman (88) were that the central wire was -60 v. with respect to the cylinder, which gave about 100 ma. of d.c. with internal resistance of about 1 megohm. The latter was found to increase very markedly at cylinder diameters over 0.25 in. Since organic vapours cause a drop in the d.c. current the signals were made positive by biasing the standing current with a dry cell and recording the unbalance current of this when vapours enter the discharge.

Increased gas flow and pressure led to reduction of the d.c. current which was, however, increased considerably by elevation of the cell temperature. However, the more significant effect of increased temperature on the rate of removal of solvent from the chromatographic column actually caused the R.F. voltage to decrease with raising of over-all temperature. To avoid this effect detector and column were thermostatted separately. It seems probable that a double cell system, operating from a pair of identical columns, would be beneficial. This presents little difficulty besides being common to many detectors.

The detector can be operated quite well with neon as carrier, but less so with argon. It seems certainly to be the case, however, that it functions best with helium, a situation which may to some extent limit its utility. The sensitivity in helium is reputedly linear over a wide range of vapour concentration and as little as 10^{-13} moles of injected sample can be detected, it is claimed (88). This puts the detector close to the first rank, in so far as sensitivity is concerned. Direct comparison of chromatograms obtained with this instrument and a katharometer yielded very close agreement on quantitative analysis with an approximate sensitivity ratio of 250 in favour of the discharge.

No doubt, this detector has considerable possibilities and as pointed out (88) may well be capable of improvement. One drawback which is evident is that associated with the very considerable ancillary equipment requirements which seem to be greater than those of any other detector, and this, to some extent, offsets the advantage gained by working at high pressures. Even so, a commercial chromatograph incorporating the device is now available, and it is possible that the detector may eventually find widespread use.

THE IONISATION GAUGE

Ionisation gauges have long been used for pressure measurement and are widely available commercially. Basically, they are triode systems comprising filament, grid and plate. The potential difference between filament and grid accelerates electrons which may ionise any gas in their path. Helium has the highest ionisation potential known (24.5 e.v.) and so, if the grid potential is maintained just below this value, helium is not ionised. Thus, no current flows in the plate circuit. If, however, the helium contains any contaminant whatever, this will be ionised and the positive ions then travel to the plate, the current recorded being a measure of the ion concentration.

Ryce and Bryce (84) first realised the possibility of using an ionisation gauge in gas chromatography, modifying a commercial gauge in such a way that it was fed with column effluent through a controlled leak and maintained at constant low pressure by a manostat. They found that over the range 0.02 to 1.5 mm. the sensitivity of the device as a chromatographic detector was more or less proportional to the pressure, but that at fixed pressure it was virtually entirely insensitive to flow variation. They chose, for convenience, to work always with the detector pressure controlled at 0.7 mm. Hg. The grid current giving maximum sensitivity in these conditions was found to be 18 v. and not 24 v. as might have been expected. Ryce and Bryce explained this as being due to the fact that electrons emitted from the filament have a Maxwellian velocity distribution, and so above 18 v. applied potential, some electrons are energetic enough to start ionising helium. The background current derived from the ions then reduced the sensitivity towards contaminants. However, this explanation has been challenged by Hinkle, Tucker, Wall and Combs (112) who pointed out that, in the gauge used by Ryce and Bryce, the a.c. filament heater current had a peak potential of about 7 v., which when added to the experimental value of the grid potential would explain the apparent anomaly. However, this cannot entirely explain the situation since even with the more stable d.c. filament heating they found a spread of 1.55 e.v. in the energy of emitted

electrons. By use of a suitable collimating device they reduced this to
0.4 e.v. and so were able to work with a grid voltage of 23.5 v. This is
adequate to ensure ionisation of all but helium and so the detector responds
to all contaminants and gives maximum response if other important parameters are properly adjusted. Both groups of workers are agreed that the
grid voltage is the most important sensitivity and stability determining
factor, and stabilisation to 0.01 per cent is considered essential (112). Plate
voltage should be about −15 v. according to Ryce and Bryce, since above
this secondary emission and other processes occur.

The sensitivity claimed originally (84) was between 30 and 100 times that
of a katharometer, but Hinkle et al., operating at 0.002 mm. Hg detector
pressure and incorporating the improvements mentioned earlier, have
attained sensitivities up to 200 times greater. This puts the ionisation gauge
on a par with the best detectors. However, one very important requirement
for the attainment of these sensitivities is the use of pure helium. Ryce and
Bryce were required to employ a charcoal trap at −50°C. to remove O_2, N_2
and water, while Hinkle et al. showed that these impurities were, in fact,
responsible for only 80 per cent of the observed noise, the remaining noise
coming, unlikely as it seems, from back diffusion of pump vapours. Thus,
a purifying trap seems to be needed at both ends of the gas flow line. It
seems possible, in the light of these findings, that the lack of an outlet trap
may have contributed significantly to the rather high noise level observed
in Pitkethly's studies of the glow discharge.

The response to concentration change has been shown to be linear over
the range 1 p.p.m. to 10^4 p.p.m. of hydrocarbon vapour in helium, and, no
doubt, extends even farther. Hinkle et al., in fact, believe that it may be
possible to arrange operating conditions such that linearity could be
achieved over the range 0 to 95 moles per cent of vapour in carrier gas.
However, one practical drawback to the use of this detector is that metal
filaments are very prone to oxidation and other reactions, and hence to
variable emission and sensitivity. Tungsten is particularly bad in this
connexion but the problem can, to some extent at least, be eliminated by
use of rhenium (112) or tantalum (85).

There is no doubt that this detector has a number of very attractive
features, but again, like the glow discharge, demands a pumping system;
in this case with very close pressure control. When these requirements are
compared with those of the flame ionisation detector, for instance, they
may appear excessive. A further point which is of importance in many
areas is the fact that the detector is clearly best suited for use with helium as
the chromatographic carrier gas. Doubtless, it could be operated with
hydrogen, nitrogen, argon or neon, but in so doing much of its attraction
would be lost.

RADIOLOGICAL DETECTOR

The earliest radiological detector used in gas chromatography was the cross section of capture β-ray instrument described by Deal, Otvos, Smith and Zucco (89) and Boer (90). Its basis of operation lies in the fact that if a β-ray source ionises surrounding gas, the ions formed carry current under the influence of a potential gradient. The current increases to a saturation value with increasing applied potential, at which point all the ions and electrons reach the electrodes before recombining. The applied potential/ saturation current relationship for a pure gas is, therefore, a complex function of electrode spacing, gas pressure and temperature. Thus, dimensions and conditions must be critically related to the energy of the emitted electrons if only a small part of the latter is to be dissipated in the gas. The latter condition is necessary if the current is to be linearly connected with the gas concentration. Presuming this to be so, then expressing the gas concentration c in molecules per ml., this and the molecular cross section of capture Q are related to the current by

$$i = kc\text{Q}$$

For a gas mixture of j components

$$i = \frac{kP}{RT}\sum_j x_j \text{Q}_j$$

where P and T are total pressure and absolute temperature, respectively, and x represents mole fraction. An alternative approach is that the net saturation current of a gas mixture $i_n{}^s$ is the sum of the individual contributions of the component gases, thus,

$$i_n{}^s = \sum (x_1 i_1{}^s + x_2 i_2{}^s)$$

and, for a two component mixture,

$$\Delta i^s = i_1{}^s - i_n{}^s = x_2(i_1{}^s - i_2{}^s) \tag{12.6}$$

where Δi^s is the saturation current change corresponding to the presence of the mole fraction x_2 of impurity in the carrier gas of saturation current $i_1{}^s$. Δi^s should be a linear function of mixture composition and should be greatest when the cross sections of capture for carrier and contaminant differ as much as possible.

A device of this sort is not restricted to use with β-rays; α or γ radiation could also be employed. The latter, however, have a low ionisation efficiency and also introduce serious shielding problems. An α-ray detector has been described recently by Graven (91), the source being aged Ra-D. The performance of this detector, however, does not appear to be very impressive, for example, 10 moles per cent of oxygen in helium gave a signal of only 4 mv. There seems little doubt that β-emitters represent a better radiation source, probably in consequence of the greater penetrating power of the electron.

The cell design for a detector utilising the above principles is relatively simple. An 0.5-in. hole drilled through a metal block contains a needle or button source of radioactive material and a central metal electrode; inlet and outlet gas ports are provided and the block acts as the second electrode (90). The standing current can be biased off electrically (89) or, perhaps better, balanced in a double cell system (90). To reduce radiation hazards the block can be sheathed in lead but even then low energy X-rays may be emitted. The radio source originally used was ^{90}Sr but others are now available which give greater radiation intensity. In the double cell arrangement (90) the opposed ionisation currents passed through a common high resistance ($\sim 10^{10}$ ohms) and any voltage developed was fed to a recorder through an impedance convertor of the vibrating reed type, although a d.c. electrometer amplifier can be used (89).

The detector has been found to be virtually completely flow insensitive but has to be manostatted and thermostatted reasonably closely. For example, operated in nitrogen at 50°C. at about atmospheric pressure the base line shift per mm. Hg change of pressure was about 0.5 mv. (89) while the sensitivity to heptane fell to almost half on increasing the cell temperature from 50° to 100°C. The response, however, under controlled conditions, was linear over a fairly wide range of composition (0 to 2 moles per cent) and according to Boer (90) the highest sensitivity attainable is comparable to that of a very good katharometer. Further, this sensitivity is much the same whether nitrogen or hydrogen is the carrier gas, in contrast to the performance of many other detectors. The dependence of sensitivity upon pressure and temperature is much the same for all gases and so relative calibrations in terms of concentration are more or less independent of all variables. In some systems it is possible to predict such relative calibrations from literature data for Q, while for hydrocarbons these can be calculated on the basis that Q per carbon atom $= 4.16$ while Q per hydrogen atom $= 1.00$. Verification of this is due to Boer, who, knowing Q for nitrogen and hydrogen, computed Q for a number of hydrocarbons and then used a correction factor

$$\underline{C}' = \frac{Q_2 - Q_1}{(\text{molecular weight})_2}$$

(cf. p. 302) to convert peak areas on a chromatogram to weight percentage. All peak areas were multiplied by $\underline{C}'$, the products added and each product evaluated as a percentage of the sum. The results calculated by this means were in excellent agreement with the known composition by weight of a number of mixtures. It is not known whether such a priori calculations can be extended to other classes of compounds.

Despite the many attractive features of the detector it has been little used, possibly because it was not significantly better in performance than the katharometer, but also because of the emergence of the argon modification described in the following pages. With a more intense source its sensitivity could undoubtedly be improved, but this is probably not worth the effort of development.

ARGON β-RAY IONISATION

The absorption of radiation by gases may not only produce ionisation, but also atoms or molecules excited to one or other of their resonance levels. The lifetime of such metastable atoms or molecules is normally so short that they rapidly return to the ground state with emission of light. Some metastable states, however, are sufficiently long lived that they may make many collisions before radiating and if the other molecule involved in collision has a suitable energy level there may be a return to the ground state through a transfer of energy which raises the second molecule to a resonance level or, if the energy is great enough, to ionise it. A familiar example of this process is photosensitisation by mercury but the low energy involved (ca. 5 e.v.) is about 4 e.v. below the ionisation potential of most organic molecules, so that ionisation rarely occurs. The rare gases, on the other hand, have first excited states in excess of 9 e.v. and so should be able to ionise most organic molecules; metastable helium, in fact, at ∼24 e.v. is capable of ionising anything it collides with.

In the cross section of capture detector previously described, the total ionisation produced depended both upon the cross section of the electron and its residence time in the system. The latter is of course extremely short. One method of increasing the sensitivity of the device, therefore, would be somehow to increase the length of time spent by the electrons in the ionisation chamber without significant loss of energy. Lovelock (92) achieved this by use of argon as the carrier gas. The extent of primary electron capture by argon molecules is little different to that by other gases, but many of the argon atoms are elevated to the first resonance level (ca. 11.7 e.v.) which is long lived, and so, in effect, since these atoms are neutral and unaffected by the prevailing potential gradient, the electron transit time is greatly extended. In fact, it appears that argon ions may also be formed. Subsequent collision of foreign molecules with excited argon can lead to energy transfer, and all those substances of ionisation potential below 11.7 e.v. should ionise. Substances of even higher ionisation potential would be ionised if more energetic states or ions of argon were present. Even more effective ionisation of impurities should occur in helium because of its higher energy, but, due possibly to the presence of traces of argon and neon in commercial helium, excited helium atoms cannot readily be made in quantity since they are probably converted to excited argon. Since helium is the main rare gas impurity in argon, it should not degrade the latter, in consequence of its higher resonance and ionisation energies.

The Simple Detector. The original detector cell designed by Lovelock (92) differed little from those described earlier (89, 90). The cell itself, briefly illustrated in Figure 12a, was a brass cylinder of about one inch length and diameter and was contained within and insulated from a brass container.

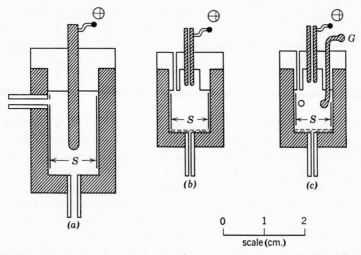

FIG. 12. Basic construction of argon type β-ray detectors; (a) simple, (b) miniature and (c) triode miniature. *By courtesy of Butterworths.*

A 10 mc. source of ^{90}Sr in silver foil covered the inner cylinder wall, and a central brass electrode, which must be 2 mm. in diameter, was mounted in Teflon insulation and fitted through one end. For use above 200°C. ceramic insulation was necessary. It was found to be essential that the electrode tip was rounded and smoothed. Gas flow ports were provided, one through the central electrode or nearby through the side wall, and one at the other end of the cell. The cell itself acted as the second, earthed electrode.

The radioactive source must provide an ionisation current of between 10^{-9} and 10^{-8} amp. since smaller currents demand expensive amplification. With much higher currents trouble has been experienced through space charge effects. The d.c. ionisation current was conveyed to a recorder through a current amplifier. With pure argon in the ionisation cell the ionisation current was virtually constant over the range 300 to 1000 v., but at higher voltages it increased rapidly. Lovelock attributed this to the onset of large scale ionisation of the argon. At any given voltage above about 300, the introduction of organic molecules into the argon is accompanied by a large increase in the ionisation current. This results from the combined sequence of reactions

$$A + e = A^* + e$$
$$A^* + (Org.) = A + e + (Org.)^+$$

It is seen that each original electron is regenerated in a form of chain reaction, and hence, in effect, the concentration of metastable argon is unaffected by the degradative collisions. According to the theory advanced by Lovelock (92, 93, 94) the current in the presence of added organic molecules is related to their concentration c', the primary electron concentration n_e, the initial metastable atom concentration n_a, and the applied voltage V by

$$i = \frac{Ac'(n_e + n_a) + Bn_e}{A \exp\{1 - a \exp[b(V - 1)]\} + B}$$

where a, A, b and B are constants. According to this there should be an infinite current flow at some finite value of c' and, in practice, some means of limiting this rise in i may be needed. This is usually achieved by use of a linearising external resistance placed in series with the detector cell. Condon et al. (77) have shown that no single valued resistor gives a linear response over more than a restricted concentration range, and further, that the resistor makes a serious contribution to the time constant of the system. Lovelock (94) suggests as an alternative that appropriate cell design would induce an internal positive space charge which would have a linearising effect. At the highest voltages the sensitivity increases considerably due to the electron regeneration and, possibly, multiplication processes, but these equally introduce instability, and the practical limit appears to be about 1200 volts. In practice, the optimum voltage for maximum sensitivity is determined to some extent by cell geometry and source strength (77, 92).

The sensitivity of the simple detector towards different substances is large and varies relatively little if these have ionisation potentials below 11.7 e.v. but is very small and variable for those of higher ionisation potentials. This is brought out in Table 9 (92).

The fact that there is a finite sensitivity towards some substances of high ionisation potential indicates that all of the excited argon is not in the lowest resonance level, but that some may either be in some higher excited state or ionised. There is, of course, the added possibility that methane, for example, is ionised directly by electron impact but this seems less likely on the whole, especially when it is considered that the primary radio electron

TABLE 9

IONISATION POTENTIALS AND SENSITIVITY OF ARGON
β-RAY SYSTEM

Substance	Ionisation Potential e.v.	Relative Molar Sensitivity
Cyclohexane	9.2	1.00
Benzene	9.5	1.07
Ethyl acetate	10.0	0.64
n-Hexane	10.6	0.86
Ethanol	10.6	0.64
Methanol	10.9	0.64
Water	12.8	0.02
Methane	13.2	0.05
Oxygen	13.6	0
Carbon dioxide	14.4	0.01
Nitrogen	15.5	0

emission is unlikely to be monochromatic and is thus almost certain to cause excitation of argon to more than one resonance level.

The relative equivalence of the detector's sensitivity towards substances of low ionisation potential might be expected if the fate of the collisional energy in excess of that needed for ionisation is of little consequence, and if, as is suggested (94) the probability of ionisation on collision is unity for most organic molecules. In this situation the main sensitivity differences observed would be expected to arise from differences of collision frequency and hence of molecular weight. On the basis of kinetic theory Lovelock (92) calculates that the effect should be small, relative sensitivity diminishing with increasing molecular weight in approximate proportion to $M^{1/6}$. He has shown results very roughly in accord with this although contrary data were obtained for aromatics and alcohols. Condon et al. have quoted

TABLE 10

RELATIVE SENSITIVITY OF ARGON DETECTOR TO ALCOHOLS

	Relative Molar Response	Relative Weight Response
n-Propyl	1.0	1.0
n-Butyl	1.56	1.49
n-Pentyl	1.48	0.95
n-Hexyl	2.08	1.24
n-Butyl	1.00	—
Isobutyl	0.89	—
sec-Butyl	0.73	—
tert-Butyl	0.46	—

data for the sensitivity of a simple model for various alcohols which also conflict with the collision theory outlined above. Their results are listed in Table 10.

It is clear that, on a molar basis, sensitivity towards homologous alcohols increases but, strangely, molecules containing even numbers of carbon atoms give bigger signals than do those containing an odd number. On a weight basis, sensitivity falls off with increasing molecular weight, as is seen by comparing the values for C_3 and C_5 or of C_2 and C_4 alcohols. The most significant changes, however, are those depending upon molecular structure. n-Butyl alcohol is twice as readily detected as is $tert$-butyl alcohol. Evidently, there is much yet to be learned about the mode of operation of the detector.

The detector has been claimed to be virtually gas flow, pressure and temperature insensitive (77). If the argument just advanced to account for the relative sensitivity data is correct, this is surprising, since if collision frequencies are important sensitivity determining parameters, so too are pressure and temperature. Lovelock (94) on the other hand, has pointed out that in the simplest type of system the sensitivity is, in fact, sufficiently flow sensitive to suggest that solute molecules must enter the region containing excited argon atoms by diffusion. In this case the simple detector is concentration rather than amount sensitive. Large changes of temperature and pressure quite certainly alter the sensitivity (96), a result which has been attributed to their effect on the acceleration of the primary electrons. The findings, however, could be equally well if not better explained by the collision frequency argument, if this were not itself in some doubt.

The sensitivity claimed by Lovelock (92) corresponds to the detection of a sample 5×10^{-9} g. of hydrocarbon eluted from a column; this is roughly 10^{-11}–10^{-12} moles. More recently, Condon et al. have quoted a more precise value of 0.08 p.p.m. for the minimum detectable sample or, in another fashion, 260 μa. per ml. per mg. These figures indicate a sensitivity an order of magnitude less than is found for the flame ionisation detector (p. 301) by the same workers. They state also that the linearity range is about a factor of 1000 at best, and so is considerably smaller than for the flame detector, while at concentrations of about 0.1 per cent the detector becomes overloaded completely.

In common with the flame detector the argon system is insensitive or only feebly sensitive to a number of substances. Some of these are listed:

H_2 O_2 CO H_2O CH_4 CH_3CN

N_2 CO_2 $(CN)_2$ fluorocarbons C_2H_6 C_2H_5CN

On the other hand it does respond reasonably to some inorganic gases such as H_2S, NO, NO_2, NH_3, PH_3 and BF_3.

One very important point in connexion with this detector is that the presence of contaminants in the argon has a very considerable effect on the performance of the instrument. Lovelock (94) has recently shown that while up to 50 per cent of helium has no effect, the maximum permissible amounts of other likely impurities are 2000 p.p.m. of nitrogen or hydrogen; 800 p.p.m. of oxygen; 100 p.p.m. of carbon dioxide and 30 p.p.m. of water. These substances, if present in great amount, reduce the detector sensitivity enormously and may also make it non-linear and random. Commercial argon normally contains a total of about 10 p.p.m. of the gases quoted, other than water. The water content, however, may often be greater than the specified 30 p.p.m. and increases with room temperature and time of use of the cylinder. It is this which accounts for the numerous reports of day long and day to day variations in sensitivity. Thus, a very good drying agent must be incorporated in the pre-column flow stream. Another point is that rubber and plastic connexions cannot be used since, according to Lovelock (94), sufficient air can diffuse through from the atmosphere against the positive argon pressure, to upset the detector performance. Using the data quoted above, this implies that nitrogen can diffuse rapidly through to maintain a concentration of 0.2 per cent. This value seems very high indeed in the circumstances.

While it has been claimed (94) that aqueous samples can be analysed without serious difficulty, there is no doubt that peaks emerging from a column close to water cannot be used for quantitative analysis. In fact, it is often the case that there is a very protracted recovery time after analysis of aqueous samples. This is a serious drawback for many problems. Even in the analysis of non-aqueous samples it is evident that a good, gas tight injection system is required, and that hypodermic or ampoule methods are not to be recommended.

The Miniature Argon Detector.   The simple argon detector has a volume of 8 to 10 ml. and so is very slow in response and, therefore, best used at relatively high flow rates, say 60 ml. per min. To adapt the detector for use with capillary columns, which work at very low flow rates, Lovelock has developed a miniaturised detector (97). Figure 12*b* shows an outline of this design. Column effluent enters the detector chamber through the anode tip, the anode being withdrawn 2.5 mm. inside a small cavity drilled out of Teflon. A large scavenging flow of argon (ca. 50 ml. per min.) enters at the other end thus confining the column effluent to the anode chamber, since the combined flows leave through a port at the anode end of the cell. Electrons reach the anode along a very narrow path and since the electric field distribution resides close to the anode the region containing the metastable argon atoms is thus extremely small. The withdrawal of the anode has a further advantage in that it weakens the field at the cathode, and this helps develop a positive space charge at current densities greater than 10^{-8} amp. per ml. Thus, the need for a linearising external resistor is automatically overcome. The radiation source needs to be capable of giving a current of about 10^{-8} to 3×10^{-8} amp., that is, about ten times that for the simple detector, but it is found that sensitivities attainable with the miniature design are at least thirty times as high as with the simple model. Further, the signals obtained can be fed directly to any recorder of input impedance greater than 10^5 ohms.

This form of the detector is apparently less flow sensitive than the earlier

TABLE 11
ARGON DETECTOR CHARACTERISTICS

	Simple		Miniature	Triode Miniature
Gas flow, ml./min.	60	(84)	2	2
Applied potential, volts	1200	(1200)	1200	1200
Radiation source, mc.	RaD 0.07	(^{85}Kr) 10	Tritium 50	Tritium 50
Background current, amp.	7×10^{-9}	(5×10^{-9})	1×10^{-8}	3×10^{-10}
Noise, amp.	10^{-11}	(2×10^{-11})	10^{-12}	$< 10^{-13}$
Minimum detectable concentration, g./ml.	4×10^{-11}	—	10^{-12}	6×10^{-14}

type, and its response is not proportional to concentration, but to the mass of vapour entering the cell in unit time. This is presumed to be because the vapour enters the region of metastable atoms by direct mixing. A number of workers have used this design with considerable success.

The Triode Miniature Detector. A recent elaboration (94) of the miniature design is the addition of a centrally located, negatively charged ring electrode situated about 6 mm. from the anode tip. This is shown in Figure 12c. The ring electrode confines the primary electrons to a narrow beam and collects any positive ions. The latter effect separates the primary background from the signal and, since there is no primary current to offset, there is a very considerable reduction in the noise level and, correspondingly, greater sensitivity. It appears (94) that the residual noise can be reduced even farther by use of a fourth, positively charged electrode situated between the collector and either the chamber or the anode. Nothing, however, is known of the details of performance of this model.

Table 11 lists some data (94) for the three types of argon detector which indicate their capabilities. The data in parentheses, taken from Condon et al. (77), are in excellent agreement.

There is no doubt that the miniature detectors represent a very considerable advance on the simple model without introducing much more in the way of constructional or operational problems. Indeed, the most significant of the latter appears only to be the need to incorporate into the cell chamber a few layers of metal gauze to smooth the scavenger gas flow. Both miniature models can be used at high flow rates if the column effluent enters through the scavenger port and not the anode. Thus, when used with packed columns, for example, the detector is comparable in principle to the simple model except for the restriction around the anode. It seems, therefore, that the simple argon detector, now by far the most common, will, for all purposes, be superseded shortly by the miniature types.

DETECTOR SENSITIVITY

Quantitative description of detector performance requires first the formulation of some definition of sensitivity. This is less simple than it sounds, since, broadly speaking, differential detectors can belong either (a) to the class which, in principle at least, gives a response proportional to any change of concentration of material eluted in carrier gas, or (b) to the class which gives a response proportional to the rate of entry of material into the detector. In this context response can be taken to imply recorded peak height. Typical of the former class would be an ideal thermal conductivity cell while the flame ionisation and small or triode argon detectors fall into the second group. For a fixed sample size of material eluted from a column at different carrier flow rates the peak heights recorded by an ideal thermal conductivity cell would be independent of flow rate and the peak area would be inversely proportional to the flow. On the other hand, since a flame ionisation detector, for example, can only give a fixed amount of current per unit amount of material combusted, at varying flow rates with a fixed sample, it would give peaks of constant area and, hence, of height directly dependent on the flow.

The first attempt at a definition of sensitivity and the one which has been most widely employed is the sensitivity parameter S_f proposed by Dimbat, Porter and Stross (62) and which was designed for use with concentration sensitive detectors. It takes the form

$$S_f = \frac{O_p F}{W} \tag{12.7}$$

where O_p is the peak area in mv. min., F is the carrier gas flow rate in ml. min.$^{-1}$ and W is the eluted sample weight in mg. Thus, S_f has the units mv. ml. mg.$^{-1}$, that is mv. (mg. per ml.)$^{-1}$, and therefore represents a recorder response (peak height) per unit concentration of sample in the carrier gas at the detector. The concentration units, mg. ml.$^{-1}$ are not particularly useful although, for most eluted substances, any value quoted in this way would be within an order of magnitude of the corresponding number in the dimensionless quantity moles per mole, that is, parts sample per part of carrier, by volume. Young (113) has suggested that it would, in fact, be better to define detector sensitivity by

$$S_{fm} = \frac{O_p F}{m} \tag{12.8}$$

where m is the eluted sample weight in millimoles. The resulting concentration units, millimoles per ml., are somewhat more useful than those of 12.7, being a constant factor ($\sim$20) times the moles per mole ratio for all things if carrier flow, as is usual, were measured near to N.T.P.

Young's suggestion goes only half way and it would be logical to modify the expression for sensitivity even further to

$$S_m = \frac{O_m F_m}{m} = \frac{OF}{m_v} \tag{12.9}$$

where O_m is the peak area in mv. millimoles and F_m represents the carrier flow in millimoles. min.$^{-1}$ S_m would then be the mv. peak height observed for a given concentration of eluted material in moles per mole, that is, parts per part by volume of carrier. From the point of view of the calculation of S_m it would be simpler, as shown in the equation, merely to express O and F as before, and convert W to the gaseous volume m_v of the sample at the temperature and pressure at which F was measured. It is important to realise that the concentration involved is always that in the detector and not that in the original injected sample. The dilution effect in the column must always be taken into account when a value of S is used to compute the minimum amount of any component of a mixture which can be dealt with.

Onkiehong (76) has adapted equation 12.7 for use with detectors of the second class. He writes the equivalent of

$$S_q = \frac{O_a}{W} \tag{12.10}$$

and because this equation is usually only necessary for use with high sensitivity detectors, which are mostly of high impedance, he prefers to define O as the peak area in μa. sec. in order to make it independent of impedance. Thus S_q becomes the electrical response in milliCoulombs per

g. of eluted material. It would perhaps be more useful to use Young's approach and write

$$S_{qm} = \frac{O}{m} \qquad (12.11)$$

when S_{qm} would represent the peak area in milliCoulombs per mole of eluted substance. These units are attractive in that, for ionisation devices, $S_{qm}/96,500$ gives the effective ionisation efficiency of the processes occurring in the detector.

Whichever expression for S is used, it is quite clear that it represents no more than a general definition of sensitivity. This again has been pointed out by Young (113) who suggests that any quoted value of S should always refer to the situation that the relevant peak height is twice the basic noise of the system. Then any value of S represents a maximum which, although arbitrary, is based on an idea which is commonly accepted in other fields.

In continuation of the above idea, Young has proposed a new sensitivity parameter. Starting from the fact that

$$S = \frac{R}{Q}$$

where R represents the change in the electrically measured property resulting from the change Q in the gas property monitored, then, by the above definition,

$$S_{\max} = \frac{2R_n}{Q_0}$$

where R_n is the noise and Q_0 is the minimum detectable change in the value of the monitored property. Substitution for $S_{\max}$ from the earlier equations gives

$$Q_0{}^f = 2R_n \frac{m}{O_p F} \qquad (12.12)$$

$$Q_0{}^m = 2R_n \frac{m}{O_m F_m} \qquad (12.13)$$

and

$$Q_0{}^q = 2R_n \frac{m}{O_a} \qquad (12.14)$$

In the first case, $Q_0{}^f$ represents the minimum detectable concentration in millimoles per ml., while in the second, the concentration units are volume by volume. In the third equation, $Q_0{}^q$ is the minimum detectable rate of entry of material into the detector in millimoles per sec. This latter function is not easy to envisage in practical terms and Condon et al. (77) have suggested that $Q_0{}^f$ should be used even though, at first sight, it appears inappropriate.

Any form of Q function will yield a very small number and so Young, by analogy with pH, has proposed the use of the device

$$pQ = -\log Q$$

pQ will clearly be some number between about 3 and 20, increasing integral values representing improvement by an order of magnitude in actual detector performance. Such numbers are easy to remember in contrast to those obtained from the other sensitivity equations. If only for this reason, Young's method of representing sensitivity through Q and pQ is to be preferred to the S type of function, but, in addition, it is of greater value to know the minimum detectable amount of material than to know the area of a peak for a given amount of material.

TABLE 12

COMPARISON OF DETECTOR SENSITIVITIES

	S_m mv. ml. millimole^{-1}	R_n μv.	$pQ_0{}^f$	$pQ_0{}^m$
Hot wire katharometer	4×10^4	1	7.3	5.9
Thermistor katharometer	2.5×10^4	10	6.1	4.9
β-Ionisation	5.5×10^4	10	6.3	4.9
Ionisation gauge	2.5×10^6	20	7.8	6.3
Flame ionisation	7.5×10^{10}	70	11.7	10.3
Glow discharge	2×10^{10}	2×10^4	8.7	7.3

No matter what approach is used, however, comparison of the two broad classes of detectors is rendered difficult, since no one function describes the performance of both. In this connexion it seems pertinent to point out that, ultimately, the most important thing in practice is the height of the eluted peak and not its area. It is of no consequence if a peak has a large area if its height is too small for accurate measurement. Some general description of sensitivity in terms of peak height would, therefore, appear to represent the only possibility of finding a comprehensive definition of sensitivity. From this point of view, the approach adopted by Condon et al. in using $Q_0{}^f$ for the flame and argon detectors is very realistic.

Whatever system of describing sensitivity is finally adopted, it seems quite certain that there will be no number which will uniquely describe the capabilities of a given detector. Any value quoted must always refer to a specific eluted substance. Perhaps, for this reason, there would be little profit in attempting to find a unifying definition of sensitivity. Thus, the general use of S_f or S_m, or, better, $pQ_0{}^f$ or $pQ_0{}^m$ is probably the most practical course.

Table 12 lists values of S_m, R_n and pQ_0 calculated from literature data by

Young (113). Also included are $pQ_0{}^m$ values calculated by the author from the same data.

These data are not recent and higher values have since been reported. Further, as pointed out earlier, it is probable that the values quoted for the last three detectors have no more than semi-quantitative meaning. Even so, they well illustrate that the flame ionisation detector is considerably more sensitive than the others. In addition, since most of the values of S_m quoted do not refer to the condition that $R = 2R_n$, the table shows clearly how the apparently high sensitivity of the low pressure discharge, as expressed by its S_m, is largely lost in practice through the high noise level which, in turn, leads to a relatively low $pQ_0{}^f$. This detector is still, however, the second most sensitive of those listed.

TABLE 13

DETECTOR SENSITIVITIES

Detector	$pQ_0{}^m$	Detector	$pQ_0{}^m$
Hot wire katharometer	6.8	Argon detector—simple	8.5
Thermistor katharometer	6.1	small	9.3
Ionisation gauge	7.5	triode	11.8
		R.F. detector	8.7

Table 13 contains some approximate values of $pQ_0{}^m$ which have been calculated by the author for a number of detectors from more recent data. The sources are those quoted earlier in the chapter and the data represent the highest sensitivities claimed and are not necessarily those most commonly achieved.

Since these figures correspond to the minimum detectable sample in ml. per ml. entering the detector the level of detectability in terms of the injected sample will, of course, be much higher due to the dilution effect of the elution process (equation 7.29). It is not always clear in the literature whether detector capabilities are described in terms of sample or effluent concentrations, and so considerable care is necessary in evaluating such information.

DETECTOR RESPONSE TIME

Of comparable importance to detector sensitivity is the speed of response to change in the property monitored. Generally, delays in response stem from four sources:

a. Dead volume between the column and detector.

b. The time of entry of sample into the detector volume.

c. The time response lag inherent in the instrument itself.

d. The time delay in the associated electrical equipment.

The first source of delay is readily minimised by appropriate design and, provided it is not great, merely induces an overall signal delay which is common at all points of the chromatogram. If the dead volume is large, of course, gas diffusional spreading and remixing of eluted bands may occur. It is unlikely that this effect is very common since the majority of workers site their detectors as closely as possible to the column outlet.

The second source of slow response may, in addition, be responsible for unfaithful recording of the concentration profiles of eluted bands. If the volume of the sensing chamber were, for example, exactly equal to the volume of carrier containing the eluted band, at some instant the whole sample would be inside the detector. At best, the detector would then respond to the average concentration rather than the maximum. Further, during the filling and emptying of the sensing volume, the detector would be constantly averaging the concentration and an apparent peak distortion would be observed. Even if the sensing chamber is small in comparison with the eluted band some effect must arise.

A special instance of this effect is met with in side-chamber diffusion entry types of thermal conductivity cell, and perhaps also the simple argon detector (cf. p. 317). In these, since material enters the sensing area by diffusion the response cannot truly represent the concentration profile of the eluted band except at extremely low flow rates, since one Gaussian function is superimposed on another. As pointed out earlier, thermal conductivity cells of the type under discussion usually require from 10 to 20 sec. to indicate 67 per cent of an instantaneous step change of gas composition. It is clear, therefore, that the sensing volume must be kept down to a minimum, and that the rate of entry of gas into the sensing volume should be as great as possible. The problem becomes critical when highly efficient and high speed columns are used. In any detector, in which the carrier flow is direct, the time constant of filling is given by

$$\tau = \frac{V_{det}}{F}$$

V_{det} being the detector volume and F the carrier flow rate from the column. With conventional packed columns, V_{det} may be quite large without significantly slowing up response, but for capillary column analysis where often $F < 1$ ml. per min., obviously, V_{det} must be kept down to some remarkably small value.

The inherent response time of detectors is, in almost all cases, extremely small. In thermal conductivity cells, flames and radiological or other ionisation devices, the true response time is probably no more than a millisecond. Only with adsorption type detectors is it likely that time delay from this source will become important.

Quite appreciable contributions to the time constant of the detector system may come from the associated apparatus. Conventional millivolt potentiometric recorders normally require a second or more to travel full scale following an instantaneous upset in the system. In most systems this is, in fact, the limiting factor. While very fast writing pen recorders are available, they are, on the whole, very expensive, and so, in some instances nowadays, cathode ray oscillographs are being employed (114). Another important point is the combined resistance and capacitance of any electrical system used. The electrical time constant of a system is given by the product RC. With detectors of conventional sensitivity, resistances are so low that the product RC is negligible. With high sensitivity detectors, on the other hand, the over-all resistance of the system may be 10^{10} ohms or more and quite long response times may result even with very small capacitances. For example, a stray capacitance, which might well be 1 pf., would give a time constant of 10^{-2} sec. at the resistance quoted above. Even very good electronic equipment may be expected to have capacitance of 10 pf. and coaxial cable, for instance, may have capacitance as high as 10 pf. per ft. Thus, the electronic apparatus response time may well be as high as 0.1–1.0 sec. with high sensitivity detectors. This is particularly undesirable since these are, otherwise, highly suited to high speed analysis. The minimising of capacitance is thus of great importance in such systems.

REFERENCES

1. James, A. T., and A. J. P. Martin, *Biochem. J.*, 1952, **50**, 679.
2. Boer, H., *Vapour Phase Chromatography*, 1957, Butterworths, London (editor, D. H. Desty), p. 314.
3. Liberti, A., and G. P. Cartoni, *Gas Chromatography*, 1958, Butterworths, London (editor, D. H. Desty), p. 321.
4. Janak, J., *Collect. Czech. Chem. Communs.*, 1954, **19**, 684.
5. Janak, J., *Vapour Phase Chromatography*, 1957, Butterworths, London (editor, D. H. Desty), p. 247.
6. Liebnitz, E., H. Hrapia, and H. Könnecke, *Brennstoff-Chem.*, 1957, **38**, 14.
7. van de Craats, F., *Analytica Chim. Acta*, 1956, **14**, 136.
8. Sevenstr, P. G., *S. African Ind. Chem.*, 1958, **10**, 75.
9. Falconer, J. W., and J. H. Knox, *Proc. Roy. Soc.*, 1959, **250A**, 493.
10. Griffiths, J. H., D. H. James, and C. S. G. Phillips, *Analyst*, 1952, **77**, 897.
11. Griffiths, J. H., and C. S. G. Phillips, *J. Chem. Soc.*, **1954**, 3446.
12. Turner, D. W., *Nature*, 1958, **181**, 1265.
13. Martin, A. E., and J. Smart, *Nature*, 1955, **175**, 422.
14. Franc, J., and J. Jokl, *Chem. listy*, 1958, **52**, 276.
15. Liberti, A., G. Costa and E. Pauluzzi, *Chim. e ind.*, Milan, 1956, **38**, 674.
16. Johnstone, R. A. W., and A. G. Douglas, *Chem. and Ind.*, **1959**, 154.
17. Dudenbostel, B. F., and W. Priestley, *Ind. Eng. Chem.*, 1957, **49**, 99A.
18. Priestley, W., *Vapour Phase Chromatography*, 1957, Butterworths, London (editor, D. H. Desty), p. 165.
19. Janak, J., M. Nedorost, and V. Bubenikova, *Chem. listy*, 1957, **52**, 890.
20. Turkel'taub, N. M., *Zhur. Fiz. Khim.*, 1957, **31**, 2012.

21. Grant, D. W., *Gas Chromatography*, 1958, Butterworths, London (editor, D. H. Desty), p. 153.
22. Nedorost, M., *Chem. listy*, 1956, **50**, 317.
23. Phillips, G., *J. Sci. Instr.*, 1951, **28**, 342.
24. Ambrose, D., and R. R. Collerson, *J. Sci. Instr.*, 1955, **32**, 323.
25. Bolland, J. L., and H. W. Melville, *Trans. Faraday Soc.*, 1937, **23**, 1317.
26. Claesson, S., *Arkiv. Kemi. Mineral. Geol.*, 1946, **A23**, 1.
27. Davies, A. J., and J. R. Johnson, *Vapour Phase Chromatography*, 1957, Butterworths, London (editor, D. H. Desty), p. 185.
28. Norrish, R. G. W. and J. H. Purnell, *Proc. Roy. Soc.*, 1958, **A243**, 450.
29. Daynes, H. A., *Gas Analysis by Measurement of Thermal Conductivity*, 1933, Cambridge University Press.
30. Ray, N. H., *J. Appl. Chem.*, 1954, **4**, 21.
31. Ebeid, E. M., and G. J. Minkoff, *Research*, 1956, **9**, S19.
32. Ellis, J. F., and G. Iveson, *Gas Chromatography*, 1958, Butterworths, London (editor, D. H. Desty), p. 300.
33. Felton, H. R., and A. A. Buehler, *Anal. Chem.*, 1958, **30**, 1163.
34. Harvey, D., and G. O. Morgan, *Vapour Phase Chromatography*, 1957, Butterworths, London (editor, D. H. Desty), p. 74.
35. Keppler, J. G., G. Dijkstra and J. A. Schols (see ref. 34), p. 222.
36. Keulemans, A. I. M., A. Kwantes and G. W. A. Rijnders, *Analytica Chim. Acta*, 1957, **16**, 29.
37. Madden, W. F., R. K. Quigg, and C. Kemball, *Chem. and Ind.*, **1957**, 892.
38. Mellor, N., *Vapour Phase Chromatography*, 1957, Butterworths, London (editor, D. H. Desty), p. 63.
39. van de Craats, F., *Gas Chromatography*, 1958, Butterworths, London (editor, D. H. Desty), p. 248.
40. Rosie, D. M., and R. L. Grob, *Anal. Chem.*, 1957, **29**, 1263.
41. Ryce, S. A., and W. A. Bryce, *Nature*, 1957, **179**, 541.
42. Ryce, S. A., P. Kebarle, and W. A. Bryce, *Anal. Chem.*, 1957, **29**, 1386.
43. Stuve, W., *Gas Chromatography*, 1958, Butterworths, London (editor, D. H. Desty), p. 178.
44. Schmauch, L. J., *Anal. Chem.*, 1959, **31**, 225.
45. Johnson, H. W., and F. H. Stross, *Anal. Chem.*, 1959, **31**, 357; 1206.
46. Willis, V., *Nature*, 1959, **183**, 1754.
47. Davis, A. D., and G. A. Howard, *J. Appl. Chem.*, 1958, **8**, 183.
48. Musgrave, W. K. R., *Chem. and Ind.*, **1959**, 46.
49. Cowan, C. B., and P. H. Stirling, *Gas Chromatography*, 1958 Academic Press, New York (editor, V. J. Coates, *et al.*), p. 165.
50. Messner, A. E., D. M. Rosie, and P. A. Argabright, *Anal. Chem.*, 1959, **31**, 230.
51. Kaiser, R., *Gas Chromatography*, 1958, Butterworths, London (editor, D. H. Desty), p. 187.
52. Littlewood, A. B. (see ref. 51), p. 186.
53. Wirth, M. M., *Vapour Phase Chromatography*, 1957, Butterworths, London (editor, D. H. Desty), p. 154.
54. Brooks, I., W. Murray, and A. F. Williams (see ref. 53), p. 281.
55. Bohemen, J., and J. H. Purnell, *Chem. and Ind.*, **1957**, 815.
56. Bohemen, J., and J. H. Purnell, *J. Appl. Chem.*, 1958, **8**, 433.
57. Behrendt, S., *Z. physikal. Chem.*, 1959, **21**, 240.
58. Riesz, P., and K. E. Wilzbach, *J. Phys. Chem.*, 1958, **62**, 6.
59. Wolfgang, R., and F. S. Rowland, *Anal. Chem.*, 1958, **30**, 903.

60. Moussebois, C., and G. Dayckaerts, *J. Chromatog.*, 1958, **1**, 200.
61. Behrendt, S., *Z. physikal. Chem.*, 1959, **20**, 367.
62. Dimbat, M., P. E. Porter, and F. H. Stross, *Anal. Chem.*, 1956, **28**, 290.
63. Eggertsen, F. T., H. S. Knight, and S. Groennings (see ref. 62), 303.
64. Fredericks, E. M., and F. R. Brooks (see ref. 62), 297.
65. Schmauch, L. J., *Ann. Mtng. Amer. Chem. Soc.*, Sept. 1959, Atlantic City, N.J.
66. Bennett, C. E., S. dal Nogare, L. W. Safranski, and C. D. Lewis, *Anal. Chem.*, 1958, **30**, 898.
67. Green, G. E., *Nature*, 1957, **180**, 295.
68. See Lewis, B., and G. von Elbe, *Combustion, Flames and Explosions*, 1951, Academic Press, New York, p. 206.
69. McWilliam, I. G., *2nd Informal Symposium of the Gas Chromatography Discussion Group*, Cambridge, Sept. 1957.
70. McWilliam, I. G., and R. A. Dewar, *Nature*, 1958, **182**, 1664.
71. McWilliam, I. G., and R. A. Dewar, *Gas Chromatography*, 1958, Butterworths, London (editor, D. H. Desty), p. 142.
72. Harley, J., and V. Pretorius, *Nature*, 1958, **181**, 177.
73. McWilliam, I. G., *Gas Chromatography*, 1958, Butterworths, London (editor, D. H. Desty), p. 147.
74. McWilliam, I. G. (see ref. 73), p. 150.
75. Onkiehong, L. (Ph.D. Thesis, University of Eindhoven, 1960).
76. Onkiehong, L., *3rd International Symposium Gas Chromatography Discussion Group*, Edinburgh, June, 1960, Preprints, p. E.1.
77. Condon, R. D., P. R. Scholly, and W. Averill (see ref. 76), p.N.134.
78. Thompson, A. E., *J. Chromatog.*, 1959, **2**, 148.
79. Glueckauf, E., *Gas Chromatography*, 1958, Butterworths, London (editor, D. H. Desty), p. 151.
80. Purnell, J. H., and C. P. Quinn, *3rd International Symposium Gas Chromatography Discussion Group*, Edinburgh, June 1960, Preprints, p.R.154.
81. Kieselbach, R., *Ann. Mtng. Amer. Chem. Soc.*, Sept. 1959, Atlantic City, N.J.
82. Hardy, J., and V. Pretorius, *Nature*, 1956, **178**, 1244.
83. Pitkethly, R. C., *Anal. Chem.*, 1958, **30**, 1309.
84. Ryce, S. A., and W. A. Bryce, *Can. J. Chem.*, 1957, **35**, 1293.
85. Bryce, W. A. (private communication).
86. Bowman, R. L., and A. Karmen, *Nature*, 1958, **182**, 1233.
87. Karmen, A., and R. L. Bowman, *Ann. N.Y. Acad. Sci.*, 1959, **72**, 714.
88. Karmen, A., and R. L. Bowman, *2nd I.S.A. Symposium*, Lansing, Mich., June 1959, Preprints, p. 33.
89. Deal, C. H., J. W. Otvos, V. N. Smith, and P. S. Zucco, *Anal. Chem.*, 1956, **28**, 1958.
90. Boer, H., *Vapour Phase Chromatography*, 1957, Butterworths, London (editor D. H. Desty), p. 169.
91. Graven, W. M., *Anal. Chem.*, 1959, **31**, 1197.
92. Lovelock, J. E., *J. Chromatog.*, 1958, **1**, 35.
93. Lovelock, J. E., *Nature*, 1958, **181**, 1460.
94. Lovelock, J. E., *3rd International Symposium Gas Chromatography Discussion Group*, Edinburgh, June 1960, Preprints, p. 9.
95. Mason, L. H., H. J. Dutton, and L. R. Blair, *J. Chromatog.*, 1959, **2**, 322.
96. Lovelock, J. E., A. T. James, and E. A. Piper, *Ann. N.Y. Acad. Sci.*, 1959, **72**, 720.
97. Lovelock, J. E., *Nature*, 1958, **182**, 1663.
98. Henderson, J. I., and J. H. Knox, *J. Chem. Soc.*, **1956**, 2299.

99. Bullock, P., *Gas Chromatography*, 1958, Butterworths, London (editor, D. H. Desty), p. 175.
100. Primavesi, G. R. (see ref. 99), p. 176.
101. Claesson, S., *Ark. Kemi. Min. Geol.*, 1946, **23A**, 1.
102. Martin, A. J. P., and A. T. James, *Biochem. J.*, 1956, **63**, 138.
103. Munday, C. W., and G. R. Primavesi, *Vapour Phase Chromatography*, 1957, Butterworths, London (editor, D. H. Desty), p. 146.
104. Liberti, A., L. Conti and V. Crescenzi, *Nature*, 1956, **178**, 1067.
105. Zderic, J. A., W. A. Bonner, and T. W. Greenlee, *J. Amer. Chem. Soc.*, 1957, **79**, 1696.
106. Scott, R. P. W., *Nature*, 1955, **176**, 793.
107. Scott, R. P. W., *Vapour Phase Chromatography*, 1957, Butterworths, London (editor, D. H. Desty), p. 131.
108. Primavesi, G. R., G. F. Oldham, and R. J. Thompson, *Gas Chromatography*, 1958, Butterworths, London (editor, D. H. Desty), p. 165.
109. Kemula, W., and Z. Stachurski, *Roczniki Chemii*, 1956, **30**, 1285.
110. Scott, R. P. W., *Gas Chromatography*, 1958, Butterworths, London (editor, D. H. Desty), p. 176.
111. Knewstubb, P. F., and T. M. Sugden, *Nature*, 1958, **181**, 474; 1261; *Proc. Roy. Soc.*, 1960, **A255**, 520.
112. Hinkle, E. A., H. C. Tucker, R. C. Wall, and J. F. Combs, *2nd International Symposium of I.S.A.*, Lansing, Mich., June 1959, Preprints, p. 27.
113. Young, I. G. (see ref. 112), p. 40.
114. Scott, R. P. W., *Nature*, 1960, **185**, 312.

13

ANALYTICAL
TECHNIQUES

The first decision to be faced in devising an analysis is that between gas-solid and gas-liquid chromatography. Adsorption isotherms obtained with solid adsorbents are generally unfavourable to chromatography since they are commonly non-linear (p. 15) and the extent of adsorption is usually so considerable as to lead to very long retention times. In order to achieve elution in reasonable times it is thus necessary to use either short, relatively inefficient columns, or high temperatures. Combined with the commonly observed peak asymmetry, these features restrict very considerably the application of the gas solid technique at this time. Further difficulties are experienced through irreproducibility of the adsorbent from column to column and the frequent dependence of retention volumes upon the identity of the carrier gas as a result of competitive adsorption.

In general, therefore, gas-solid chromatography is most successfully applied in the analysis of those permanent gases which cannot be readily separated with gas-liquid columns. There are, of course exceptions, hydrocarbons up to C_5 have been dealt with by gas-solid methods on numerous occasions (see, for example, 1) while an even wider range of molecular weights can be dealt with if a small amount of an involatile liquid is incorporated in the column (see, 2, 3, for example). These gas solid-liquid columns may well become very important in the future since, as described later, they offer certain advantages. Equally, as exceptions to any generalisation, gas-liquid columns can often be found which will analyse certain permanent gas

330

mixtures. For example, such gases as chlorine, hydrogen chloride, hydrogen sulphide, carbon dioxide and the oxides of nitrogen and sulphur are all well retained and separated by several solvents. Nitrous oxide, for instance, is eluted coincidentally with ethylene from a squalane column operating at 25°C. (4) although ethylene and ethane are resolved.

There is, thus, no clear-cut rule governing the choice of technique and the best generalisation we can make is that it is more or less correct to say that gas-solid columns are only *essential* in the analysis of the most low boiling materials and that, otherwise, gas-liquid chromatography usually provides the more fruitful approach. The two methods are thus taken separately in the subsequent discussion, although virtually all of the methods applied and the conclusions drawn in the gas-liquid section which relate to column comparison, are directly applicable to gas-solid chromatography.

GAS-LIQUID CHROMATOGRAPHY

The first prerequisite of a gas-liquid chromatographic column is that it shall have a reasonable working life. This is entirely determined by the volatility of the solvent and, hence, the column temperature. As yet no standard value of an upper limit of volatility which is tolerable has been suggested but calculation suggests that in practice workers most commonly employ solvents at temperatures at which their apparent saturation vapour pressures are less than about 10^{-2} mm. Hg. In a carrier gas stream at about atmospheric pressure this value of the solvent vapour pressure corresponds roughly to a concentration of solvent vapour in the effluent no greater than 1 part in 10^5. Thus, very approximately, 1 g. of a solvent of molecular weight 400, which would have a vapour volume of about 60 ml. per g., near room temperature and pressure, would be lost from a column after the passage of 6000 l. of carrier, and so, at a flow rate of 100 ml. per min. this loss would occur over 1000 hr. This is, of course, a very long column life, but it must be remembered that it corresponds to the loss of a large amount of liquid since a reasonable column filling would consist of only 1 to 10 g. of solvent. If, over the lifetime of a column, a 10 per cent solvent loss is tolerable, column life in these conditions still lies between 100 and 1000 hr. Anything much less than the former period is of little use for routine quantitative purposes; thus, the vapour pressure value quoted earlier does, in fact, seem to represent a reasonable upper limit of volatility for general purposes.

However, solvents are occasionally recommended for particular problems despite their very high volatility at convenient temperatures; an instance being the use of dimethylformamide in paraffin/olefin analysis. At room temperature this solvent has a vapour pressure in the region of 1 mm. Hg and so the column life must be extremely short unless refrigeration techniques, which are not very popular, are used. Nevertheless, in qualitative studies, particularly those aimed at solute identification, such liquids can be of value.

A subsidiary problem associated with solvent loss from the column is that of the effect of the solvent vapour on the detector. With detectors of moderate sensitivity it is unlikely that effective vapour pressures of 10^{-2} mm. Hg or less would be perceptible as drift or variation in the chromatogram base line but the newer high sensitivity detectors respond in certain circumstances to solute pressures as low as 10^{-6} mm. Hg in the column effluent. This places very considerable restrictions on solvent volatility, which in most cases in practice are unlikely to be met with, since it seems probable that the background signal derived from the higher sensitivity detectors stems mainly from solvent stripping. This obviously complicates the problem of defining the temperature working range of any solvent since it may well be largely determined by the choice of detector.

At the present time little of a quantitative nature is known about effective solvent vapour pressures or loss rates from columns. What evidence there is suggests quite strongly that saturation of the carrier is never achieved since loss rates are much lower than would be calculated from vapour pressure data. For example, the rate of loss of phenanthrene at 110°C., measured by following retention volume changes, is less than 20 per cent of the calculated value (5) and appears to diminish with increasing carrier gas flow rate. This aspect of column studies is obviously of practical importance and since it could well also be used to shed light on the problem of mass transfer in the gas phase it merits more detailed study.

SOLVENT STABILITY

Of somewhat less importance than solvent volatility is the question of its chemical stability and inertness. Obviously, any solvent which is thermally unstable at the chosen column temperature is quite unsuitable for use. It may well be this factor which eventually sets the upper limit of temperature for gas-liquid chromatography, since, as a rough rule, both volatility and thermal stability decrease with increasing molecular weight. Thus, a point on the temperature scale may be reached at which the only organic liquids suitable from the point of view of volatility may be quite unsuitable because of their thermal instability. Beyond this point, therefore, it may be necessary to turn to inorganic liquids or to gas-solid chromatography. This problem has now become very important, since in the relatively recent past attempts to work as high as 1000°C. have been made with some success.

Another source of solvent instability is the possible interaction with the carrier gas. It is mainly this which rules out the use of air or superheated steam as carriers, and where unsaturated solvents are used, hydrogen is sometimes suspect. For reliability and long column life it is evidently worthwhile to feel assured of the chemical stability of the solvent and so the possible thermal effects and those of the carrier (and its impurities) should always be taken into account.

Another problem met with occasionally, lies in the possibility of reaction of some sort between the solvent and some sample component. For example, the author has experienced difficulties through progressive chlorination of hydrocarbon type solvents following repeated analyses of mixtures containing free chlorine. The observable effect was a marked change in both absolute and relative retention times, admittedly over a period of months. This, if not checked on frequently, might lead to wrong identification of peaks at some time. An alternative interaction is that in which the solvent effectively plays the part of a catalyst. Thus, for example, the terpene isomerisations discussed earlier (p. 179) could well result from exposure, not to an adsorbent surface, but to a highly polar liquid. It is, therefore, clearly worthwhile to check on the inertness of a solvent in respect to the samples to be analysed.

SOLVENT FUNCTION

Broadly speaking, solvents can be classified either as non-specific (boiling point) or as selective separators. The distinction is, of course, meaningless unless the particular solute types in question are also specified, for a solvent which is completely unselective when dealing with mixtures of, let us say, aliphatic and aromatic hydrocarbons, may differentiate sharply between either class and ketones or alcohols and, equally possibly, between the latter two compound types as well. A good example of a boiling point separation is that of straight chain aliphatic hydrocarbons of varying degrees of unsaturation by squalane columns.

A plot of log retention volume against boiling point (6) for these substances is shown in Figure 1 and clearly illustrates the point since the data plotted all lie very close to a single line. The key to the identity of the numbered substances accompanies Figure 14. It should be pointed out that the degree of separation is not necessarily that predictable from vapour pressure data since, although a straight line plot may be obtained, the slope of the line may not correspond to the ideal calculable value (equation 10.15). Also included in the figure are data for some alicyclic compounds, obtained in identical conditions to those for the aliphatics, and these again are seen to lie on a single line not, however, that for the aliphatic compounds. This would apparently indicate that squalane operates selectively in the analysis of aliphatics and alicyclics. In fact, this may be illusory. Selectivity is, by definition, a consequence of the non-ideal interaction of solutes and solvent, whereas the separation of log retention volume versus boiling point plots for different solute types reflects both interactional differences and differences in the constants of the saturation vapour pressure equations of the homologous series concerned. This point is clarified if we refer to equation 10.15 which shows that the position of a series line (if there is one) on a boiling point plot is, in the first instance, determined by the values of k_7 to

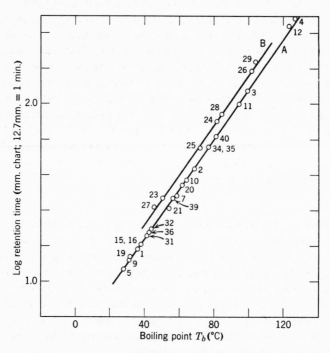

FIG. 1. Boiling point plot of log (relative retention volume) for the elution of a range of hydrocarbons from squalane at 43°C. Key to identity of the solutes accompanies Figure 14. Line A, aliphatics; line B, alicyclics.

k_{10} which come directly from the Clausius-Clapeyron or other vapour pressure equation of the pure solute.

Caution is, therefore, advisable in ascribing specificity to a solvent solely on the basis of plots such as Figure 1, and, as emphasised on p. 216, the best course is to consider first the saturation vapour pressure equation constants of the pure solutes and then to calculate activity coefficients. The equivalent graphical procedure is based on the fact that the one form of logarithmic plot which unequivocally shows up selectivity by the solvent is that of log retention volume versus log vapour pressure of the solute. That squalane can, on occasion, act selectively, however, is unquestionable, ketones, for example, are weakly dissolved whereas n-paraffins show almost ideal solubility.

This statement illustrates a further point of some importance, selectivity, when it is observed is most commonly between classes of compounds and only occasionally does a solvent behave very differently towards homologues other than the earliest series members. Thus, even solvents showing pronounced type selectivity generally act as boiling point separators when dealing with homologues. The degree of separation, however, is often other than the ideal (saturation vapour pressure ratio) value and even if it does correspond to the latter this does not necessarily imply ideal solution but only a constant activity coefficient from solute to solute. A degree of separation greater than that predicted by the vapour pressure ratio would correspond to a "superdistillation" (7), but, as yet, no system showing this type of behaviour appears to have been found. The data for elution of n-alcohols from silicone oil columns show a tendency in the right direction but marked positive deviations from ideality of solution of the individual alcohols lead to a balance of effects giving what then appears to be ideal solution behaviour if the elution data at a single temperature only are considered (8). It is these, of course, which are of analytical importance.

What variations from the ideal degree of separation are known at this time are thus all in the direction of increasing activity coefficient with decreasing saturation vapour pressure, and so lead to an analysis less effective than might be hoped for. However, it is generally the case that the changes in activity coefficient from solute to solute which give rise to this effect appear to be functions of molecular weight in general accord with equation 10.16, and so still permit linearity of log retention volume against boiling point or other plots. Exceptions are known, a particular example is met with in the analysis of certain aromatics with columns of tritolyl phosphate (8).

Interactions in Solution. The great power of gas chromatography was originally considered likely to stem from the relative ease with which selective solvents could be chosen to suit a particular problem. Nowadays it is evident that clear cut selectivity is less common than might have been hoped for. To some extent help in estimating the probable selectivity of solvents can be gained by consideration of the various forces likely to arise in solution. Briefly, the following types may be of consequence.

a. Dispersion forces which operate in all systems at all times and arise through the oscillatory motion of the nuclei and electrons of molecules. The transient dipoles set up give rise to molecular attraction and repulsion but there is no net dipole moment.

b. Orientation forces arising through the interaction of permanent dipoles located within the molecules. In the extreme case in many systems the relatively strong hydrogen bond may be set up. This can be of the type —H $\cdots$ F—, —H $\cdots$ O—, —H $\cdots$ N—, and —H $\cdots$ S—, the bond strength diminishing more or less in the same sequence.

c. Induction forces caused by the polarisation of normally non-polar molecules when they are subjected to the field of a molecule having a permanent dipole. The forces involved are almost always very small although the effect is common enough.

Each of the three forces varies inversely as the sixth or higher power of the distance between molecules, and so they each fall off rapidly with distance. Some idea of the relative magnitudes of the three types of force

TABLE 1

PER CENT CONTRIBUTIONS OF VARIOUS FORCES TO
TOTAL ENERGY OF MOLECULES

Substance	Dispersion	Orientation	Induction
CO	99.9	0.1	0.01
HCl	80	15	5
NH_3	50	45	5
H_2O	19	76	5

is gained from the data in Table 1 which lists the approximate percentage contribution of each to the total energy of a few molecules of widely different polarity.

The great majority of molecules of chromatographic interest would lie between CO and HCl in the table and in only the most polar of molecules are the dispersion forces less than about 90 per cent of the total. However, even small contributions from induction or orientation forces can give rise to quite helpful changes in the relative volatility (α) of different solutes through non-ideality of solution; a 5 per cent change of α, for example, could well reduce the theoretical plate requirement for chromatographic separation by as much as a factor of four.

The application of these considerations to the choice of solvents for gas chromatography can obviously be little more than qualitative. Basically, the first approach adopted is that of the "like dissolves like" principle by which it would be expected that non-polar solutes were best separated by non-polar solvents while, of course, polar solutes were best dealt with using polar solvents.

Again, when dealing with mixtures of non-polar and polarisable molecules advantage might be taken of the induction effect of a polar solvent on the latter. Thus, for example, naphthenes and aromatic hydrocarbons of about the same saturation vapour pressure are more readily separated by polyethylene glycol than by octadecane, in fact the order of elution is inverted as a consequence of the polarisability of the aromatics. Even so, the polyglycol, and also such solvents as phthalate esters, are good solvents for non-polar molecules. An example of the converse situation is the analysis of the methyl esters of higher fatty acids with columns of Apiezon-M grease and polyethylene glycol adipate (9). The specific retention volumes of the esters are as much as fifteen times as great with the hydrocarbon as with the polar ester although, on the principle expressed above, the reverse might have been anticipated. At the same time, the polyester offers quite excellent separations of the esters of the various unsaturated acid isomers in consequence of their polarisability differences while doing little in resolving saturated branched chain isomers; the reverse is true of the hydrocarbon grease columns.

Thus, to some extent the behaviour of these solvents is predictable while in other ways it is not. One possible explanation is that even though the solvent molecule may be quite polar it is so large that the dipole is effectively buried, and so exerts relatively little in the way of an external field except when in the vicinity of another polar or of a polarisable molecule. Thus, phthalate esters may be able to behave as though they were non-polar in the analysis of non-polar materials but as though they were polar when dealing with other molecules.

There are, however, other contributory factors to the difficulty of theoretical predictions of solvent solute behaviour. There is growing evidence that gas liquid chromatographic systems are often to be regarded on something of the same basis as high polymer solutions (10, 11) (see p. 422), the difference being that the work is carried out at the opposite end of the concentration scale. Thus, the geometry of the molecules may be more important than their polarity, volume fractions may be of greater significance than molar fractions, and nearest neighbour group interactions rather than interactions of the molecule pairs as a whole may determine the total energy. Perhaps the most important evidence for this point of view is the fact that most often the non-ideality of solution encountered in gas chromatography can be traced in large measure to entropy effects.

An interesting approach to solvent selectivity is that in which quite definite chemical bonding, as opposed to physical forces, is brought in. Complex molecule formation is assumed to occur when salts of transition metals salts of fatty acids are used as solvents (12), while an extreme case about which there is no doubt is met with in the use of silver nitrate/glycol mixtures as solvents in the analysis of saturated and unsaturated aliphatic hydrocarbons (13). The unsaturates form complexes with the silver salt and so are highly soluble, while the saturates are virtually entirely insoluble and emerge from columns in more or less the same time as air. This is, so to speak, an absolute selectivity and is therefore very useful, in particular when dealing with very complex mixtures.

Moderate chemical type selectivity, depending as it does on relatively small differences in non-ideality of solution, however, can often introduce as many problems as it solves. For example, paraffin/olefin analysis with octadecane or squalane columns is not particularly difficult, the major problem being the resolution of the paraffin and olefin of the same carbon number. Columns containing β-β' oxydipropionitrile simplify this particular problem very considerably, since the peaks of corresponding paraffins and olefins are well separated, so much so, in fact, that a new problem is introduced, that of separating the olefin from the next higher paraffin.

Thus, on the whole, there is some justification for the belief that, for single column analysis, moderate class selectivity is of greatest use with simple mixtures, and that in the long run, if it is desired to deal with complex mixtures with a single column, it is just as well to employ a relatively non-selective solvent and accept the need for long columns of high efficiency. However, even the most moderate selective powers can be turned to good use if two or more analyses of the same sample, employing different solvents of different selectivities each time, are carried out, since in this situation complete resolution of all mixture components with any one column is never required and column efficiency requirements are greatly reduced.

It is quite clear that at this time there are few hard and fast rules to guide the choice of solvent, and it is the case that most analysis is done with one or other of only about half a dozen solvents. With time, however, there is every reason to suppose that such rules may emerge. In the meantime it is still necessary to rely mainly on trial and error, although, undoubtedly, the list of probable solvents can be reduced to a manageable number on the general lines described above. This empirical approach is not to be decried since already it has yielded satisfactory results in the analyses of almost all chemical types. There is, therefore, in the literature already a great deal of useful information and a preliminary literature survey is almost certain to be very helpful. This procedure has been considerably facilitated by the recent emergence of *Gas Chromatography Abstracts* (14). Although the abstracts themselves are very brief the volumes contain a most comprehensive listing of papers indexed under various headings in such a way that those relevant to the analysis of particular solute types can be found in a very short time. In consequence of this, and because the number of solvents described in the literature already runs into hundreds, the inclusion of a detailed list of solvents here would be pointless. Table 2, therefore, represents only an abbreviated list representing those liquids most commonly used for general purposes and which, incorporated in a series of columns, would provide a good basic reserve in any laboratory.

These six solvents are by far the most widely used and a set of columns containing these represents an excellent basis on which to commence any investigation. There is no doubt that the various silicones find the widest application, the data for these in the table embracing a wide variety of silicones ranging from oils through greases to the elastomers. Surprisingly, they differ little in their retentive capacities and selectivities and the choice of silicone is usually dictated by availability and the analysis temperature chosen. The greases are said to function more reproducibly and over longer periods of time if washed before use with ethyl acetate. Octadecane or medicinal paraffin could be substituted for squalane without great change and in fact, the Apiezon greases are also very similar to these paraffins in their performance. Apart from minor selectivity differences, again it is the working temperature which mainly dictates the choice between squalane and Apiezon. The data in the column headed di-alkyl phthalates relates to the di-octyl, di-nonyl and di-decyl esters. There is nothing to choose between these and ready availability is usually the deciding factor.

The two solvents which show the greatest degree of selectivity and non-ideal behaviour of those listed are tricresyl phosphate and the polyglycols. It is frequently very useful to employ one or both of these as a foil to one of the other four. The term polyglycols is very broad since it embraces ethylene and propylene glycols and also the ethers and a number of esters. Broadly speaking, they differ little in performance, but different ethers and esters show slightly different selectivities and for particular problems, therefore, some one or other may be preferable. The polyglycols and their derivatives are especially good in the analysis of polar mixtures, partly, it is supposed, because of their hydrogen bonding ability. This is more likely to be true of polyethylene than of polypropylene glycols which, as seen earlier (p. 222) behave rather more ideally.

One interesting departure from convention which may be commented on here is the introduction of inorganic solvents for both inorganic and organic sample analysis. The approach appears to have been initiated by Juvet and Wachi (147, 148) who used the molten eutectics $CdCl_2/KCl$; $AlCl_3/NaCl$ and $BiCl_3/PbCl_2$ to separate the volatile chlorides of tin, antimony and titanium. Following this the gas chromatographic analysis of a Zn:Cd alloy by use of a LiCl column at 620° was reported (194) while more recently, Hanneman has used molten eutectics such as those of the nitrates of lithium, sodium and potassium to analyse very high boiling organic mixtures, for example those of the higher hydrocarbons (150).

THE APPROACH TO QUANTITATIVE SOLVENT COMPARISON

While it is not at all easy to draw up rigorous rules for solvent selection, once a preliminary short list has been devised it is certainly possible, after a

TABLE 2 SOLVENTS OF WIDEST APPLICATION AND

Di-alkyl Phthalates	Squalane	Silicone Oils and Greases
Amines	Aromatics	Aldehydes
Alcohols	Aliphatic sulphides	Alcohols
Allylic halides	Aromatic sulphides	Aromatics
Alkyl halides	Boron hydrides	Aromatic amines
Alkyl nitrates	Naphthenes	Aliphatic amines
Aldehydes	Pyridines	Alkyl sulphides
Aromatics	Thiophenes	Boron hydrides
Ethers	All types of	Carbohydrate
Fluorocarbons	aliphatic hydro-	derivatives
Ketones	carbons	Ethers
Nitriles		Esters
N-trifluoroacetyl		Fluorocarbons
amino acid esters		Fatty acids
Naphthenes		Germanes
Oximes		Halogenated
Peroxides		hydrocarbons
Phenols		High boiling
Pyrazine bases		fatty acid esters
Silanes		Isocyanates
Thiols		Ketones
All types of		Phenols
aliphatic hydro-		Phosphonitrile
carbons		chlorides
		Phthalate esters
		Pyridine bases
		Silyl ethers
		Silanes
		Sterols
		Terpenes
		All types of
		aliphatic hydro-
		carbons

minimum of experimentation, not only to make a reasonably quantitative comparison of their capabilities, but also to calculate, at least approximately, the most probable operating temperature and column length which will eventually be required.

The most common method of reporting gas chromatographic information is in the form of relative retention data (α), some solute being chosen as the standard and the retention volumes or times of other solutes being

SAMPLE TYPES FOR WHICH THEY HAVE BEEN USED

Tricresyl Phosphate	Apiezon grease	Polyglycols
Aldehydes	Aromatics	Aromatics
Alcohols	Alkyl sulphides	Aldehydes
Alkyl halides	Alkyl chlorides	Alcohols
Alkyl sulphides	Ethers	Alkyl halides
Esters	Carbohydrate	Alkaloids
Boron hydrides	derivatives	Carbohydrate
Ketones	Fatty acid esters	derivatives
Mercaptans	Metal alkyls	Ethers
Naphthenes	Mercaptans	Esters
Olefins	Naphthenes	Halogenated
Paraffins	N-acetyl amino	aromatics
Phenols	acid esters	Ketones
Pyridine bases	Phenols	Metal alkyls
Terpenes	Terpenes	Naphthenes
Thiophenes	All types of	Nitroparaffins
Water	aliphatic hydro-	Nitriles
	carbons	Oximes
		Picolines
		Pyridine bases
		Terpenes
		Water
		All types of
		aliphatic hydro-
		carbons

given as a ratio to this. The values of α so obtained are clearly of value and the use of the relative method is attractive in that it eliminates all need to make corrections for pressure gradient, solvent weight etc. In passing, however, it should be pointed out that, before use is made of such listed values, care must be taken to ascertain that the air peak (column dead volume, V_d) retention time or volume has been allowed for in computing α. Surprisingly, this point is not always appreciated and since the inclusion of

V_d relates any α to a specific piece of apparatus such values are only of use when the retention volumes are very considerably greater than V_d.

It is certainly the case that the largest practically attainable value of α usually leads to the simplest analysis. This clearly follows from equation 7.44 from which it is seen that the degree of difficulty of separation of two substances is proportional to $(\alpha/\alpha - 1)^2$. Thus, if α can be increased even slightly by change of solvent or temperature, great benefit can be obtained. For example, the theoretical plate requirement diminishes by almost exactly half if α can somehow be increased from 1.10 to 1.15 without change of k'. This latter condition is difficult to achieve and so the use of α values as the sole criterion of solvent capability can be misleading. This follows from a closer study of equation 7.44, which for convenience in discussion is reproduced here.

$$N_{\mathrm{req}} = 36\left(\frac{\alpha}{\alpha - 1}\right)^2\left(\frac{1 + k'}{k'}\right)^2 \tag{7.44}$$

It is obvious that for a true appreciation of the capabilities of a solvent we must take account not only of α but of k' because a low value of the latter may vitiate any advantage deriving from a high value of α. Hence, since k' is, among other things, a function of solvent volume, information as to the weight (and density) of solvent, as opposed to solvent/support ratio, is desirable. The truth of this is best illustrated by an example. Consider the separation of two substances X and Y which when eluted in that order from columns containing solvents A and B, respectively, present in the same solvent support ratio, have the values of α and k' listed in Table 3.

TABLE 3

Solvent	$\alpha_{YX} = (V_R)_Y/(V_R)_X$	k_Y'
A	1.10	0.5
B	1.05	5.0

On the basis of the relative retention values alone, A would immediately appear superior to B. However, when 7.44 is used to compute the number of theoretical plates required for the separation it is found that, in consequence of the difference in k', a column of solvent B would need to be equal to only 23,000 plates in order to separate X and Y completely, while one of A would need to have 40,000 plates. If identical plate heights were attainable in each case, from the point of view of ease of separation, that is column length, alone, solvent B would be a better choice than solvent A although analysis with solvent A would be considerably faster. Thus, values of α alone can be misleading since, ignoring the time aspect, A would only be a better choice than B if used at a higher solvent/support ratio or at a lower temperature; both expedients which lead to increased k' and a lower N_{req}. With only relative retention data available these conclusions could never be drawn.

The example quoted is perhaps even more pertinent in illustrating the dangers inherent in comparing solvents on the basis of relative retention data obtained with columns operated at different temperatures. In fact, it is in this situation that the greatest differences in k' commonly arise, and so, although the disparity in k' used in the example might be regarded by some as extreme, this is not in fact the case since, even for a given solvent, k' can change by an order of magnitude over as little as 50°C. There is no doubt, therefore, that at least some of the expressions of opinion on the relative merits of solvents to be found in the literature are founded on false premises.

From what has been said it follows that, although a study of relative retention data is useful, for a truly unequivocal assessment of the merit of any solvent or solvents on a quantitative basis, it is necessary to know the relevant specific retention volumes and their dependence upon temperature. Aiven this information we obviously have α in any case, and at all temperatures, while k' can always be calculated, since the column dead volume is close to a constant fraction of thé total packed volume (see p. 62). In the following pages an outline is given of the way in which ab initio calculation can be carried out not only to compare solvent capabilities, but also to elucidate the most probable optimum packing composition, column length and elution temperature. Even if the results obtained in this kind of calculation are only good to 10 or 20 per cent, they can still save months of experimental effort. In order to simplify the discussion, several examples of increasing severity will be considered.

Single Solute Type Mixtures. The separation of the components of a mixture composed entirely of homologues constitutes one of the simplest of gas chromatographic problems. It is very commonly found that the relative retention volume ratio of successive homologues is nearly constant and, most often, exceptions to this generalisation involve only the earliest series members. As the first example of the quantitative approach to column selection and design, we can consider the separation of the C_1 through C_4 n-fatty alcohols, since specific retention volume data for two solvents over a range of temperatures are available for these (15, 16, 103) and in addition, both systems show an anomaly in α for methanol and ethanol. The specific retention volumes, α's and theoretical plate requirements, assuming k' for the moment to be very great with each solvent, for elution at 80°C. are listed in Table 4.

TABLE 4

V_g, α AND N_{req} DATA FOR n-ALCOHOLS (C$_1$ TO C$_4$) AT 80°C.

	Silicone 702			Tricresyl Phosphate		
	V_g(ml.)	α	N_{req}	V_g(ml.)	α	N_{req}
MeOH	6.0			27.3		
		3.23	76		1.51	318
EtOH	19.4			41.2		
		2.28	113		2.29	110
PrOH	44.2			94.2		
		2.15	127		2.16	130
BuOH	94.8			204.0		

It is interesting to see that α's for the pairs of alcohols above C$_2$ are virtually identical for the two solvents and so, if methanol were not present, the tricresyl phosphate would represent the better choice in virtue of the more than twofold greater V_g's. However, the very unfavourable α for C$_2$/C$_1$ with this solvent, in contrast to the very large value observed with the silicone, alters the situation completely if methanol is present. A comparison of the data in the table certainly indicates the choice of the silicone, but it should be borne in mind that the difference in V_g already commented on might affect conclusions based on equal and low values of k', although the direction and magnitude of the discrepancy in the α's for C$_2$/C$_1$ make this highly unlikely.

Since the condition for fastest analysis is that k' for the second eluted of the pair offering most difficulty in separation is in the region of two, we can most profitably evaluate N_{req} for this condition. Table 5 contains the results of these calculations with ethanol placed at $k' = 2$ for both solvents and n-propanol also being placed at $k' = 2$ for the silicone. α(C$_2$/C$_1$) is so small with tricresyl phosphate that there is little point in evaluating the effects of placing the propanol at $k' = 2$ with this solvent.

TABLE 5

RECALCULATED N_{req} FOR n-ALCOHOLS

	Silicone 702		Tricresyl Phosphate
	$k' = 2$ (ethanol)	$k' = 2$ (propanol)	$k' = 2$ (ethanol)
MeOH			
	170	350	720
EtOH			
	170	255	160
PrOH			
	140	190	160
BuOH			

The data show clearly that the low α and high N_{req} with tricresyl phosphate are still the deciding factors and hence the silicone is certainly the better choice at this temperature. This result clearly illustrates the point that at equal k', the relevant α's determine N_{req} entirely. It now remains to calculate the probable optimum column conditions for the silicone. On comparing the values of N_{req} and α for the two situations discussed for this solvent it is obvious that there is something to be gained by placing the

TABLE 6
CALCULATED COLUMN LENGTHS, SOLVENT/SUPPORT RATIOS AND RETENTION VOLUMES (V_R).

	Silicone 702		Tricresyl Phosphate
	$k' = 2$ (ethanol) V_R (ml.)	$k' = 2$ (propanol) V_R (ml.)	$k' = 2$ (ethanol) V_R (ml.)
MeOH	1.8	1.65	15.8
EtOH	5.8	5.1	24.0
PrOH	13.3	11.6	55.0
BuOH	28.5	25.8	119.0
Col. length	7 in.	14 in.	29 in.
Solvent/ support	24% w/w	10.6% w/w	11.2% w/w

propanol at $k' = 2$ and accepting the need for a longer column. This situation is uncommon and arises only because of the very large α for ethanol and methanol.

If we now make some assumptions about column parameters, which are in fact close to the original data quoted (103), we can calculate the necessary column lengths, solvent/support ratios and resulting retention volumes. A column of 5-mm. I.D. packed with Celite (packing density $\rho_b \simeq 0.35$ g. per ml.; true density $\rho_s \simeq 2$ g. per ml.) would have a gas free space (V_d) of about 5 ml. per ft. and would contain about 1.25 g. per ft. of solid. Either column would be capable of giving about 300 theoretical plates per ft. (103), dividing this figure into the N_{req} for either column gives the length needed and from this V_d and hence, $2V_d = V_R$ can be calculated. The ratio V_R/V_g gives the weight of solvent required and since, from the column length and packing density, the weight of support can be determined, the solvent/support ratio can be found. Table 6 lists these calculated values.

The silicone column offers a slightly faster analysis with the lower solvent/support ratio at greater length but, in fact, the chromatograms

TABLE 7

COMPARATIVE DATA FOR THE RETENTION AT 110°C. OF AROMATICS
BY SEVERAL SOLVENTS

Ref. No.	Component	B. Pt.	Benzyl Diphenyl	Di-n-propyl Tetrachlor- phthalate	7,8-Benzo- quinoline	Phenan- threne
1	Benzene	80.1	61	70.5	68	57
2	Toluene	110.8	128	153.6	113	129
3	Ethylbenzene	136.1	242	265	214	249
4	n-Propylbenzene	159.5	441	471	384	485
5	n-Butylbenzene	180.0	877	834	780	935
6	o-Xylene	144.4	326	411.5	300	357
7	m-Xylene	139.1	265	310.5	241	286
8	p-Xylene	138.5	256.5	323	226.5	273
9	1-Me, 2-Et-Benzene	162.0	572	651	53?	640
10	1-Me,3-Et-Benzene	162.5	485	507	434	520
11	1-Me,4-Et-Benzene	162.0	478.5	531.5	424	511.5
12	1,2,3-Trimethyl-benzene	176.1	972	1044	864	1025
13	1,3,5-Trimethyl-benzene	164.6	542	581	517	—
14	1,2,4-Trimethyl-benzene	169.2	638	803	601	740

produced either way would look very similar and there is virtually nothing to choose. The important point emerging is the great speed with which the analysis might be done since the calculated total retention volume of less than 30 ml. for n-butyl alcohol (which would be slightly higher when allowance was made for carrier gas compressibility) could well require no more than 10 to 30 sec.

Consider now the much more complicated problem encountered when isomers, for instance, occur in single solute type mixtures. As an example we have the fourteen aromatic hydrocarbons listed in Table 7. These cover a boiling range of 80 to 175°C., include several sets of isomers and, that the analysis is by no means simple can be judged from the quoted boiling points. Particular difficulty may be expected in the separation of meta and para-xylene and of the three methyl ethyl benzenes, respectively. A number of solvents have been recommended for aromatic analysis and the xylene separation, in particular; four of these have been studied in some detail by, among others, Langer and the author (10). Table 7 also lists their data for the specific retention volumes in millilitres, recalculated from 0° to 110°C. ($V_g{}^T$), of fourteen solutes eluted from each of the four solvents. The particular temperature chosen for this preliminary evaluation is dictated by the extraordinarily short working temperature range of one solvent, phenanthrene, which melts only at 100°C. yet vaporises very rapidly at 120°C., while the list of solvents is limited by the shortage of specific retention volume data.

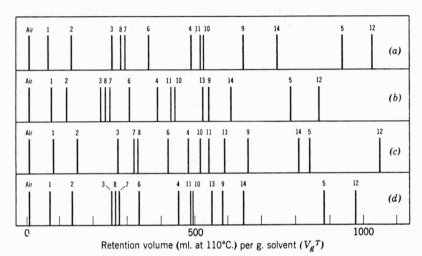

FIG. 2. Calculated sketelal chromatograms for the elution at 110°C. of the substances listed in Table 7 from columns containing 1 g. each of (a) phenanthrene, (b) 7,8-benzo-quinoline, (c) di-n-propyl tetrachloride and (d) benzyl diphenyl. Allowance has not been made for the gas compressibility effect.

Figure 2 shows in skeletal form the chromatograms which would be obtained at 110°C. with columns containing 1 g. of each of the four solvents. If this weight of liquid were distributed on 6 g. of Sil-O-Cel (16 per cent w/w) the total column dead space (V_d) would be, as assumed in constructing the figure, about 10 ml. Inspection of Figure 2 immediately shows which separations will present the greatest difficulty with each solvent and application of equation 7.44 to the data for these pairs then tells us the theoretical plate requirement for complete resolution in each case. The results of such calculations are shown in Table 8.

With all four solvents the *meta/para* xylene separation is difficult. For this analysis there is no doubt that, at the chosen temperature, 7,8-benzo-quinoline is the best of the solvents since it requires only 10,000 plates, in contrast to benzyl diphenyl, the least useful solvent, a column of which would need to have about 36,000 theoretical plates to bring about complete resolution. However, the separation of 1, methyl-3, ethyl-benzene from 1, methyl-4, ethyl-benzene is even more difficult than that of the xylenes, except when di-n-propyl tetrachlorphthalate is used as solvent. This liquid, in turn, makes hard work of the separation of n-butyl benzene and 1,2,4-trimethylbenzene. Even so, if all fourteen components are present in a mixture, the tetrachlorphthalate appears the best solvent choice, since only 26,500 theoretical plates would be needed for complete resolution in

TABLE 8
MOST DIFFICULT SEPARATIONS IN MIXTURE OF TABLE 7 AND CALCULATED (EQUATION 7.44) VALUES OF N_{req}

Solvent	Difficult Separation	N_{req}
Benzyl diphenyl	m and p-Xylene	36,000
	1, Me-3, Et-benzene⎤ 1, Me-4, Et-benzene⎦	190,000
Di-n-propyl tetrachlorphthalate	m and p-Xylene	24,000
	n-Butyl benzene ⎤ 1,2,4-Trimethylbenzene⎦	26,500
7,8-Benzoquinoline	m and p-Xylene	10,000
	1, Me-3, Et-benzene⎤ 1, Me-4, Et-benzene⎦	68,000
Phenanthrene	m and p-Xylene	17,000
	1, Me-3, Et-benzene⎤ 1, Me-4, Et-benzene⎦	136,000

comparison with the 68,000 required of the next best choice, 7,8-benzoquinoline. If roughly equal theoretical plate heights were attainable with each solvent, the tetrachlorphthalate column would thus need only to be about one-third the length of the next best, and would, correspondingly, yield a threefold faster analysis at a given flow rate since there is relatively little difference in V_g^T for the last eluted component (1,2,4-trimethylbenzene), no matter which solvent is used.

A point of interest which emerges from Table 8 is that benzyl diphenyl is not a particularly good solvent for the analysis of aromatic mixtures containing isomers, although many suppose otherwise. Further, phenanthrene, although reasonably effective for xylene separation, is of little use in resolving the methyl ethyl benzenes. In conjunction with its undesirable physical attributes, this conclusion leads to the view that this solvent and benzyl diphenyl need not be seriously considered for aromatic analysis under any conditions.

For the fourteen component analysis the choice of solvent clearly lies between the tetrachlorphthalate and benzoquinoline, the former appearing the more likely prospect. However, it is unsafe to depend upon conclusions arrived at on the basis of data for a single temperature and it may be that, at some temperature other than 110°C., the benzoquinoline might be preferable. The simplest way to check this possibility is to refer to plots of log V_g against $1/T$ such as those shown in Figure 3, and to read off values of α for, say, 60°C. This temperature represents the minimum possible with

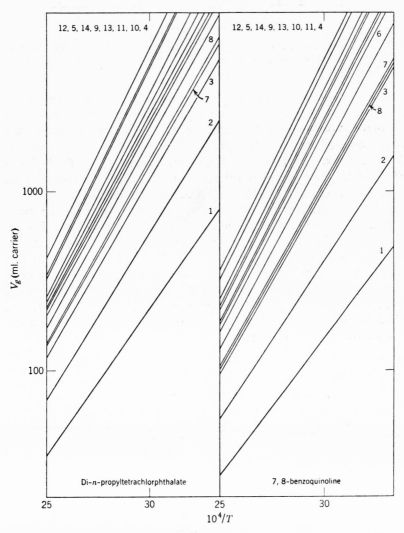

FIG. 3. Plots of log V_g against $1/T$ for the systems of Figure 2.

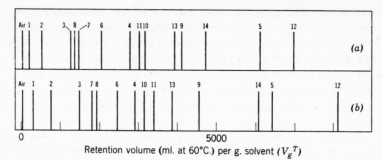

Retention volume (ml. at 60°C.) per g. solvent $(V_g{}^T)$

FIG. 4. Calculated skeletal chromatograms for the elution at 60°C. of the solutes of Table 7 from columns containing 1 g. each of (*a*) 7,8-benzoquinoline and (*b*) di-*n*-propyl tetrachlorphthalate.

benzoquinoline since it is close to its melting point. If, for any reason, a lower operating temperature is contemplated there is no alternative to the use of the chlorphthalate. This procedure further illustrates the advisability of quoting published retention data in the Clausius-Clapeyron or Antoine forms, as has several times been strongly recommended (15, 16). It should be noted that it is necessary to use log V_g rather than log $V_g{}^T$ plots since the latter are sufficiently curved to make extrapolation unreliable.

Figure 4 represents the skeletal chromatogram drawn for the hypothetical 60°C. elution of the fourteen components, the data being deduced from the log V_g versus $1/T$ plots shown in Figure 3. The retention volumes were, for uniformity, changed to $V_g{}^T$ data before plotting. The analysis time is increased by a factor of seven over the 110° elution but this is of no consequence at this point. The most difficult separations to achieve are exactly those found for 110°C. Application of equation 7.44 to the data yields the values shown in Table 9 for the number of theoretical plates required to effect complete separation at 60°C.

TABLE 9

Solvent	Difficult Separation	Plates Required
7,8-Benzoquinoline	*meta* and *para*-Xylene	9,800
	1-methyl, 3-ethyl benzene and 1-methyl, 4-ethyl benzene	24,500
D-*n*-propyl tetrachlorphthalate	*meta* and *para*-Xylene	10,500
	n-butyl benzene and 1,2,4-trimethyl benzene	13,000

The reduced theoretical plate requirements illustrate the advantage which often comes through the increased α resulting from the use of low elution temperatures. As at the higher temperature the benzoquinoline provides the better xylene separation although the difference between solvents is less clear cut than it was at 110°C. This may to some extent derive from the uncertainty involved in the extrapolation of $1/T$ plots which, in this case, would probably flatter the chlorphthalate. However, as before, the chlorphthalate appears the better choice for the full fourteen component analysis in virtue of the lower over-all theoretical plate requirement (13,000 as against 24,500).

Even the calculations carried out so far are not conclusive, however, because the values of k' relating to the most difficult separations deduced from Figure 4 are so great that for practical purposes a much lower solvent/support ratio than the assumed 16 per cent w/w would be very necessary. It is often the first difficultly separable pair to be eluted which determines the over-all theoretical plate requirement (column length), since the latter increases very rapidly with decreasing k'. Thus, in reducing k' for a xylene, for example, a condition can possibly be achieved when despite the fairly big value of α, the separation of benzene and toluene would be more difficult than that of the xylenes. In order to check this, consider now the consequence of attempting to achieve maximum analysis speed by arranging column conditions such that, with the chlorphthalate as solvent, p-xylene was eluted at $k' = 2$ (p. 156) while, with 7,8-benzoquinoline, m-xylene was eluted at the same point. This would entail using the former solvent in a column at about 0.16 per cent, and the latter at about 0.21 per cent w/w solvent to Sil-O-Cel. The retention volumes (inclusive of $V_d = 10$ ml.), k' and theoretical plate requirements then become as listed in Table 10.

As we consider first the benzoquinoline data, the perhaps not surprising fact emerges that the separation of ethyl benzene from p-xylene is now more difficult than that of the xylenes from each other, although by far the most difficult separation is still that of the methyl ethyl benzenes. For fastest analysis with this solvent, therefore, 1,methyl-4,ethyl-benzene should be brought out of the column closer to $k' = 2$ and so the theoretical plate requirement for the full analysis would rise even farther than the 28,000 now calculated as necessary.

With the tetrachlorphthalate, on the other hand, the *meta/para*-xylene separation is still the most difficult and so the siting of these in the neighbourhood of $k' = 2$ represents the most reasonable choice for fastest analysis. This solvent is, therefore, to be preferred to the benzoquinoline and the finally chosen operating conditions should be (assuming 10 ml. column dead volume per 6 g. of support as before), a column of about 0.2 per cent w/w solvent to support operating at 60°C. Assuming very reasonably that an efficiency of 500 theoretical plates per foot of column were readily attainable, then the columns would need to be about 40 ft. long, the corresponding analysis time being equivalent to a total carrier gas flow of only 85 ml. This flow of course, is that corresponding to the compressibility corrected value and so, in practice, a somewhat higher value would be observed. It is, thus, clearly possible to carry out the analysis in a matter of minutes.

It can be very reasonably argued that work with packed columns of such length and at such a low solvent/support ratio is difficult and inevitably

TABLE 10

Di-n-propyltetrachlorphthalate			7,8-Benzoquinoline		
V_g^{60} (ml.)	k'	N_{req}	V_g^{60}	k'	N_{req}
Benzene 13.1	0.31		Benzene 12.7	0.27	
		515			515
Toluene 17.75	0.775		Toluene 17.1	0.71	
Ethyl		385	Ethyl		250
benzene 25.5	1.55		benzene 27.5	1.75	
		5150			17800
p-Xylene 28.7	1.87		m-Xylene 28.7	1.87	
		19200			14800
m-Xylene 30.0	2.00		p-Xylene 30.0	2.00	
n-Butyl			1-Methyl,		
benzene 73.2	6.32		3-ethyl		
			benzene 51.1	4.11	
		14900	1-methyl,		28200
1,2,4-			4-ethyl		
Trimethyl					
benzene 76.8	6.68		benzene 53.0	4.30	

demands the use of non-adsorptive support. However, work with long columns has been carried out on numerous occasions in the past and packed columns up to 100 ft. in length are not out of the question, while various methods of pre-treatment are available to reduce adsorption. On the other hand, a capillary column would undoubtedly function well for this analysis in the calculated conditions, and would probably be easier to fabricate. It is questionable, however, whether the equivalent solvent loading to the 0.2 per cent packed column could be readily achieved. However, capillaries have been very successfully used by Desty, Goldup and Swanton (17) for separation of the xylenes, although the analyses were not particularly fast. When relatively long columns are required the choice between capillaries and packed columns is, to a large extent, determined by personal choice. The complexities involved in either approach having already been discussed, they will not be enumerated further.

An Optimum Solvent Support Ratio Equation. The calculation of the solvent/support ratio giving fastest analysis at any temperature for a packed column can be somewhat simplified and reasonably accurately worked out from an equation derived in the following way. Assuming for our present purposes the reasonable approximation that the condition $k' = 2$ for the second eluted of the most difficultly separable pair of substances represents the optimum for speed, we have by definition

$$2 = \frac{KV_l}{V_d}$$

Elaborating the statement made earlier concerning the relationship of V_d with packing volume it is evident that for any given column we can write

$$V_d = \omega V_s$$

where V_s is the true volume of the support solid and ω is some proportionating constant whose value is approximately 5 for Sil-O-Cel and 6.5 for Celite 545. With reproducible packing density, obviously ω would have a constant value from column to column for a given support and, since this is not far from the situation attainable in practice, it will be assumed true here. Then, as a generalisation we have,

$$\frac{V_l}{V_s} = \frac{2\omega}{K}$$

and, if w and ρ represent weight and true density respectively, the subscripts being as before,

$$\frac{w_l}{w_s} = \frac{2\rho_l \omega}{K\rho_s} \tag{13.1}$$

This equation is exact for any solute eluted at $k' = 2$. In order to generalise it further we can assume that for siliceous supports, $\rho_s \simeq 2$, when, for Sil-O-Cel columns

$$\frac{w_l}{w_s}\% \simeq \frac{500\rho_l}{K} \tag{13.2a}$$

and for Celite

$$\frac{w_l}{w_s}\% \simeq \frac{650\rho_l}{K} \tag{13.2b}$$

where K represents the partition coefficient of the second eluted of the most difficulty separable pair in any mixture.

A rough check of the utility of this equation can be made with the aid of the date of Table 7 for 110° elution of aromatics from the tetrachlorphthalate column. The approximately 16 per cent w/w column gave $V_g{}^T = 323$ for p-xylene with $V_d = 10$. Hence, for p-xylene to be eluted at $k' = 2$, a column (16 × 20)/323 per cent of solvent should be used, that is, a 1 per cent solvent support ratio. The density of the tetrachlorphthalate at 110° is about 1.4 g. per ml. hence, using equation 13.2a we find (500 × $\rho_L)K =$ 700/450 per cent, that is, it suggests the use of a column of 1.5 per cent solvent to Sil-O-Cel support. The use of more precise values of solid density etc. would have yielded a closer agreement, of course. Obviously, if some criterion other than $k' = 2$ is shown to represent the optimum for fastest analysis, equations 13.2 can be modified accordingly. Their use as they stand, however, can clearly indicate the upper limit of solvent/support ratio, since the optimum condition is much more likely to be $k' < 2$ than $k' > 2$. A point of interest which emerges from this discussion is that for a comparable analysis, solvent/support ratios must be chosen in proportion to the packing density of the supports, that is, allowance must be made for differences in ρ_s. Thus, comparison of support performance at the same solvent/support ratio is incorrect.

Mixtures Containing Different Solute Types. Often, although not always, the occurrence of different chemical types in a mixture makes for increased difficulty of analysis. As a first example of a problem in this class we can consider the separation of the methyl esters of higher fatty acids, a problem which has received much attention in view of its great biochemical importance. The problem is complicated first because of the enormous number of geometrical and structural isomers possible in long chain molecules and, secondly by the occurrence not only of saturated but also of unsaturated acids which may differ not only in the position of the multiple linkage but also in the number of such linkages in the molecule.

Notwithstanding the difficulties, a great deal of success has been achieved in this kind of work and, as might be expected from what was said earlier, columns containing both polar and non-polar solvents have been found useful. While little of the large volume of published retention data is in the form of specific retention volumes, the work of one group, Farquhar and his associates (9) has, fortunately for our present purposes, been provided in the necessary form for ester elution from columns of Apiezon-M grease and polyethyleneglycol adipate. These results are not only of interest in the present connexion, but also, as pointed out earlier, because of the light they throw on solvent function.

Table 11 lists retention data for the elution at 197°C. of a large number of esters of acids in the range C_{14} to C_{20} which are identified by the number of carbon atoms in the acid and the number of double bonds. Thus, for example, 16:2 represents a straight chain C_{16} acid containing two double bonds. The symbol "br" indicates side branching.

Before proceeding to discuss the details of analysis it is of interest to compare the functioning of the two solvents. It has already been pointed

TABLE 11

RETENTION DATA AT 197°C. FOR METHYL ESTERS OF FATTY ACIDS OF MENHADEN BODY OIL (15)

Acid C number	Ethylene Glycol Polyadipate V_g (ml.)	$V_g^{197°}$ (ml.)	Apiezon-M V_g (ml.)	$V_g^{197°}$ (ml.)
14:0	53.0	91.5	424	730
14:0 br	—	—	378	652
14:1	60.2	104.2	388	670
15:0	70.6	122	665	1150
15:0 br 1	—	—	580	1005
15:0 br 2	—	—	560	968
15:0 br 3	—	—	531	920
16:0	96.7	167.5	1035	1795
16:1	112.0	194	896	1550
16:2	136.5	236	880	1520
16:3	160.0	277	790	1365
16:4	—	—	765	1326
17:0	129.5	224	1600	2760
17:0 br 1	—	—	1215	2100
17:0 br 2	—	—	1360	2350
18:0	175	303	2430	4215
18:1	197	341	2110	3660
18:2	236	410	1945	3370
18:2*	253	440	—	—
18:3	304	528	1945	3370
18:4	349	606	1770	3060
19:0	237	412	3800	6600
20:0	322	560	5840	10100
20:1	357	620	4590	8400
20:2	410	712	4550	7860
20:2*	434	752	4340	7500
20:3	490	352	4030	6970
20:4	538	930	3590	6200
20:5	681	1150	3590	6200

Solutes are designated by carbon number and number of double bonds; e.g., 14:1 br is a C_{14} acid, branched and with one double bond in chain. Asterisk is a difference (unspecified) symbol.

out that for all types of ester, V_g is much bigger with Apiezon-M than with the polar polyadipate as solvent, a result which would not have been predicted on general grounds. To go further, Table 12 summarises values of α deduced from the data of Table 11 on the assumption that within each series of compounds there is a constant α from member to member. This view, which is not far from the truth, even in the worst case divergences are

TABLE 12

AVERAGE CLASS RELATIVE RETENTION DATA REDUCED
FROM TABLE 11

Solutes	Ethylene Glycol Polyadipate α	Apiezon-M α
Successive straight chain saturates	1.34	1.55
Straight chain saturate/ nearest eluted branched isomer	1.00 (?)	1.14
Straight chain saturate/ nearest eluted un- saturate	0.89	1.15
Successive straight chain unsaturates of same carbon number	1.15	1.07

no greater than about 6 per cent from the average, simplifies discussion considerably.

There is little to choose between the solvents in the separation of straight chain saturates from unsaturates, the main difference being in the order of elution, while the Apiezon grease is clearly superior when dealing with saturated homologues. Even more marked is its superior ability to separate straight from branched chain saturates, the value $\alpha = 1.00$ (?) quoted in this case for the polyadipate being deduced from the fact that no resolution was apparently achieved (9). This value cannot be taken too seriously since, evidently, α is almost certain to be greater than unity and it is probable that the true value was simply too small to be measured in the conditions employed. The one separation where the polar nature of the polyadipate really is of value is that of unsaturated isomers from each other, the differences in α with the two solvents being most marked for these compounds. However, one consequence of this selectivity, as was earlier suggested to be likely, is that other separations are made difficult. For example, we see

from the data of Table 12 that while the adipate column will readily separate the unsaturated esters 18:1, 18:2, 18:3 and 18:4, the separation of
18:2 from the saturate 19:0 is virtually impossible, while that of 18:4
from 20:1 is quite difficult. Thus, again, moderate selectivity, while
solving one problem, introduces another.

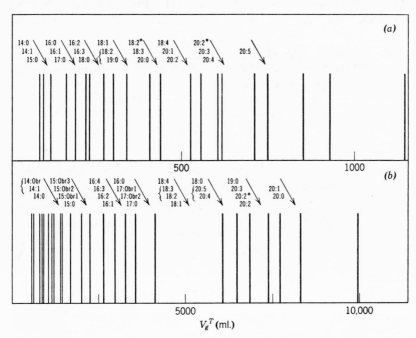

FIG. 5. Calculated skeletal chromatograms for the elution at 197°C. of the methyl
esters of fatty acids listed in Table 11 from columns each containing 1 g. of (a) polyethylene glycol adipate and (b) Apiezon-M.

Figure 5 shows the skeletal chromatograms drawn for columns containing 1 g. of each solvent, the specific retention volumes having been converted from V_g to V_g^T for the purpose. It should be noted that the time
scale for the Apiezon-M analysis is ten times that of the other, while in
addition, the chromatogram appears somewhat worse because a number of
branched chain saturates are resolved. A study of the figure indicates
immediately which will be the most difficult separations, and the use of
equation 7.44 then permits calculation of the column efficiency required for
complete resolution. Assuming again that we are dealing with 16 per cent
w/w solvent/support columns of $V_d = 10$ ml. the values obtained are those
listed in Table 13.

Clearly, with either solvent a number of separations appear impossible, or, at least, may require millions of theoretical plates even with the high k' values relevant to the calculations up to this point. To achieve these separations would thus demand both extremely long columns and analysis times. The situation could not be ameliorated by use of a capillary column, no matter how long, since the present calculation is based on a very high value of k' for either solvent and at the lower values attainable with capillaries even greater efficiencies and times would be required. It can, therefore, be

TABLE 13

CALCULATED THEORETICAL PLATE REQUIREMENTS FOR THE MOST DIFFICULT SEPARATIONS SHOWN IN FIGURE 5

Ethylene Glycol Polyadipate		Apiezon-M grease	
Solute pair	N_{req}	Solute Pair	N_{req}
16:2 ⟩ 17:0	15,100	14:0 br ⟩ 14:1	65,000
Saturated ⟩ Isomers	∞	15:0 br 1 ⟩ 15:0 br 2	24,200
18:2 ⟩ 19:0	∞	16:1 ⟩ 16:2	145,000
18:4 ⟩ 20:1	64,000	18:2 18:2* ⟩ 18:3	∞
		20:2 ⟩ 20:2*	16,000
		20:4 ⟩ 20:5	∞

concluded with reasonable certainty that single column analysis with either of the solvents discussed here cannot provide complete resolution of even this restricted list of esters.

Turning to those separations which are feasible we see that an Apiezon column of 150,000 theoretical plates and one of polyadipate of only 70,000 plates would suffice to give complete resolution of all but two small groups of compounds. The important point emerging from the discussion is that the groups of esters which are unresolved differ with the two columns and so duplicate analysis can provide the equivalent of complete separation. This is clearly the most satisfactory approach. Having established this point, detailed study of the probable optimum conditions can be attempted.

There is little point in recapitulating the procedure for choice of working temperature, particularly since in this instance the high boiling points of the solutes make the use of much lower temperatures than the one quoted difficult through sampling and sample size problems. In order to increase the speed of analysis, a study of the effect of placing the various pairs of difficult separation at $k' = 2$ can also be made as before. The consequence of this, for 197°C. elution, with the polyadipate column is to reduce the time of each analysis (in volume flow units) by a factor of thirty as compared with the chromatograms of Figure 5, but to increase the theoretical plate requirements to 150,000. Similarly, the Apiezon-M column would require to have about 330,000 plates, corresponding to a time reduction of about a factor of eighty. Because of the very high plate requirements and low solvent/support ratios required (about 0.5 and 0.2 per cent w/w respectively) the analyses might best be attempted with a non-porous (glassbead) support or with capillary columns in which solid adsorptive effects would be a minimum. If a porous solid support were used, either some form of pre-treatment would almost certainly be essential, or a higher temperature would have to be employed.

The very high efficiencies calculated as necessary derive mainly from the difficulty of the separations of esters 18:4/20:1, 14:0br/14:1 and 16:1/16:2 and so a final possibility of reducing the difficulty and time of the analyses lies in finding a third solvent capable of separating these pairs, if no others. If such a solvent were found, the theoretical plate requirements of the columns used would be reduced almost tenfold and almost any type of column might be used, since inordinate lengths would not be required. The type of solvent likely to be capable of facilitating the above separations can only be guessed at, but it is most likely, on general grounds, to be something polar, since all the pairs involve unsaturated esters.

As a final example, and one which illustrates a situation in which triplicate analysis turns out to be the most economical approach in terms of time and practical requirements, is that described (4) in connexion with the study of the pyrolysis of acetaldoxime. The reaction product mixture normally consisted of the seventeen substances named in Table 14, which lists also the columns, flow rate and inlet and outlet pressures finally chosen for the analyses. The compounds determined quantitatively with each column are shown in order of elution, those not appearing in any list either emerged more or less coincidentally with the "air" peak or were retained so long that they were eluted at concentrations below the level detectable.

Generally speaking, each gas liquid column splits the mixture into two, the low to medium boiling materials being analysed with the high solvent weight squalane column, while the highest boiling substances were separated with the low solvent weight polyglycol column. The silica gel gas solid column was needed to resolve the two otherwise inseparable pairs, $N_2:CO$ and $N_2O:C_2H_4$. No one of the three columns, no matter how long, could have brought about complete resolution of all seventeen compounds, because of the extreme theoretical plate requirements. The triple column approach, on the other hand, gave the equivalent of complete resolution in a time of about 20 min., the three analyses being conducted consecutively.

That multiple analysis leads often to simplification and speedier analysis has been verified several times (18, 19, 20) and examples where the use of as many as four (21) and five (22) separate columns was advantageous, are known.

TABLE 14

PYROLYSIS PRODUCTS OF ACETALDOXIME; ELUTION
BY HYDROGEN

20% w/w Squalane/Sil-O-Cel (8 ft.; $N \simeq 5000$)	2% w/w Polyethylene Glycol 600/Celite 545 (3 ft.; $N \simeq 1200$)	Silica Gel (7 ft.; $N \simeq 1000$)
25°C.	55°C.	85°C.
200 ml./min.	150 ml./min.	120 ml./min.
(at 15 p.s.i.)	(at 15 p.s.i.)	(at 15 p.s.i.)
95 p.s.i.–75 p.s.i.	23–15 p.s.i.	35–15 p.s.i.
(N_2, CO)	CH_3OH	N_2
CH_4	(CH_3CN, HCN)	CO
CO_2	CH_3NO_2	CH_4
(N_2O, C_2H_4)	H_2O	C_2H_6
C_2H_6	syn-CH_3CHNOH	N_2O
C_3H_6	anti-CH_3CHNOH	CO_2
C_3H_8		C_2H_4
HCN		
CH_3CHO		
CH_3CN		
Analysis time	Analysis time	Analysis time
8 min.	3 min.	7 min.

MULTIPLE COLUMN METHODS

The last two examples indicate the importance of multiple column methods, and so it is worthwhile considering in some detail the various possible ways of employing such techniques. The various alternatives which suggest themselves are:

a. The use of the chosen columns separately for consecutive analysis.

b. The simultaneous use of the columns operated in parallel.

c. Series operation of the columns.

d. The use of a single column containing a mixture of the sorbents (solids or liquids) selected.

The method (*a*), examples of which have already been given, involves taking as many samples as there are columns, a feature which can sometimes be undesirable due to irreproducibility of sampling procedures or limited supplies of sample. Further, it may not always be a simple matter to tie the several chromatograms together quantitatively. If this is necessary it is best to ensure that some particular component is clearly resolved with each column so as to act as a reference. Alternatively, a substance having this property can always be added to the mixture although this method opens up possibilities of error in manipulation. Probably the best course, although it is not the simplest or always applicable, is to eschew comparative methods and to have absolute detector calibrations and highly accurate and quantitative sample injection.

Other problems met with in this approach are those associated with the different pressure drops, flow rates and temperatures likely to be needed for each column. Separate thermostatting is a simple matter, while operation of the columns from a single gas supply presents little difficulty. One real obstacle is that for financial, if no other reasons, a single detector-read out system is usually desirable. Differences of flow and temperature with each column might introduce problems of stability, base line drift and possibly of solute condensation, if a single detector were used. This aspect of the problem would require serious consideration, but it is obviously worthwhile to attempt to overcome the drawbacks. The analysis can be speeded up somewhat when a single detector is used by starting the second analysis before the first is completed, the time overlap being equal to the "air" elution time of the second column.

Method (*b*) offers several advantages over (*a*). First, it may well be possible to carry it out faster, secondly, it can be arranged so that a single sample only is required, and thirdly, a single detector-read out system is easier to operate. Consider first how faster analysis may be achieved. The simplest way is to stagger injection times into the columns such that superimposed chromatograms do not contain superimposed peaks. Figure 6 shows the skeletal chromatograms obtained with the systems defined in Table 14, the chromatograms being stepped in time such that with a single read out system, at the quoted column efficiencies, all peaks would be resolved. The use of a single detector would demand that the total carrier gas flow from all columns was mixed at all times and so each peak would be diluted by the effluent from other columns. With the detectors now available this presents no real sensitivity problem and little trouble should be experienced through base line instability. Evidently, as many samples as columns are needed with this method, but a considerable saving in time is often achieved.

A more complicated parallel column approach, but one which would be at least as fast, would still employ a single detector and would require only a single sample, is that in which column compositions (or lengths) and carrier flow rates are adjusted so that all components would appear resolved on a single chromatogram. Figure 7 shows the skeletal chromatogram for the mixture of Figure 6 which would be obtained with single sample injection into the three columns of Table 14 if they were operated in parallel

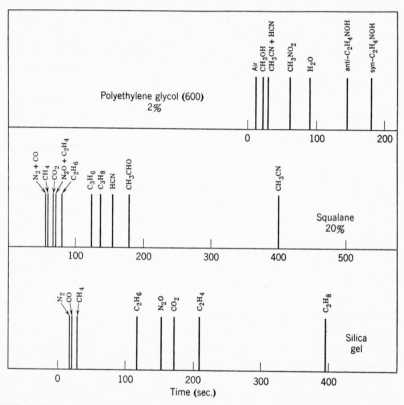

FIG. 6. Illustration in skeletal form of the chromatogram obtainable by a three sample, time-staggered injection of the mixture of Table 14 into the three columns listed and operated in parallel.

in the quoted conditions, altered only in that the polyethylene glycol column was of 6.2 per cent w/w, the squalane column was of 10.6 per cent w/w and the silica gel column was reduced from 3 ft. to 2 ft. 6 in. in length. It is seen from the figure that the most difficult "separation" is that of methyl cyanide and water, the separation actually being achieved by two columns. The width of the former compound peak must correspond to a column efficiency of about 1800 theoretical plates for there to be no peak overlap in the normal case. However, the water peak is so asymmetric that its front rises almost instantly to the peak maximum. This reduces the plate requirement for the cyanide to only about 500, a value readily attained in the conditions as is seen from Table 14.

An interesting feature of the chromatogram is the fact that although peaks 6 to 9 are so close together that it is difficult to resolve them, this is, in fact, unnecessary, since, each is resolved elsewhere on the chromatogram. Again, since C_2H_6 (peak 10) is readily resolved (900 plates) from peak 9 and C_3H_8 appears well separated as peak 22, these paraffins, when they occur

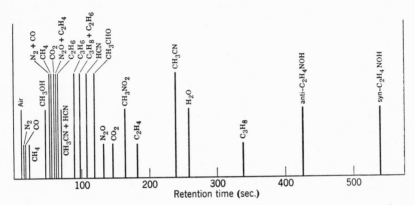

FIG. 7. Illustration in skeletal form of the result of adjustment of column solvent/support ratios (see text) for parallel operation and single sample injection of the mixture of Table 14.

again on the chromatogram, can be superimposed as peak 12, thus leading to a considerable speed-up of analysis.

It is quite certainly true that multiple column, single sample analysis of this type may not always be possible, although the advantages deriving from the single sample for quantitative analysis make it very worthwhile to study the system carefully with a view to its application. One important consequence of using a single sample technique is that the sample will be divided between columns in proportion to the gas flow rate through each. If the apportioning is so extreme as to lead to difficulty in quantitative analysis, this can, at least to some extent, be redressed by appropriate detector sensitivity adjustments during a run or by the use of columns of different diameters chosen so as to balance out flow rates. However, solvent/support ratios must then be changed in inverse proportion while if gas-solid columns are used column lengths may have to be modified. The parallel column technique seems to have been little used, perhaps because on an empirical basis it offers difficulties. Amberg, Echigoya and Kulawic

(23) have described a system capable of parallel operation, but it is not clear which approach was employed, or the extent to which the system was used.

The operation of several columns in series—method (c)—is considerably simpler technically than the approaches already discussed, since only a single gas flow system and sample are required. However, the method is somewhat less flexible in that adjustment of elution times is less readily brought about; it is only in exceptional cases that all the individual columns can be operated at their optimum flow rates. Again, if different column temperatures are necessary, problems may be encountered through condensation of vapours and possible excessive dead volume between columns as well as the difficulty in the construction and adequate operation of several thermostats in close proximity.

However, the difficulties are clearly readily overcome, since this method has been very widely employed (24 to 32) for such mixtures as ketones, hydrocarbons, halogenated hydrocarbons, phenols, exhaust gases, permanent gases, crude oils and aldehydes.

Obviously, a series operated system must show retention volume ratios which lie between those for the individual columns, since the total retention volume is the sum of the component parts. For example, if we designate the true retention volume of solute A with each of two solvents 1 and 2, as V_1^A and V_2^A and, similarly, for solute, B, V_1^B and V_2^B, we know that

$$\alpha_1 = \frac{V_1^B}{V_1^A} \quad \text{while} \quad \alpha_2 = \frac{V_2^B}{V_2^A}$$

and so

$$\alpha_{12} = \frac{V_1^B + V_2^B}{V_1^A + V_2^A} = \left(\frac{V_1^B}{V_1^A + V_2^A}\right) + \left(\frac{V_2^B}{V_1^A + V_2^A}\right)$$

Hence we see that α_{12} varies between α_1 (when V_2^A and V_2^B are zero) and α_2 (when V_1^A and V_1^B are zero) and also that the actual value of α_{12} achieved in practice depends upon the ratios V_2^A/V_1^A and V_2^B/V_1^B and thus, not only on α_1 and α_2 but also upon the solvent support ratios employed in the two columns. The critical nature of this latter quantity has been discussed by Martin and Winters (31). It is evident that multiple column techniques are only necessary when there is more than one difficult separation, since otherwise a single column of a selective solvent would suffice. Thus, since the most favourable ratio of V_2^A/V_1^A is not necessarily the same as that relevant to some other difficult separation which it is hoped also to achieve, some compromise must inevitably be accepted. Thus the choice of solvent weights and temperatures is less free than in the other methods discussed.

An example is shown in Figure 8, which illustrates a hypothetical skeletal chromatogram of a seven component mixture A-G obtained with a column (I) containing 1 g. of solvent 1 and the corresponding chromatogram obtained with a column (II) containing 1 g. of solvent 2. With column I the components C and D are unresolved, while with column II these are easily separated. On the other hand, with column II not only are E and F coincident, but, as is commonly experienced, there is an inversion in the order of elution relative to (I) since G emerges before E. The consequence of running the two columns in series (column III) is shown in Figure 8 (III),

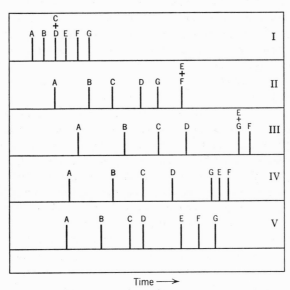

FIG. 8. Calculated skeletal chromatograms illustrating the use of series operated columns of solvents designated 1 and 2. Relevant solvent weights are (I) 1 = 1 g.; (II) 2 = 1 g.; (III) 1 = 2 = 1 g.; (IV) 1 = 0.68 g., 2 = 1 g.; (V) 1 = 1.5 g., 2 = 0.5 g.

which shows that while the separation of C and D is easily achieved, E and G are now coincident. It is apparent that if we attempt to keep C and D as far apart as possible by having the ratio of solvent weights in favour of solvent 2, the best we can hope to achieve is to have E midway between G and F. This situation is depicted in Figure 8 (IV), and results from the use of a composite column with only 0.68 g. of solvent 1 and 1 g. of solvent 2 in columns of the original length. The theoretical plate requirement is 5500 for the separation of E and F. The obvious course to simplify the problem is to accept a reduction of the separation of C and D, which is so great anyway as to pose no real problem. This means using more of solvent 1 than of solvent 2. The chromatogram resulting if, again at the same column lengths, a double column (V) containing 1.5 g. of solvent 1 with only 0.5 g. of solvent 2. The theoretical plate requirement is now only 1500 for the separation of F and G and is less than 1000 for C and D. Evidently, the over-all requirement could be reduced to about 1200 theoretical plates by slight further adjustment of solvent weights. The example shows both how the series column approach can solve difficult problems and how, at the same time, permissible solvent weight ratios are rather restricted.

Since, in the series operated system, the columns operate separately, the efficiencies should be additive. Barnard and Hughes (18), however, have claimed that series columns are less efficient than the individual columns, or even than mixed solvent columns. Primavesi (19) has more recently shown that their studies were carried out with inconstant solvent/support ratios and that, in fact, when allowance was made for this, their results were in accord with expectation.

Method (d), in which mixed solvents in a single column are used, would not be expected to differ from method (c) in the results it gives unless the eluted vapours had solubilities different in the mixture from those in the separate solvents. Nothing is known of such non-ideal effects in mixed solvent systems, what work has been reported has, in any case, always been carried out with immiscible liquids. Studies with silver nitrate saturated ethylene glycol/tri-isobutene mixtures obtained are identical with those computed from separate column data and those obtained with series operated columns of the same overall length and solvent weights. Further, the retention volumes of individual solutes were shown to vary linearly with the composition of the solvent mixture. Other workers (35, 36) who have successfully used mixed solvent columns did not comment on these points and presumably, therefore, observed no anomalies. It must be expected that some mixed solvents, particularly those showing partial or complete miscibility, may show unexpected solubilities for certain vapours and it may well be that a search for these would reveal some interesting and useful selectivities.

ISOTOPE SEPARATIONS BY GAS-LIQUID CHROMATOGRAPHY

Isotope effects are of great use in all types of chemical studies. There are numerous instances of the use of gas chromatography to separate mixtures into fractions, each fraction then being examined mass spectrometrically or with some radiation measuring device to determine the percentage isotopic content. However, a problem of greater interest is that of direct gas chromatographic separation of molecules differing only in containing isotopes of one or more constituent atoms. In particular, interest centres around the separation of hydrogenated and deuterated varieties of the same compound. That such separations are feasible has been demonstrated by Wilzbach and Riesz (145) who obtained partial resolution of cyclohexane and cyclohexane-d_{12} with a didecyl phthalate column of only 2500 theoretical plates

($k' \simeq 20$) at 53°C. The measured α was 1.08, which indicates that a column of 7000 theoretical plates would have given complete resolution. The high value of α derives from substantial differences in zero point energy, and hence saturation vapour pressure, of the molecules, and not from solution interaction differences, and it gives hope, with more efficient columns, for the much more difficult separation of mixtures of partially deuterated molecules. Experiments with tritiated benzene (145) gave evidence of resolution from the ordinary variety also and so there is clearly much to be gained from studies in this field.

GAS-SOLID CHROMATOGRAPHY

The apparatus required in this technique is identical with that for gas liquid analysis, what differences there are between the methods being in the operating conditions necessary. In explaining this it is simplest to list the problems met with in gas-solid systems which are either non-existent or of minor significance in gas-liquid chromatography.

a. Partition coefficients and, hence, retention volumes or times, are generally very much greater for adsorption than for solution.

b. Non-linear partition isotherms are common to all but the most low boiling materials. This leads to considerable peak asymmetry which, since in most instances adsorption is of the Langmuir type, takes the form of sharp fronts and diffuse tails. Linearity of isotherms is approached more closely at elevated temperatures.

c. As a consequence of (*b*), peak shape and width is sometimes very sensitive to sample size and also to sample composition. For the best results extremely small samples must thus be used.

d. Solid adsorbent properties depend very markedly on their origin, pretreatment and subsequent history. The reproducibility from batch to batch is thus not high, and column characteristics frequently alter markedly during use.

e. A serious problem arises through the possible catalytic activity of the adsorbent. This may be hundreds of times greater than in a gas-liquid column of comparable dimensions and even there, many workers consider the effects to be serious.

The consequence of (*a*) is that, in general gas-solid columns are operated at higher temperatures for a given analysis than would gas-liquid columns. One reason for this is that the low efficiency (*b*) does not permit the use of shorter columns to reduce analysis time and so temperature elevation is the only alternative. A second reason for the use of higher temperatures is the improved linearity of the adsorption isotherms (p. 16) and hence the greater peak symmetry. While these views imply that gas-liquid analysis is likely to be better for high boiling mixtures it equally predicts, as indeed is found, that gas-solid chromatography is superior in the analysis of low boiling mixtures. This arises because, in the separation of hydrogen and nitrogen, for example, because of solvent freezing and slow diffusion, no gas liquid column can be operated at a low enough temperature to increase k' sufficiently to bring $N_{req.}$ down to a reasonable level. On the other hand, the partition coefficients pertaining to adsorption of each of these substances by most active solids is high enough to require relatively small values of $N_{req.}$ even at temperatures as high as 100°C. or more.

The small sample problem (c) is probably not very serious in these days of super sensitive detectors and (d) and (e), which to some extent are interconnected, are of much greater importance. The irreproducibility of adsorbent is highly undesirable and normally difficult to overcome. Perhaps the most displeasing aspect of this is the fact that recorded data for retention volumes are unlikely to be of universal application. One approach to overcoming this is to use chemical or physical methods for surface modification and while there have been relatively few quantitative studies along these lines, there is sufficient evidence to show that it is a profitable approach. The whole question of solid activity assumes even greater significance in the light of (e). Most active solids have adsorptive surface areas in the region of 100 m.² per g. and are almost all capable of catalysing some reaction or another. Since the relatively inactive molecular sieves, Linde 13X, for example, have been shown to catalyse the conversion of cyclopropane to propylene at only 115°C. (53) the more active solids must be very suspect. This clearly makes vapour analysis at high temperatures somewhat dangerous. Some kind of study of such effects would undoubtedly be worthwhile, since for extremely high temperature analysis (ca. > 300°C.) there are so few solvents of sufficient stability and involatility that gas solid chromatography may well represent the most profitable, indeed the only possible, approach.

The following conclusions may be drawn from this discussion. First, gas-solid chromatography is superior in the analysis of very low boiling materials, and is also likely to be superior both at very low and very high column temperatures. Secondly, at this time the gas-solid and gas-liquid techniques are essentially complementary and compete only in the analysis of what we may call substances of intermediate boiling point such as the small group of inorganic and organic liquids boiling between about −50°C. and 0°C. In this region there is relatively little to choose between the two approaches and any final decision between them rests entirely on personal preference and the details of the analysis to be accomplished.

COLUMN PACKINGS

Virtually all the gas-solid chromatography reported up to now has involved the use of one or other of the activated adsorbents, carbon, alumina, silica gel or the molecular sieves. An outline of the results of studies with such solids and an indication of the types of analyses for which they are best suited is given below.

Carbon. There are, of course, many varieties of active carbon characterised by differences in activity stemming from differences in porosity and available area, the extent of oxygen and water adsorption and possibly of surface hydroxylation. Almost the only study of the effect of any of these quantities on the level of activation and, in turn, on the gas chromatographic performance is that of Habgood and Hanlan (37). These workers found that the highest column efficiency was obtained with the most active carbon, a result which they attributed to reduced resistance to mass transfer to and from the solid surface. This result conflicts with the experience of most workers who, in fact, attempt to reduce the activity either by chemical or physical pre-treatment or by the use of combined gas solid-liquid columns. If for any reason enhanced activity is desired, this can be achieved by pre-reaction to remove water with sodium or potassium, as has recently been described (38). Carbon columns have been used almost exclusively in permanent gas analysis, the most striking example probably being that of mixtures of H_2, air, He, CO, Ne, A and low boiling hydrocarbons, analysed in a single run (39).

Alumina. In contrast to carbon, alumina columns are very little used for permanent gas analysis. In fact, apart from the separation of hydrogen isotopes, every reported application involves hydrocarbon mixtures, usually of aliphatic compounds in the C_1 to C_5 range. Working with alumina deactivated by addition of inorganic bases and water it has, however, proved possible to analyse paraffin wax (C_{15} to C_{36}) at temperatures between 250° and 400°C. (40). This result accords with the suggestion made earlier that it is in very high temperature applications that gas solid chromatography may find its widest use for vapour analysis. In this connexion alumina appears at this time to offer advantages over other adsorbents, particularly in its adsorptive characteristics for organic vapours (41) and because it seems also to be the one which can most readily be prepared in a reproducible way (42, 43).

Of the adsorbents discussed here, alumina has been the subject of most detailed chromatographic study (2). The effect of changing degrees of hydration on both retention volumes and selectivities for paraffins and olefins was determined, the extent of hydration being varied by pre-heating the alumina at selected temperatures in the range 200° to 1000°C. As the water content was reduced by pre-heating from 200° to 500°C. the selectivity, as defined by the relative retention of olefin/paraffin, increased faster than the overall increment in retention volumes.

Further experiments in which 500°C. treated material was treated with increasing amounts of water substantiated the findings, which were then taken to indicate that adsorbed water covered highly active sites which interacted preferentially with the olefin. The results obtained also indicated that there was a minimum selectivity at some definite percentage of ad-sorbed water and that the quantity of water necessary to achieve this con-dition was a function of the available surface area of the alumina. Calcul-ations suggested that this minimum selectivity corresponded to monolayer coverage by water and that selectivity was more a function of the extent of this coverage than of intrinsic surface area of the solid. Alumina, heat treated progressively from 500° to 1000°C., gave correspondingly decreasing retention volumes for the paraffins, but those of olefins were little affected. In consequence, alumina heat treated at 1000°C. was so selective towards olefins that ethylene was eluted well after propane. Studies of the effect of varying treatment time at constant temperature showed that there was little change after one hour and this, therefore, represents a generally accep-table period for activation whatever temperature is chosen.

The considerable variations in chromatographic behaviour with pre-treatment indicate clearly the significance of the problem of irreproduci-bility. If reasonably highly activated aluminas are to be used it is evidently necessary to exclude water completely from the carrier gas stream and sample since otherwise the column continually hydrates and alters in retention characteristics. The most suitable condition from the point of view of reproducible column construction appears to be that of minimum selectivity, that is, relatively low activity (2), but even in this state it was found necessary to pre-saturate the carrier gas with water for routine analysis. An example of an excellent, although slow, analysis of a hydrogen C_1 to C_4 hydrocarbon mixture of fourteen components is shown in Figure 9 and it illustrates the advantages of controlled water deactivation, since the column efficiency approaches 300 theoretical plates per foot, a figure far higher than could be achieved with a normal activated solid.

Silica Gel.   This material has been by far the most widely used adsorbent, although its properties and selectivity differ little from those of active carbon if the types of analysis performed are anything to judge by. It has been used almost exclusively in permanent gas and low boiling hydro-carbon analysis. It is an interesting point that by far the greatest proportion of chromathermographic analysis appears to have been performed with silica gel columns.

As found for alumina, the activity of the material depends very markedly on its history and the level of water adsorption. Turkel'taub et al. (44), in a study of the chromatographic performance of a variety of silica gels, each at different extents of hydration, found that the driest samples were of little value and that for each type of gel there was an optimum extent of wetting. This result was confirmed by Schulze and Schmidt-Kuster (45) who concluded that, as a rough generalisation, material dried over a period at 250°C. had the most desirable chromatographic properties in terms of peak symmetry. A study of the effect of pore size in the range 10 to 70 Å on the adsorptive properties of silica gel (46) has shown that, to a large extent,

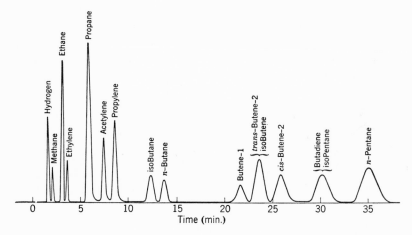

FIG. 9. C_1 to C_4 hydrocarbon analysis with a water deactivated alumina column (2). *By courtesy of the Institute of Petroleum.*

selectivity of the solid derives more from the effect of the molecular shape and size of the adsorbate than from its polarity. Although these studies were not so comprehensive as those of alumina discussed overleaf, the results obtained are so similar that the findings for alumina can probably be extrapolated with fair certainty to silica and even carbon.

The types of analysis best carried out with silica gel columns are exemplified by that quoted earlier for carbon columns (39) and the mixture carbon monoxide and dioxide, nitrogen, oxygen and the C_1 to C_4 hydrocarbons (47). Separations of the oxides of nitrogen (48) and of sulphur (49) have also been reported. In the author's experience silica gel columns are to be preferred to carbon columns since efficiencies seem to be higher, retention times are more reproducible, while relative retentions appear to be little different.

Molecular Sieves. The term "molecular sieve" is applied to inorganic compounds such as the calcium zeolites, which, having an open and well defined structure of molecular dimensions are able to trap molecules small enough to enter the zeolite structure, but not others. The process is sometimes called "persorption." An excellent review of the use of porous crystals as filters and the possibilities of their modification for specific purposes has recently been given by Barrer (50). The sieves most readily commercially available at this time are all calcium aluminium silicates, although other types of compounds, urea for example, have similar properties. Those which have received widest use gas chromatographically are the Linde sieves 4A, 5A and 13X. The numbers do not denote network dimensions, although they do not differ significantly from these quantities. In the 4A variety, for example, the average interatomic distance is about 3.8 Å. These materials have been studied crystallographically (51) and shown to have a common building block unit of 24 silicon and aluminium ions interconnected with 36 oxygen ions; the 4A and 5A sieves have these units in cubic array while the 13X has them tetrahedrally arranged. A fairly detailed study of the properties of the 5A sieve has been carried out by Janak, Krejci and Dubsky (52). They first studied the effect of pre-heating and found that above about 100°C. occluded water only is released, but that above 300°C. lattice bound water comes off. It is the removal of the latter that confers its sorptive properties on the material and so activation above 300°C., before use, is always necessary. The extent of this activation is important since it has been shown (52) that again, as for alumina and silica, the amount of residual water in the sieve determines selectivity in a number of cases. For example, at 2 per cent w/w of water, Linde 5A sieve columns retain carbon monoxide about twice as strongly as methane; at 4.5 per cent water the two substances are inseparable, while at 9 per cent water methane is retained twice as long as carbon monoxide. The residual water level is primarily determined by the activation temperature which should lie between 300° and about 600°C.; above the latter temperature lattice breakdown through crystallisation, sintering and melting is likely to occur. Similar changes in selectivity following addition of water and also of such substances as ammonia and methylamine have been demonstrated for a number of sieve type materials by Barrer and Rees (129).

It is a point of interest that the inversion of the elution order of carbon monoxide and methane as the water content of the sieve is reduced implies almost certainly that there is at least some true adsorption of the former. This conclusion is likely to be quite general and so separations achieved with molecular sieves are not due solely to simple cageing of molecules. Some cases where anomalous orders of elution are encountered are thus to be expected. It is to be anticipated also that water will be irreversibly sorbed by highly activated sieves and, indeed, this property can be utilised in pre-columns designed to remove water from samples, or in pre-injection point columns incorporated to produce very dry carrier gases such as are necessary with many gas-solid columns and the argon detector. Carbon dioxide also interacts with the commercially available molecular sieves, probably to produce calcium carbonate, and so cannot be used as carrier. Even the analysis of samples of mixtures containing this gas leads eventually to breakdown of the packing and, in contrast to the case of water sorption, the sieve columns cannot then be re-activated. Similar effects are also sometimes observed through interaction of organic materials with silicate networks (54).

Almost any mixture of permanent gases can be separated by use of molecular sieve 4A columns and they provide, in the author's experience, by far the simplest separation of oxygen and nitrogen. The 5A sieve, in addition, retains n-paraffins but not their isomers (straight but not branched or cyclic molecules) and, in consequence, excellent analyses of the *normal* paraffins (C_3 to C_6) in petroleum and kerosenes have been achieved (52, 92), while there is evidence that n-paraffins as high as C_{40} can be dealt with.

Other Adsorbents. The amount of work carried out with adsorbents other than those discussed earlier is negligible. Glemser and Rieck (58) have used iron oxide and claimed greater selectivity, and stronger adsorption of low boiling materials than with the particular alumina used by them. Certain varieties of coal (59), magnesium silicate (60) and Fuller's earth (61) have been successfully employed in the analysis of C_1 to C_5 hydrocarbons, the coals, in addition, being found very effective for the separation of hydrogen, carbon monoxide and methane and also of all the rare gases except radon. An adsorbent of quite different type is ammonium phosphomolybdate, for which application in the analysis of some low boiling substances has been claimed (62).

Perhaps the most interesting approach in the search for new adsorbents is that initiated by White and his colleagues (63 to 66). These workers utilised the fact that the sodium ions in naturally occurring clays, such as bentonite, could be replaced by such things as amines and organic bases. They have studied the gas solid chromatographic properties of dimethyldioctadecylammonium bentonite, prepared through the use of the appropriate quaternary ammonium salt, in some detail, and shown it to be capable of excellent separations of aliphatic and aromatic hydrocarbons, the eluted peaks being very symmetrical. To some extent it seems likely that such adsorbents can be "tailored" to suit particular separations and this field offers considerable promise for the future.

The possibilities of mixed solid packings are evident but as yet the field has hardly been touched. That improved separations can be achieved in this way is shown by the work of Krejci, Tesarik and Janak (67) who greatly simplified the analysis of a mixture of krypton, nitrogen and methane by use, at 20°C., of a column containing active carbon and Linde sieve 4A in the ratio 1:10 by weight.

HYDROGEN ANALYSIS

Both hydrogen and deuterium can exist in *ortho* or *para* forms, distinguished by the way in which the nuclear spins are coupled. In addition, they can react together to produce the mixed molecule HD. Thus, in principle, a sample of "hydrogen" might well correspond to a five component mixture. The *ortho/para* and the $H_2/HD/D_2$ conversions are extensively employed in fundamental studies of reaction kinetics and so the analysis of such mixtures is of considerable importance. This, and the fact that the gas chromatographic solution to the analytical problem involved probably represents the most spectacular demonstration of the power of the technique, are sufficient reason to justify separate discussion of the approaches so far adopted.

The earliest indication of the likely success of gas chromatographic analysis came in the work of Glueckauf and Kitt (68) who, using the displacement method, achieved an adequate separation of H_2 and D_2 with a column of palladium black distributed on asbestos. They eschewed the elution method since palladium catalyses the reaction forming HD and, since this is an equilibrium situation, quantitative analysis would be impossible. This view was later confirmed independently (69).

The undoubted superiority of the elution method, however, prompted numerous efforts to overcome the problems involved. The complete separation of o-H_2 and p-H_2 was soon achieved by Moore and Ward (70), using an alumina column at 77°K., and since then van Hook and Emmett (71) have shown that the analysis can be extended to include D_2. While Moore and Ward described partial resolution of o-D_2 and p-D_2, the latter workers do not appear to have observed this. At the same time, they have also shown that HD cannot readily be separated from o-H_2 and that the combined peak tails sufficiently to overlap the D_2 peak somewhat. For quantitative analysis of $H_2/HD/D_2$, therefore, two correction procedures were found to be necessary. First, either the o-H_2/p-H_2 or the HD/D_2 ratio had to be found. The former is normally 3, and in many cases this figure sufficed as the correction; if it did not, however, the latter ratio had somehow to be measured. Second, graphical allowance was necessary for the (o-H_2 + HD)/D_2 peak overlap. It was found that, following these allowances, when HD was present in large amounts, analyses corresponded to those conducted mass spectrometrically to within 1 per cent for each component. At low HD content, on the other hand, discrepancies of up to 14 per cent were noted.

In general, workers are interested either in *ortho/para* separation or in $H_2/HD/D_2$. Thus, the approach already described may often be over-elaborate and an obvious way of resolving the situation for the second of the above mixtures would be to prevent resolution of the *ortho* and *para* hydrogen. This can readily be achieved by utilising the fact that at low temperatures, paramagnetic adsorbents strongly catalyse the *ortho/para* conversion. Thus, while alumina, being diamagnetic, separates the two forms, iron oxide, chromia or carbon, for example, would continually equilibrate the separated materials and thus provide only a single, although perhaps rather broad, hydrogen or deuterium peak. This approach was adopted by Smith and Hunt (72, 73), who used a mixed, water deactivated alumina/chromia column to obtain an excellent $H_2/HD/D_2$ separation.

What is described as an even more successful approach is that of using diamagnetic and paramagnetic columns in series (74). The first column, 2 m. of alumina, gave the separation p-$H_2/(o$-$H_2 + HD)/D_2$, while the second column, 50 cm. of mixed iron oxide and alumina simply maintained the original p-H_2/o-H_2 separation but resolved the o-H_2, HD and D_2. Both columns were maintained at 77°K. In the iron oxide column, of course, the two forms of hydrogen originally separated were equilibrated to the composition corresponding to the column temperature ($\sim$1:1) but this was of no consequence since the chromatogram still showed four peaks. Since the four component analysis can, thus, be achieved, there is every reason to suppose that the technique can be extended to include o-D_2 and p-D_2 separation also, and thus give complete analysis of all the forms in a single run.

The importance of this result is unquestionable, since gas chromatography can now replace the much more expensive mass spectrometer in many of the applications where the latter has, up to now, still held sway. Further, extension of the technique to the preparative scale should eventually make it possible to prepare reasonable quantities of highly pure samples of any or all of the five varieties of hydrogen. While virtually pure p-H_2 and o-D_2 can be prepared at this time it has never previously been possible to obtain better than 75 per cent o-H_2 or 67 per cent p-D_2 since these represent the high temperature equilibrium values.

GAS LIQUID-SOLID CHROMATOGRAPHY

The use of mixed liquids in gas liquid chromatography and of mixed solids in gas solid chromatography has already been discussed (pp. 366, 374). It is not surprising, therefore, that columns composed of active solids coated with an involatile liquid should also have been used. Such columns are generally regarded as belonging to one of two classes, the first being that in which the involatile liquid is added merely to reduce the solid activity somewhat and so yield more symmetrical elution peaks (tailing reducers), the second being that in which, in effect, the active solid acts as a support for the liquid and functions as a selectivity modifier. Since, in any combination column the retentive properties of both phases must be experienced by any eluted material, the effects of the two phases cannot be immediately divorced and therefore, irrespective of the proportions of liquid and solid, such columns will be described here as gas solid-liquid columns.

The earliest work in the field is that of Eggertsen, Knight and Groennings (75) who added up to 1.5 per cent by weight of squalane to a Pelletex carbon column and thereby vastly improved the resolution of lower hydrocarbons through enhanced peak symmetry. The considerable tailing obtained with Pelletex alone was, in fact, virtually entirely eliminated. Since this work, numerous tailing reducer liquids have been employed with good effect, the most comprehensive study being that by Scott (2). His results for water deactivation of aluminas have already been described and he showed that silicone oil, diglycerol, polyglycols or dimethyl sulpholane could be used in place of water with much the same result. However, in contrast to the results of water deactivation, no region of minimum selectivity could be found, since the combined retentive effects of the two sorbent phases were continuous with composition. This results because the total retention volume is the sum of the individual retention volumes due to the uncovered solid and the liquid present. Thus since

$$V_{R(\text{total})} = V_{R(\text{uncovered solid})} + V_{R(\text{liquid})}$$

as the proportion of liquid increases so does $V_{R(\text{liquid})}$; $V_{R(\text{solid})}$ meanwhile being reduced. The equivalence stated above has been substantiated by Grubner and Smolkova (76) over a wide range of liquid/solid ratios. Thus, even where liquids are added merely as tailing reducers they exert a sufficient effect on retention times to alter completely the characteristics of the packing.

Figure 10 shows a chromatogram of a C_1 to C_4 hydrocarbon mixture obtained (2) with a column of alumina partially deactivated by water carrying 2 per cent by weight of silicone oil. It is quite as good as that shown in Figure 9, where water deactivation alone was used and, after allowing for the difference in flow rates, is rather faster on the basis of equal weights of packing. The main problem encountered in the routine use of these columns is again the affinity of the uncovered solid for water but, with its rigorous exclusion, it is perfectly possible to work with such systems over long periods. In order to illustrate the comparison with gas-liquid chromatography, Figure 11 shows chromatograms obtained for low boiling hydrocarbons with an alumina/silicone oil and a squalane column (77). It is only in analyses of this type of mixture that the methods compete (p. 330) and, in this instance, the alumina/silicone column offers certain advantages, since the α's are more favourable and so permit faster analysis.

A number of workers have employed gas solid-liquid columns at liquid

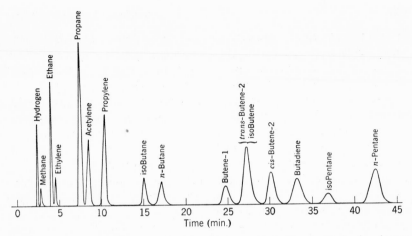

FIG. 10. C_1 to C_4 hydrocarbon analysis with 2 per cent silicone oil-alumina (water deactivated) column (2). *By courtesy of the Institute of Petroleum.*

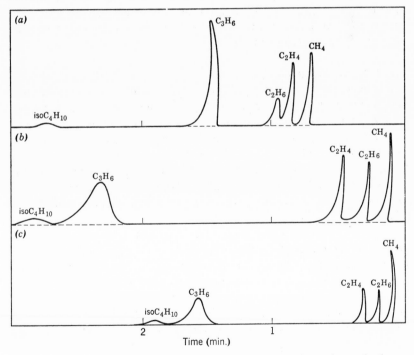

FIG. 11. Comparison of chromatograms of the major pyrolysis products of *n*-butane obtained with columns containing (*a*) 18 per cent w/w squalane/Sil-O-Cel and (*b*) 2 per cent silicone/alumina. The analysis time has been adjusted to show clearly the greater α for olefin/paraffin obtained in (*b*); trace (*c*) shows the higher speed attainable in consequence of the higher α. Recorder chart has a curved scale. Isobutane occurs as impurity ($<0.05\%$) in reactant.

377

loads as high as 20 to 30 per cent. Thus, Norrish and the author (78) used silica gel/dibutyl phthalate columns to achieve very effective paraffin/olefin separations while the same problem has been solved by others by use of alumina coated either with dimethylformamide (79) or by propylene carbonate (80). Alumina carrying up to 20 per cent of dioctyl phthalate has proved very useful in the analysis of Freons (81), and when coated with a variety of liquids is suitable for phenols and aromatics in general (82).

There is no doubt that gas solid-liquid chromatography can be a very powerful tool, since it has a somewhat greater flexibility than either component technique alone. Thus, in the analysis of complex mixtures such as, for example, the fatty acid ester mixture discussed earlier (p. 355), small changes in α might be induced by incorporation of small amounts of alumina or silica gel into the support and these small changes might conceivably reduce the very high column efficiency requirements by an order of magnitude or more. At this time, the technique has been applied almost exclusively to the analysis of low boiling materials. It remains to be seen whether, at relatively low column temperatures, it has any application in the higher range of boiling points.

CHOICE OF CARRIER GAS

The identity of the carrier gas used in gas-liquid chromatography may affect the theoretical plate height markedly, but has no discernable effect on compressibility corrected retention volumes. In gas-solid chromatography, however, not only is column efficiency affected but retention volumes also depend upon the identity of the carrier gas. This is a consequence of the fact that the carrier is itself adsorbed and so competes with the sample components for adsorption sites and, effectively, reduces the available area. Obviously, the effect will be most marked for components which are weakly adsorbed and will become progressively less pronounced as we pass along the time axis of the chromatogram. The phenomenon has been studied and verified by a number of workers (55 to 57).

Some idea of the magnitude of the effect can be gained by the following retention time data of Greene and Roy (57) for elution of methane by various carriers from a carbon column at 25°C. at fixed flow rate; helium, 34 min.; argon, 22 min.; nitrogen, 16 min.; air, 15 min.; acetylene 5 min. Compressibility corrections for the different pressure gradients prevailing would modify these figures somewhat, but the effect is evidently very significant and could be misleading if not recognised. It should be borne in mind also that if retention volumes are a function of carrier gas identity they must also depend upon its pressure. Thus fairly close pressure control is demanded for routine analysis. However, the effect of carrier identity and pressure could be turned to good account since it represents a technique of modification of the adsorbent which should be extremely flexible and reproducible.

SPECIAL TECHNIQUES

PRE-COLUMN ABSTRACTORS

Among the more serious problems met with in quantitative analysis is that in which one or more components are present in great excess and so render accurate analysis of the trace components difficult because of band overlap through spreading and distortion. In many instances the major component is water, which introduces even greater difficulty because, at best, it gives very poor elution peaks. A specialised application of the series operated multi-column system is employed to overcome this problem.

Ahead of the main column or columns is sited an abstractor column, the desirable property of the packing being its ability to retain the undesired component or components very strongly; so strongly, in fact, that the column need be only very short. For the removal of water from hydro-carbons, for instance, a short length of Linde molecular sieve 4A can be used (83). This packing can be used for many analyses since the water is irreversibly adsorbed up to the saturation point. Alternatively, glycol or glycerol pre-columns will remove water from many systems, but in this case, either a new pre-column must be used for each analysis or during the analysis by the main column the pre-column must be cleaned out by passage of a high gas flow directed to waste. (Depending on the direction of the waste flow this technique is described either as forward or back flushing.) A system of this type has been described by Rysselberge (84) who used an Apiezon-M grease pre-column to remove higher hydrocarbons from crude oil analysed with a di-nonyl-phthalate main column.

A similar approach to the same problem was adopted by Lichtenfels, Fleck, Burow and Coggeshall (85) who, however, used a single column 8 ft. in length with a tapping point 1 ft. along from the injection point. At some appropriate time this first short section was bypassed so that only hydro-carbons $<C_7$ occurring in the crude oil samples entered the main section of the column. The bypassed section was cleared of higher boiling hydro-carbons by a high gas flow directed to waste. A very interesting variation of this latter method has been described by Mackay, Lang and Berdick (56). A 1-in. pre-column was maintained at a temperature 100°C. lower than the main column, the two being of identical composition. Very large samples of human breath ($\sim$500 ml.) were then injected and the compounds responsible for breath odour, which were present at very low concentra-tion, were effectively trapped in the pre-column. Following elution of the air, and if necessary, after several injections, the pre-column temperature

was rapidly raised to that of the main column. The abstractor thus acted first as a concentrating device and secondly as an efficient injector system for the very small samples involved.

A number of pre-column packings operating on the basis of specific, irreversible chemical reaction with a given chemical substance or species have been employed with success. For example, silica gel impregnated with molten maleic anhydride removes excess conjugated hydrocarbons such as 1,3-butadiene from complex hydrocarbon mixtures (87) while carbon carrying irreversibly adsorbed bromine (88) and silica carrying concentrated sulphuric acid remove olefins from mixtures with other hydrocarbons (89). Other examples are the use of silver nitrate to remove secondary and tertiary alkyl bromides from mixtures with the primary compounds (91) and mixtures of sodium hydrogen sulphite and ethylene glycol for aldehyde removal.

Abstractor columns can be used to simplify analysis of very complex mixtures as well as to remove components present in excess. For example, Linde molecular sieve 5A retains n-paraffins strongly but not the isomers, and so complex paraffin mixtures can be analysed by duplicate analysis, with and without a molecular sieve pre-column (92); no resolution of an n-paraffin from its isomers is required and so, relatively inefficient main columns of short length can be used. This approach reduces analysis time considerably, especially when wide boiling range samples are used. A similar technique has been used for paraffin/olefin (89) and aldehyde/ketone (90) analyses and it is interesting to speculate on the possibilities inherent in a single main column, multi-pre-column method of analysis. In many respects this approach might be more fruitful for very complex mixtures than would any straightforward single or multi-column technique since the pre-columns confer an absolute selectivity to the system, a state of affairs shown earlier to be the most desirable, and one not very readily achieved by the more conventional means. Further, the main column employed would then need to have no special selective properties and any suitable boiling point separating solvent could probably be used.

CHEMICAL CONVERSION TECHNIQUES

It is often found that while the components of certain mixtures are well separated in analysis there is sufficient band distortion that the resolution is low. This situation often arises, for example, in fatty acid analysis and conversion of the free acids to their esters before analysis commonly provides a solution (9). Another instance of improved analysis is that obtained for aqueous alcohol mixtures with silicone grease columns after prior esterification with nitrous acid (94). Often, too, pre-reaction can be of help when sample components are involatile and possibly thermally unstable. The conversion of amino acids to aldehydes by oxidation with ninhydrin (93) is a good example of this, while it has been shown (95) that the silyl ethers of phenols, produced by reaction with hexamethyldisilazane, chromatograph better than the phenols themselves. They are also so much more volatile that the comparison of chromatograms of treated and untreated phenol containing samples is a great aid to phenol identification.

At the present time the trend in this field is in the direction of incorporation of the reactant in a pre-column. The ninhydrin conversion of amino acids, for example, has been elegantly brought about by Zlatkis and Oro (96) in a short pre-column heated to 140°C. An alternative approach of great ingenuity is the so-called flash exchange technique initiated by Ralls (97, 98). Basically, this method involves production of solid derivatives of certain of the sample components in a short pre-column, the solid derivatives formed being by choice relatively thermally unstable and regenerating the parent compound on heating, either alone or in the presence of some other substance. Thus, after the desired components have been held back by reaction in the pre-column they can be regenerated and separately analysed by rapid heating of the abstractor. The types of compound so far dealt with in this way are the fatty acids through conversion to their potassium salts and carbonyl compounds which were converted to 2,4-dinitrophenyl hydrazones. The adequacy of the method for carbonyl compounds has been independently verified by Schepartz and McDowell (99). The regeneration time at 300°C. was in each case only a few seconds.

An alternative approach in the use of pre-column micro reactors lies in their application to reaction kinetic studies, in particular of heterogeneous catalysis. The pre-column in this instance is actually the kinetic reaction vessel and injection of the unreacted sample leads first to reaction, and then to rapid injection of the products into the column (100 to 102). This technique is as yet in its infancy and there are doubtless several problems to be overcome. Some of these have been discussed by Keulemans and Voge (130) who found, in particular, that the kinetic data obtained differ somewhat from those obtained by more conventional means. There is no doubt, however, that it represents a very promising field of study.

PRE-COLUMN REACTORS FOR QUALITATIVE STUDIES

A special application of pre-column chemical reactors is in the identification or characterisation of high polymers, fats or waxes, lacquer components and involatile materials in general. In this method, closely controlled pyrolysis (or perhaps oxidation) of the involatile material is brought about in a pre-column reactor and the products are then analysed. The method is not intended to be quantitative and is designed only for identification purposes, the success of the procedure resting on the reproducibility of the chromatographic silhouettes obtained. The technique was first used by Davison, Slaney and Wragg (140), and has since been extended considerably (141 to 144). In the most recent work the reactor takes the form of a platinum filament on which the material to be pyrolysed is coated in milligram quantities when cold. The filament can be raised electrically to 1000°C. or more from cold in a matter of seconds, and the gaseous products are then swept into the analysing column. The usefulness of the method is limited by the reproducibility of the pyrolysis. This, however, does not seem to be a great problem at this time, although if attempts are made to refine the technique so as to distinguish between very closely related substances it might become important.

TEMPERATURE PROGRAMMING

The isothermal analysis of wide boiling range mixtures frequently leads to a very wide spread in retention times and, through the increasing dilution of components of increasing retention volume, a progressive diminution of detector sensitivity towards components results. Quantitative measurement of peaks appearing late is thus often difficult if not impossible. There are several ways to obtain more satisfactory results, the most obvious being the use of one or other of the multi-column or pre-column methods already discussed. An alternative approach, initiated by Drew and McNesby (104), employs a single column, the temperature of which is raised progressively as analysis proceeds. Thus, successively eluted substances experience increasingly higher average temperatures and so emerge from a column more rapidly than they would in isothermal conditions.

Before going farther we may consider the possible theoretical consequences of temperature programming. Obviously peaks, which eluted isothermally at the lowest temperature of the programme would be spread out, are brought closer together by programming and so, since this means that α for successive pairs is decreased relative to the isothermal values, greater column efficiency is necessary to provide a separation. At the same time, since the specific retention volumes are also decreased in comparison with the programme starting temperature isothermal values, k' for each component is reduced and so further raises the efficiency requirements of the column. Thus, unless the column efficiency increases faster with increasing temperature than does N_{req}, the programmed temperature technique cannot provide as good a result as would the isothermal method operating at the *starting* temperature of the programme. While it is true that most evidence supports the view that theoretical plate heights decrease with rising temperature, this state of affairs is very much dependent upon the chosen column and operating parameters (see p. 194). Even if H does not decrease significantly with increasing temperature, however, it must be borne in mind that, with very complex mixtures, low temperature isothermal analysis might be a very time consuming process and the programming technique would then offer the only practicable approach. The several claims of improved resolution when using the programming method (104 to 110), which embrace solute types as diverse as hydrocarbons, esters and sulphur containing compounds, need not be contested since, in each case, the isothermal run used for comparison was not that conducted at the starting temperature of the programme but something intermediate or even close to the finishing temperature. The comparisons were thus conducted at "practical" temperatures and this illustrates the important point that it is in the use of low starting temperatures, and not in the more rapid elution of slowly eluted substances at the finishing temperatures, that the real advantage of programming lies, for starting temperatures very considerably lower than could be tolerated isothermally can be used. Thus, in some instances, analyses can be started even at liquid nitrogen temperatures (104) and startling resolution of early peaks obtained as a result. Because of the low initial temperatures, columns can be operated such that the partition coefficients of the substances eluted early are much higher than would be suitable for isothermal elution of all components.

Figure 12, taken from the work of dal Nogare and Horden (111) shows a comparison of temperature programmed and isothermal analyses of a C_5 to C_{10} paraffin mixture. This diagram illustrates each of the points made above. Thus, while the starting temperature for chromatograms A and B was 40°C. the final temperatures being A, 190° and B, 90°C., respectively, the isothermal chromatogram C was obtained at 75°C. There is no doubt that C appears the least satisfactory chromatogram while, comparing either A or B with C we see, as expected, a considerable time reduction and a greatly increased resolution of the early peaks. However, resolution of the later peaks in C is somewhat better than in A and B, and, in fact, three trace components appearing in C are not visible at all in A and B. Since the detector sensitivities in chromatograms A and B are greater than in C the trace components are presumably unresolved from the adjacent major peaks. Had the isothermal analysis been carried out at 40° and not 75°C., the resulting chromatogram would, on the evidence, have been superior to either A or B, but the time of analysis would possibly have been a hundred times greater, and the peak heights would have been very low. In this situation quantitative analysis might be difficult, if not impossible, with the column used. Thus, there are clearly situations in practice when compromise is necessary and the programmed temperature method is not only the more suitable but possibly the only feasible approach.

One thing which emerges from this discussion is that for programming to be of value peaks appearing late must be very well separated in an isothermal analysis conducted at the programme starting temperature. Indeed, if this is not the case, components can be missed out completely in programmed analysis and great care must thus be exercised in order to be sure that the improvement in the chromatogram obtained is not more apparent than real.

Experimentally, several extra practical problems are introduced by the use of varying column temperature. First, the continuously rising viscosity

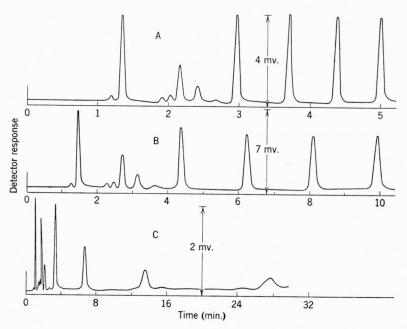

FIG. 12. Comparison of temperature programmed and isothermal analyses of C_5–C_{10} aliphatic hydrocarbon mixture. A, heating rate 30°C. per min. (40° to 190°C.); B, heating rate 5°C. per min. (40° to 90°C.); C, isothermal run at 75°C. *By courtesy of Analytical Chemistry.*

of the carrier gas throughout the analysis leads to a corresponding fall in the flow rate which may cause drift of the base line with flow sensitive detectors. Flow, as opposed to a pressure regulation, is thus indicated (111) although an alternative approach (104), operation of the column with a very small pressure differential by restricting the outlet flow, is claimed to be effective. The reason for this is not very clear. A very simple and effective constant flow device has been described by Knox (128). The second problem likely to be encountered is that the changing temperature of the outlet gas may also lead to base line drift with many detectors. This can be eliminated by incorporating a large body of metal around the connexion between the column and detector (111). Care is necessary to ensure that condensation of high boiling components does not occur.

The apparatus for programmed temperature work differs little from the conventional, the only significant addition being the programme control system. A relatively simple arrangement for this is that described by dal Nogare and his colleagues (111, 112). This consists of a closed loop proportional controller, which is illustrated diagrammatically in Figure 13. The two Helipot variable resistors P_1 and P_2 form a Wheatstone bridge powered by a 3-v. dry cell in series with any one of a number of resistors of

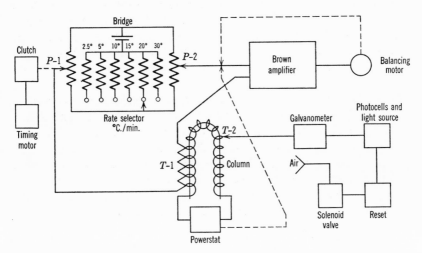

FIG. 13. Plan of programmed temperature apparatus. *By courtesy of Analytical Chemistry.*

different size. The bridge is driven off balance by a synchronous motor (3 r.p.h.) connected to P_1, the off balance output being fed to an amplifier and thence to a phase sensitive motor which re-balances the bridge by operation of P_2 and is also coupled to the Powerstat and so controls the heat input to the column. Although the bridge off balancing rate is constant, suitable selection of the battery series resistor offers a choice of column heating rate through variation of the bridge voltage and hence the magnitude of the rate of change of the off balance voltage (mv. per min.) fed to the balancing motor. The thermopile T_1 in series with the bridge provides negative feed back and, should the column temperature overshoot, this causes reduction of the heat supplied to the column in proportion to the feed back. The galvanometer and photocell arrangement shown is an elaboration which provides both automatic cut off of heat at the end of analysis and, through simultaneous actuation of the solenoid valve, directs a forced draught of cold air into the heater chamber in order to cool the column rapidly.

The question of the time of cooling back to the starting temperature is quite important since, in badly designed or very simple apparatus, any time advantage deriving from temperature programming of analysis may be more than lost between runs. One important requirement in the speeding up of cooling is that all materials used in the heating chamber should be of low heat capacity; this, of course, also facilitates fast heating rates. The majority of workers employ a linear heating programme and rates up to 50°C. per minute with a 600-w. heater can be achieved. Claims have been made, however, for non-linear programming (113) the main benefits being a considerable reduction in the necessary precision of the programme controlling mechanism and faster analysis. It has been suggested, though (111) that a linear temperature programme yields the most uniform distribution of peaks in time.

The retention time of a solute eluted by temperature programming is obviously dependent on several factors extra to those pertaining to isothermal elution. Thus, heating rate, mass flow of the carrier and its temperature range used are all significant. Theoretical attempts to take account of these and to correlate thereby isothermal and programmed temperature retention times have recently been made with some success (112, 114). Although the necessary further refinements in technique deriving from the extra variables might seem to make programming somewhat unattractive, these can be sufficiently readily dealt with to make it possible for several very reliable instruments to be available commercially.

CHROMATHERMOGRAPHY

A second variation of the non-isothermal technique is that known as chromathermography, in which an electrical ring heater, or some equivalent device, is moved along a column at fixed speed and so provides a continuously changing thermal gradient along the column. This method dates from the displacement work of Turner (115, 116) but its subsequent development, all in the field of elution chromatography, has been almost entirely by Turkel'taub, Zhukhovitskii and others in the U.S.S.R. (117 to 123). One advantage offered by this method is that, in consequence of the temperature differential between the front and back of any solute band, the bands are self sharpening and a given length of column is thus more efficient than when operated either isothermally or in a temperature programme. Nerheim (124) has studied this effect and found, for example, that, in runs conducted with the same column, n-octane eluted after 65 min. chromathermographically had the same band width as n-hexane eluted isothermally after only 20 min. This corresponds, if all other things were equal, to a ten-fold difference in efficiency which seems rather high. He further claimed that if the gradient is moved down the column several times even greater sharpening of peaks is observed.

The speed of individual bands down the column is governed by the factor $\Delta H/T$ relevant to each, ΔH being the heat of sorption and T the absolute temperature. Eventually a steady state condition is achieved, the various bands moving at the speed of the furnace, so thay cannot be further separated since pairs of components (A and B) then travel at a mutual distance Δl given by

$$\Delta l = \frac{T_A - T_B}{dT/dl}$$

The moving temperature field, however, not only creates a longitudinal gradient but also a radial gradient. This tends to spread the moving bands since it is equivalent to channelling of the column (125). In narrow columns where radial diffusion can effectively obliterate the effects of the radial gradient the latter is of little consequence, but as tube diameters are increased, reduced efficiency must result. It should be pointed out that a similar phenomenon must also occur during programmed temperature analysis, particularly at high heating rates and so this technique too is restricted to narrow columns, as has been shown by Glueckauf and Kitt (126).

Chromathermographic studies reported in the literature have so far involved mostly gas solid analyses of hydrocarbons of low boiling point and permanent gases, but halomethanes (122) have also been analysed in this way. Such mixtures are relatively simple and can be rapidly, and, so far as can be judged, as well or better dealt with by conventional means. Evidence on this point comes from the fact that the isothermally simple analysis of permanent gases and lower alkanes apparently required, in certain cases, the use of a number of columns in series when analysed chromathermographically (120), while halomethane separation required quite efficient columns in contrast to the situation in isothermal analysis, where columns less than 6 in. long have been shown to be adequate (127).

PROGRAMMING OF OTHER VARIABLES

There are, in principle at least, two programming techniques other than that of column temperature which might be valuable. The first of these is the programming of carrier gas flow rate. This approach would certainly lead to results equivalent in most respects to those of temperature programming, and if a reasonably efficient column having a very broad minimum on plots of H versus $\bar{u}$ were employed, flow changes of up to an order of magnitude might be employed in a single run without much loss of efficiency. The method is attractive for two reasons, first, since it is iso-thermal there is no change in partition coefficients during analysis and, secondly, programming of flow is obviously technically simple. There have, as yet, been no published accounts of work with systems operated in this way. The second approach is that of effectively programming k' along a column by gradually reducing the solvent/support ratio or adsorbent activity on going from the column inlet to outlet. It is not immediately obvious what advantage this offers, but Porath (192) has used an alumina column, deactivated progressively with stearic acid in the appropriate manner, for displacement and frontal analyses and claims highly beneficial results.

PEAK IDENTIFICATION

The successful analysis of any mixture depends upon three things, first, the devising of a reliable basis for the method and the construction of dependable apparatus, secondly, unequivocal identification of all the components to be analysed, and finally, the finding of means of accurate determination of each eluted component. Up to this point the discussion has been primarily concerned with the first of these, but now we turn our attention to the latter two.

Clearly, identification of the components to be analysed must precede their determination and, in gas chromatography, it is most often the more difficult operation of the two. The problem of identification exists, gener-ally speaking, at three levels of difficulty which we may list in order of increasing severity.

I. Where gas chromatography replaces an established technique or tech-niques the major components, at least, are likely to be known. Difficul-ties then arise only when, as is common, chromatography shows up the presence of hitherto unsuspected materials in the mixture under study.
II. Where gas chromatography represents the only possible method of value.
    a. If the material to be analysed derives from the reaction of known materials then the range of chemical types and perhaps the individual compounds likely to be derived from them must be fairly well pre-dictable.
    b. Mixtures deriving from unknown sources or of natural products, for example, could embrace the whole range of chemical species.

The situation described under (IIb) offers the greatest difficulty, but can to some extent be simplified by the use of ancillary techniques such as mass spectrometry, ultra-violet or infra-red spectroscopy, chemical methods and the like. These can be employed either with the bulk material or with com-ponents trapped out separately after chromatography. The present day trend towards smaller and smaller samples, however, sets a limit to the utility of ancillary techniques. Such methods, when they can be used, are obviously of great value but, since in most cases they are more likely to define the classes of compound present than individual identities they are of greater value for mixtures of type (II*b*) than of (II*a*). Non-chromatographic methods of identification are quite widely employed but, in the nature of things, can never provide the whole answer. Peak identification, therefore, at some point always becomes a chromatographic problem and the various approaches which can be employed are outlined in the succeeding discussion.

RETENTION TIME COINCIDENCE

This is by far the most frequently used method and involves no more than comparing the retention times of unknown peaks with those, obtained in identical conditions, for a whole range of standard materials. In effect, all that is done is to determine α's relative to some arbitrary standard. Thus, tables of relative retention data to be found in the literature can often be used to reduce the amount of experimentation necessary. Unfortunately, the simplest approach in which a single column and temperature are used is susceptible to gross errors, and it is an unhappy state of affairs that so many workers have such faith in it. Mere coincidence of retention times with a single column at a single temperature, at best, only serves to produce a short list of possible compounds. Only in the case of permanent gases or low boiling liquids eluted from solid adsorbents can reasonably positive identification be made. This arises because retention times here are most often very specific because non-ideality of sorption varies widely and, in addition, the number of substances to be considered is small. Even so, it is occasionally found that two such compounds have the same retention times in the same conditions.

SERIES RELATIONSHIPS

Many workers base their identifications on comparisons of retention data for unknowns with those for standard substances plotted in the form of log retention time or volume (usually relative to some standard) against either boiling point or the number of structural units in the molecules of members of chemical series. The theoretical basis of such plots has already been given (p. 219) and, in fact, the approach is basically the nomographic equivalent of the retention time coincidence method. It has, however, certain advantages over the latter. For example, any attempt at confirmation of identity by retention time coincidence may well involve much inspired guesswork and quite certainly demands a supply of standard samples of the substances which may be supposed to be present. It is commonly the case that pure samples of many things are not available. Detailed study of the nomograms, however, often reveals systematic variations in retention with structure and identifications can then be made with reasonable certainty by extrapolation.

Figure 14 illustrates a boiling point plot of some data obtained by Kallend (6) for a wide variety of aliphatic compounds eluted at 43°C. from

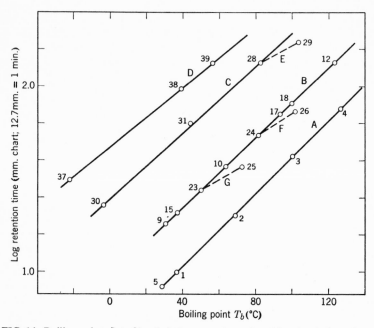

FIG. 14. Boiling point plot of log (relative retention volume) for the elution of a range of hydrocarbons from β,β'-oxydipropionitrile at 43°C. Solutes are (1 to 4) C_5–C_8 n-paraffins; (5 to 6) 2-methyl (butane and pentane); (7) 2,3-dimethyl butane; (8–12) C_4–C_8 1-olefins; (13, 15, 17) *trans*-(but-2-ene, pent-2-ene and hept-2-ene); (14, 16, 18) *cis*-(but-2-ene, pent-2-ene and hept-2-ene); (19, 20) 2-methyl (but-1-ene and pent-1-ene); (21) 4-methyl pent-1-ene; (22) 2-methyl but-2-ene; (23, 24) cyclo(pentane and hexane); (25, 26) methyl cyclo(pentane and hexane); (27, 28) cyclo(pentene and hexene); (29) 4-methyl cyclohexene; (30) 1,3-butadiene; (31, 32) *trans* and *cis* 1,3-pentadiene; (33) diallyl; (34, 35) *trans* and *cis* 2-methyl-1,3-pentadiene; (36) cyclopentadiene; (37) propyne; (38, 39) pent-1-yne, pent-2-yne; (40) benzene.

a column containing β,β'-oxydipropionitrile. Different compound types are seen to lie on different lines. Thus, line A is made up entirely of data for saturates; line C connects data for dienes, while line D represents triply bonded unsaturates (ynes). For the types of compounds falling on any given line the solvent acts as a boiling point separator. However, the degree of separation is considerably less than ideal, since the slopes of the lines lie between 0.009 and 0.100, whereas the approximate ideal slope (5/T) is 0.0158. The highly non-ideal behaviour of this solvent may be compared with that of squalane (Figure 1 of this chapter) with the same solutes, where there was only a minor class differentiation and where the line slopes were within 5 per cent of the approximate ideal values.

Consideration of the diagram illustrates clearly the dangers inherent in the simple retention coincidence method. The compounds used to construct the plot are but a small proportion of the number of aliphatic hydrocarbons possible in the range C_4 to C_8 and yet it is seen that pent-2-yne, cyclohexene and oct-1-ene (peaks 39, 28 and 12) are all eluted coincidentally while *trans* hept-2-ene, methyl cyclohexene and *n*-octane (peaks 17, 26 and 4) are also virtually inseparable. Thus, a chromatogram of a mixture corresponding to the compounds used to construct the figure would contain two peaks which were of three components. In addition, a further two peaks would be double, hex-1-ene + methylcyclopentane (10, 25) and *n*-hexane + *trans* pent-2-ene (2, 15). Thus, even the quite comprehensive experiments carried out to construct Figure 14 would be insufficient to provide positive identification of ten compounds and it is clear that alternative experiments would be required.

A useful feature of plots such as Figure 14, in addition to the broad classification they provide, is illustrated by the broken lines, E, F and G. Each of these lines connects data for some compound with its methyl derivative and in each case we see that the increment in log retention is 0.125. Thus, a line through 25 and 26 in the figure would be parallel to B and it is not an unreasonable assumption that if more data were available they too would lie on this, a new series line. Numerous structural relationships of this sort have been observed and they can often be used to predict the retentions of unavailable compounds in the same way as line A, for example, might be used with reasonable confidence to predict from their boiling points the data for paraffins above C_8.

THE MULTI-COLUMN METHOD

Ambiguities in identification with single columns, such as those pointed out above, can usually be resolved by use of further columns containing different solvents. This approach is based on the view that coincidence of retention of two solutes in a given analysis results from a self-cancelling, so to speak, of the various terms in the relevant retention equations. That this state of affairs should apply with a different solvent is unlikely, although other components may be unresolved in this case.

Figure 15 shows a log-log plot of retention data for much the same group of substances as in Figures 1 and 14 (6), when eluted from columns of β,β'-oxydipropionitrile and polyethylene glycol (M.W.600). Obviously, there is no need for the columns to be operated at the same temperature, in this case the temperatures were 43° and 25°C. respectively. Further, as in all these series plots, relative retention data are adequate provided conditions in the standardising and experimental runs are closely fixed. One feature of these log-log plots which should be pointed out is that there is no point in using two completely non-selective solvents since the combined data tell no more than either set separately. One, at least, of the solvents

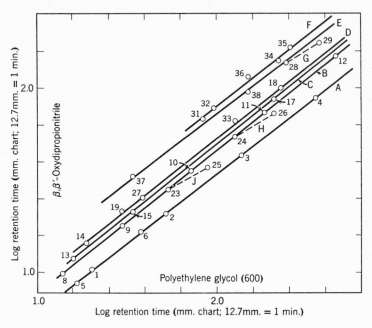

FIG. 15. Two solvent, log (relative retention volume) plot for solutes listed in Figure 14. Solvents are β,β'-oxydipropionitrile (43°C.) and polyethylene glycol 600 (25°C.). Lines connect; A, saturates; B, 1-olefins, naphthenes, and methyl derivatives of both; C, *trans* 2-olefins; D, *cis* 2-olefins, and their methyl derivatives; E, triply bonded compounds; F, dienes (straight, branched or cyclic).

used must thus show a reasonable degree of type selectivity. This selectivity, it should be noted, need not be such as to facilitate separation. In fact, the chromatograms obtained for complex hydrocarbon mixtures with the two solvents quoted in this section differ little in overall appearance although the selectivities, and hence the substances whose peaks coincide, are not always the same.

Referring to Figure 15, we see that type selectivity is more pronounced than with β,β'-oxydipropionitrile alone (Figure 14) and some six class lines (A-F) are seen. As before, line A represents data for saturated compounds, but line B groups together data for 1-olefins, naphthenes and the methyl derivatives of both. Line C represents data for *trans* 2-olefins, while those for *cis* 2-olefins and the methylated derivatives lie on line D. Triply bonded aliphatics yield line E while, finally, line F ties together data for dienes, whether straight, branched, *cis* or *trans*.

Returning to the problem posed by the data of Figure 14, the inability to distinguish between the groups of substances, 4:17:26, 12:28:39, 10, 25 and 2:15, we see from Figure 15 that 26 can now be clearly differentiated from 4 and 17 and in addition, 12:28 and 39 can be identified. This, however, is the limit to which Figure 15 can be usefully pushed and, in fact, it was found necessary (6) to use two further solvents (three log-log plots in practice) to give unambiguous identifications. Since, as has already been pointed out, the data relate to only a fraction of the total number of compounds likely to be met with in mixtures in the range C_4 to C_8 the magnitude of the identification problem is obvious.

A final point of interest in connection with Figure 15 is that again we see that, for some compound types, introduction of a methyl group gives rise to a retention increment (broken lines, G, H and J). Since this increment is again close to 0.125 (cf. Figure 14) in each case, it can be concluded that the polyglycol does not differentiate in this way and this particular selectivity derives entirely from the nitrile.

TEMPERATURE VARIATION OF RETENTION

An extension of the retention time coincidence methods which makes them much more reliable is that based on the fact that the temperature dependence of retention time or volume for two substances with any solvent is likely to differ. Thus, although at some column temperature two substances might give coincident peaks, at any other temperature they are likely to be at least partly resolved. Consider the example of two substances *A* and *B* eluted from the same column, and for which the specific retention volumes depend upon temperature according to the equations

$$\log (V_g)_A = \frac{1000}{T} - 2.50$$

and

$$\log (V_g)_B = \frac{1200}{T} - 3.17$$

When eluted at 27°C. both *A* and *B* would have specific retention volumes of 6.75 ml. and would thus coincide ($\alpha = 1$). If eluted from the same column at 0°C., however, $(V_g)_A = 14.5$ ml. while $(V_g)_B = 17.4$ ml. ($\alpha = 1.2$) and the ambiguity arising in the 27°C. result would be resolved.

This approach adds an extra degree of freedom to any form of single temperature identification, but is itself alone no more reliable, since instances of near identical temperature dependence of retention volume are known. However, combined with multi-column methods the temperature dependent peak shifts can provide reasonably positive identifications and it is highly advisable that this approach should be used. One argument often advanced against it is the considerable amount of extra labour it involves. Following what was said in the earlier sections, it is clear that, in fact, the extra effort need involve only those substances about which any doubt remains after isothermal studies and so should not be very great.

CHEMICAL ABSTRACTOR METHODS

Although this aspect has not been extensively exploited, it is evident that much useful qualitative information may be derived from the use of pre-column abstractor units. Again, as for the temperature change method, they are probably used most profitably when the greater part of the identification work has been accomplished. In this situation the specificity demanded of the abstractor can be more clearly defined and the choice simplified as a result. As an example, supposing that some peak could represent either or both of a straight and a branched chain hydrocarbon. The use of an appropriately chosen molecular sieve column ahead of the main column would immediately provide a positive result. Again, in a complex mixture of alcohols, ketones, aldehydes etc., pre-columns of sodium bisulphite or esterifying compounds could help considerably. Clearly, the reactions utilised must be rapid to be effective, but it follows that any pre-column abstractor suitable for more conventional needs (p. 379) would suffice.

PEAK SHAPE COINCIDENCE

A test of identity which in certain circumstances is very sensitive has been described by Pratt (131). It is based on the fact that the theoretical plate height measured for any column varies, often widely, from solute to solute. Thus, by determining peak widths of standards at fixed sample size and comparing these with that of the unknown, an identification can often be made. The method is obviously not very reliable when used alone, but can be very useful as a confirmatory test.

DOUBLE DETECTOR METHODS

The possibility of class identification by comparison of detector responses was initiated by Grant (132). He compared the chromatographic peak heights obtained for various substances with a flame emissivity detector and with a katharometer and Table 15 shows in abbreviated form a rough approximation to the figures he obtained. In each case, the response values are relative to an equal weight of benzene.

There is clearly a great difference in R_e/R_K for the various chemical types and this can be used to identify classes, if no more. Although the differences in R_e/R_K are, if anything, smaller than those in R_e alone the double detector method is necessary since the use of R_e values alone would demand that a quantitative analysis had already been performed in which case, presumably, identification would be unnecessary. With the two detectors used in series or parallel, however, if their calibrations for concentration are linear, there is no need for quantitative analysis, since the chromatogram can be recorded simultaneously from the detectors and R_e/R_K directly measured from the charts. In order to facilitate this, benzene, or some other chosen standard, could, if desired, be added to the original sample.

TABLE 15

RESPONSE COMPARISON OF DETECTORS

Substance Type	Emissivity Response, R_e	Katharometer Response, R_K	R_e/R_K
n-Paraffins	0.14	1.0	0.14
Aromatics	1.25	1.0	1.25
Naphthenes	0.22	0.5	0.5
Halomethanes	0.14	1.2	0.12

For this approach to be most profitable, one of the detectors used should differentiate sharply between chemical types. The other, of course, acts merely as a reference. Thus, detectors should be used in a way which, for quantitative analysis, might normally be undesirable. Thus, a katharometer should function best for identification purposes if the carrier gas were nitrogen and if flow rates were high. Obviously, there are many combinations of detectors which would be of value in this connexion. Particularly useful would be the gas density balance (p. 270) since the area response relative to that of some known substance would give the relative molecular weight of the unknown at least approximately, while the response ratio for the peaks recorded by the two detectors would help to classify it. Again, McWilliam has suggested (133) that a hydrogen flame detector, operated simultaneously as a temperature and ionisation device, would provide a single identification unit.

At the present time, identification of unknowns by Grant's method has not been extensively employed, but it clearly has great potential and should find increasing use in the future.

IDENTIFICATION WITH THE ELECTRON IMPACT DETECTOR

In any gas irradiated by electrons the following equilibrium is set up

$$M + e \rightleftharpoons M^- + E \text{ (energy)}$$

wherein E is the electron affinity of the molecule M. Gases such as hydrogen, helium and nitrogen have little affinity for electrons and so the equilibrium lies well to the left and the principal negative charge carriers are the electrons. Organic vapours, on the other hand, have considerable affinity for electrons and so, when these are added to nitrogen, for example, much of the negative charge is carried by the M^- ions. Since large negative ions, in contrast to electrons, have a high probability of collision and, hence, of combination with positive ions, the addition of organic vapour to nitrogen at constant low applied voltage leads to a reduction of current in the system. This mechanism is the basis of operation of the original modification of the β-ray detector (p. 311).

The processes occurring in electron irradiated gas mixtures, however, are somewhat more complicated than the picture given above. For example, with sufficiently large applied voltages, M^- ions would be capable of becoming highly energised between collisions and would thus tend more and more to dissociate. In other words, as in the case of supplying heat to an exothermic reaction, the equilibrium shown above would be driven to the left. The consequence of this is that with increasing applied voltage less and less of the current in an organic/nitrogen mixture would be carried by M^- ions and at some particular potential gradient, electrons alone would again carry all the negative charge. The applied voltage (V_0) at which the transition occurs is clearly closely related to E which itself differs very widely from one class of compound to another. Thus, the applied voltage corresponding to no change of current when an organic substance is introduced into the carrier is reasonably specific for chemical type. In fact, V_0 is determined to a small extent by temperature, pressure and cell geometry, but this is not significant in most cases, since all these can be controlled.

The precise location of V_0 is aided by the fact that one further process occurs in the irradiated system. This is,

$$M + e = X^+ + Y^- + e$$

This goes on under all conditions, but if the energy of the primary electrons is low the process contributes little to the electrical characteristics of the system. However, at voltages greater than V_0, any contribution from the break-down reaction must become discernable as a *gain* in cell current. Thus, over a range of voltage the signal goes from negative through zero to positive.

The potentialities of the electron impact detector as a *qualitative* detector were brilliantly realised by Lovelock and Lipsky (134) who, having advanced the arguments described above, proceeded to justify them by showing that if chromatograms of a complex mixture were run at a number of applied cell voltages, different peaks showed positive at different voltages.

Simple calibration experiments determined the value of V_0 for most of the major chemical classes and quite positive class identifications were thus made in very short times. Whether or not the method can eventually be used to distinguish between very closely related classes of compounds remains to be seen, but there can be no doubt that it must become very important. An intriguing possibility discussed by Lovelock and Lipsky is that of devising means such that argon may be used as carrier gas so that the detector becomes, at one and the same time, both a qualitative and a quantitative device.

METHODS OF QUANTITATIVE ANALYSIS

In this section we are concerned with the procedures available in the conversion of chromatograms into quantitative information. The only useful integral detectors directly record some bulk quantity and so our interest centres only on chromatograms obtained with differential detector systems. The conversion of peak parameters, obtained with such devices, into terms of quantity is effected in one or other of three basic ways depending on the method of detector calibration employed. Each of these in turn may be used either with peak height or peak area evaluation.

ABSOLUTE CALIBRATION

In this, the obvious approach, the detector response is calibrated as a function of weight or volume of each component to be dealt with. The technique is rather laborious and is, in fact, difficult in the situation when quantities of liquid of 10 μg. or less are to be dealt with, since accurate introduction of such small samples into a column presents formidable problems. However, if the liquids can be vaporised, or if the samples are normally gaseous, the measurement of pressure in fixed volumes provides a simple and accurate method of introducing as little as 10^{-2} μg. of material into a column. Even smaller quantities can be injected if dilution in inert gases is practised, since quite high pressures of mixed gas, which can be measured with great accuracy, may represent extraordinarily small amounts of the sample component.

INTERNAL STANDARDISATION

A variant of the absolute method is that known as internal standardisation. In this, some resolvable substance is added in known amount to a known amount of sample and peak heights or areas are converted to quantities by reference to those of the standard. Clearly, preliminary calibration of the detector in terms of the relative sensitivities of components and the standard, is required, and so the method is at this point absolute. One apparent advantage offered, however, is that the sample size need not be very carefully controlled but of more importance is the fact

that when the complete analysis has been performed the calculated concentration of standard should correspond with the known value. Failure to
achieve this condition indicates either loss of components or inaccurate
detector calibration.

It has been pointed out (135) that because of possible preferential loss of
certain components during the initial handling and injection of sample, the
use of a single standard is unsatisfactory. Thus, the use of two or more
standards, of widely different retention volume, is to be advocated.

INTERNAL NORMALISATION

This method differs only from the previous one in that the standard used
for reference is some component of the mixture to be analysed. In other
words, taking all individual heights or areas and assuming all components
to have been eluted we can say that

$$\text{Per cent component} = 100 \left(\frac{\text{area of component}}{\sum \text{area}} \right)$$

It will usually be necessary to multiply each area by some correction factor
derived from an absolute calibration and so the method has little to
commend it in the normal course of events. In some instances, and this
applies to the other methods also, the correction factors can either be
predicted theoretically or are unity. The former is hardly to be relied upon,
but instances of the latter, such as the detection of hydrocarbons in helium
by thermal conductivity, are known. At best, however, only approximate
data can be obtained in this way and so it is clear that in the last analysis
absolute calibration is the most important method.

PEAK HEIGHT OR AREA

The measurement of peak height is more rapid and, probably, more
accurate than that of peak area. Thus, wherever possible, it is the more
desirable quantity for use. Unfortunately, however, plots of peak height
against sample size are more often non-linear than are the corresponding
plots for peak area. The reason for this is that theoretical plate heights,
and thus peak heights and widths are frequently very dependent upon
sample size and sample feed volume, whereas the total area under the peak
is not. Thus, any variable which can affect the theoretical plate height must
be rigorously controlled if the best results are desired from peak height
measurements. Thus, this method is likely to be most reliable with very
small samples.

Both peak height and area calibration curves can be affected by carrier
gas flow rate and, indeed, in most cases this is the most important factor.
First, the theoretical plate height is dependent upon carrier gas flow rate,
and so again this contributes to non-linearity of peak height but not of peak

area calibrations. More significant is the fact that with quantity sensitive detectors the peak area is independent of flow rate and so the peak height is directly so, whereas with concentration sensitive devices the peak height is, in principle, flow independent, but the area varies inversely as the flow. Since, for many substances, it is perfectly feasible to operate columns in conditions in which H/u plots show broad minima, the effect of flow variation on H can often be more or less entirely eliminated. Then, the flow dependence of calibration curves is most likely to stem from the detector rather than the column.

It is clear that if very close carrier flow control is exercised there is little to choose between height and area measurement, other than in the accuracy of evaluation of either from chromatograms, if samples are less than about 10 μg. with packed columns and perhaps 10^{-1} μg. with capillaries. With larger samples area determination may well always be better. If, on the other hand, flow control is not very precise, with small samples, area measurement is best with detectors such as the argon or flame ionisation models, while height measurement is most reliable with the katharometer, density meter etc. It appears that most work is conducted with flow controlled to better than 1 per cent, and so, in fact, this latter conclusion is not often likely to apply. A detailed study of the reproducibility and accuracy of peak height and peak area measurements conducted by Krejci and Janak (136) led them to conclude that the former was always the more reliable, because of the uncertainty involved in area measurement.

MEASUREMENT OF PEAK AREA

There are a number of ways in which peak areas may be evaluated manually from elution curves. Krejci and Janak (136) have made a detailed comparison of these and the order of accuracy they found is as follows:

   a. Cutting out and weighing.

   b. Counting of squares.

   c. Approximation of curve to triangle drawn through the inflexion points and calculation from (base × height/2).

   d. Planimetry.

The weighing method is usually quite unsuitable, since chromatograms are destroyed and, in addition, the moisture content of the paper may change with time and so preclude the keeping of quantitative records. The counting of squares is extremely tedious, while planimetry with such small areas as are usually encountered is both tedious and unreliable. The triangulation method is thus almost certainly the most useful in the long run. In the author's experience triangulation gives areas within 2 per cent of weighing and if calibration is also done by triangulation, this error can be reduced further.

The evaluation of areas may, of course, be carried out by some sort of integrator. Numerous electronic or mechanical type instruments specifically designed for gas chromatography are now available commercially. In every case, the accuracy of integration is claimed to be better than 1 per cent and so compares with or exceeds the accuracy attainable by manual methods. With the advent of higher analysis speeds the computation of areas or heights is often by far the slowest part of the analysis. Thus, we may expect to see an even wider use of integrators, particularly those with a numerical as opposed to graphical read-out, in the near future.

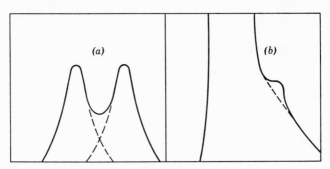

FIG. 16. Illustration of peak overlap and methods of evaluating individual areas: (*a*) components present in about equal amount, (*b*) trace component following major peak.

ANALYSIS WITH UNRESOLVED PEAKS

It is frequently found that a certain degree of overlap of peaks must be accepted if analysis is to be conducted most expediently. A number of workers have turned their attention to the problem of evaluating the separate heights or areas in this situation (137, 138, 139). Broadly speaking, there are two separate problems here, the first is that of dealing with the situation where the peaks are of the same order of magnitude, the second is that where, in effect, a trace component appears as a hump on the tail of a major peak. The two situations are illustrated in Figure 16. In (*a*) the broken lines show the individual curves as they would appear in the absence of the other component. Since the broken lines meet the base line before the peak maxima are reached, peak height analysis would be perfectly satisfactory in the situation shown. In fact, this situation persists, for Gaussian peaks, up to a peak maximum separation of three standard deviations, at which point in any case, two peaks could hardly be discerned. If it is desired to use areas, either of two methods may be used. First, a perpendicular which is taken as the dividing line, may be dropped from the minimum of the saddle between the peaks or, secondly, tangents may be drawn to the inflexion points on the overlapping sides of the curves and these taken as the curve boundaries. Both methods have been shown to be perfectly adequate, with the first slightly the better, even when the peaks differed by an order of magnitude in size (139). The areas evaluated differed by less than 1 per cent from those measured when the peaks were completely resolved. Peak overlap of the type shown in Figure 16b offers rather more difficulty in quantitative interpretation. The only method adopted up to now is that of drawing the continuation under the minor peak of the smooth curve of the major peak. This artificial base line method has several times been checked with synthetic mixtures and, while the accuracy is considerably less than is normal in chromatography, it is still reasonably high and very much better than can be achieved by other methods.

ACCURACY AND REPRODUCIBILITY

The accuracy and reproducibility achieved in gas chromatographic analyses obviously depends upon many things, among them the correct choice of column, temperature, flow rate, sample size, detector and injection system. The most satisfactory performance thus demands considerable understanding of the chromatographic process and of the effects of change in an unusually large number of variables. Notwithstanding this, even with quite ill designed apparatus, analyses can usually be conducted with an accuracy better than ± 10 per cent per component, and the results are reasonably reproducible. When precautions are taken, however, an accuracy and a reproducibility of about ± 1 per cent per component is attainable, as has often been demonstrated. This value represents reasonably closely the likely errors introduced by the sampling, detector, read-out and flow systems, and it is doubtful, therefore, whether, in the ordinary course of events, anything much better than the figure quoted can be achieved. While there have been several claims to the contrary, it seems likely that any real gains in accuracy would probably demand prohibitive elaboration of apparatus and technique, which in most cases would be relatively unprofitable.

REFERENCES

1. Patton, H. W., J. S. Lewis and W. I. Kaye, *Anal. Chem.*, 1955, **27**, 170.
2. Scott, C. G. S., *J. Inst. Petrol.*, 1959, **45**, 115.
3. Eggertsen, F. T., and S. Groennings, *Anal. Chem.*, 1958, **30**, 20.
4. Pratt, G. L., and J. H. Purnell, *Proc. Roy. Soc.*, 1961, **260A**, 317.
5. Langer, S. H., and J. H. Purnell, (unpublished results).
6. Kallend, A. S., and J. H. Purnell, (unpublished data).
7. Hoare, M. R., and J. H. Purnell, *Trans. Faraday Soc.*, 1956, **52**, 222.
8. Purnell, J. H., *Vapour Phase Chromatography*, 1957, Butterworths, London (editor, D. H. Desty), p. 52.
9. Farquhar, J. W., P. Insull, P. Rosen, W. Stoffel and E. H. Ahrens, *Nutrition Reviews*, 1959, **17**, Supplement, No. 8, Pt. II, 1.
10. Langer, S. H., and J. H. Purnell, (unpublished work).

11. Ashworth, A. J., and D. H. Everett, *Trans. Faraday Soc.*, 1960, **56**, 1609.
12. Barber, D. W., C. S. G. Phillips, F. G. Tusa and A. Verdin, *J. Chem. Soc.*, **1959**, 18.
13. Bradford B. W., D. Harvey and D. E. Chalkley, *J. Inst. Petrol.* 1955, **41**, 80.
14. *Gas Chromatography Abstracts*, Vols. I and II, 1958 and 1959, Butterworths, London (editor, C. E. H. Knapman).
15. Ambrose, D., A. I. M. Keulemans and J. H. Purnell, *Anal. Chem.*, 1958, **30**, 1582.
16. Ambrose, D., and J. H. Purnell, *Gas Chromatography*, 1958, Butterworths, London (editor, D. H. Desty), p. 369.
17. Desty, D. H., A. Goldup and W. T. Swanton, *Nature*, 1959, **183**, 107.
18. Eggertsen, F. T., and S. Groennings, *Anal. Chem.*, 1958, **30**, 20.
19. Madison, J. J., *Anal. Chem.*, 1958, **30**, 1859.
20. Taylor, G. W., and A. S. Dunlop, *Gas Chromatography*, 1958, Academic Press, New York (editor, V. J. Coates et al.), p. 84.
21. Brodskii, A. I., R. A. Kalinenko and K. P. Lavroskii, *Problemy kinetiki i Kataliza*, 1957, **9**, 399.
22. Skrivan, J. F., and H. E. Hoelscher, *A. I. Ch. E. Journal*, 1959, **5**, 348.
23. Amberg, C. H., E. Echigoya and D. Kulawic, *Can. J. Chem.*, 1959, **37**, 708.
24. Ausloos, P., and E. Murad, *J. Amer. Chem. Soc.*, 1958, **80**, 5929.
25. Fredericks, E. M. and F. R. Brooks, *Anal. Chem.*, 1956, **28**, 297.
26. McFadden, W. H., *Anal. Chem.*, 1958, **30**, 479.
27. Nunez, L. J., W. H. Armstrong and H. W. Cogswell, *Anal. Chem.*, 1957, **29**, 1164.
28. Fitzgerald, J. S., *Australian J. Appl. Sci.*, 1959, **10**, 169.
29. Hurn, R. W., J. O. Chase and K. J. Hughes, *Ann. N. Y. Acad. Sci.*, 1959, **72**, 675.
30. Murakawi, Y., *Bull. Chem. Soc. Japan.* 1959, **32**, 316.
31. Martin, R. L., and J. C. Winters, *Anal. Chem.*, 1959, **31**, 1954.
32. Murad, E., and W. A. Noyes, *J. Amer. Chem. Soc.*, 1959, **81**, 6405.
33. Barnard, J. A., and H. W. D. Hughes, *Nature*, 1959, **183**, 250.
34. Primavesi, G. R., *Nature*, 1959, **184**, 2010.
35. Zlatkis, A., L. O'Brien and P. R. Scholly, *Nature*, 1958, **181**, 1794.
36. Tenney, H. M., *Anal. Chem.*, 1958, **30**, 2.
37. Habgood, H. W., and J. F. Hemlan, *Can. J. Chem.*, 1959, **37**, 843.
38. Anon., *Chem. Eng. News*, 1960, **38**, 38.
39. Janak, J., *Chem. Listy*, 1953, **47**, 464.
40. Scott, C. G., and D. A. Rowell, *Nature*, 1960, **187**, 143.
41. Greene, S. A., and H. Pust, *Anal. Chem.*, 1957, **29**, 1055.
42. Harris, M. R., and K. W. Sing, *Chem. and Ind.*, **1957**, 1573.
43. Wohlleben, G., *J. Chromatog.*, 1958, **1**, 271.
44. Turkel'taub, N. M., A. I. Kolyubyakina and N. S. Selenkina, *Zhur. Anal. Khim.*, 1957, **12**, 302.
45. Schulze, G. R., and W. J. Schmidt-Kuster, *Z. anal. chem.*, 1959, **170**, 232.
46. Goertner, K., and R. Griessbach, *Kolloid-Z.*, 1959, **162**, 25.
47. Brenner, N., and L. S. Ettre, *Anal. Chem.*, 1959, **31**, 1815.
48. Smith, R. N., J. Swinehart and G. D. Lesnini, *Anal. Chem.*, 1958, **30**, 1217.
49. Juranek, J., and A. Ambrova, *"Gas Chromatography,"* 3rd *Conf. Anal. Chem.*, Prague, Sept. 1959.
50. Barrer, R. M., *Brit. Chem. Eng.*, 1959, **4**, 267.
51. Broussard, L., and D. P. Shoemaker, *J. Amer. Chem. Soc.*, 1960, **82**, 1041.
52. Brenner, N., and V. J. Coates, *Nature*, 1958, **181**, 1401.
53. Bassett, D. W., and H. W. Habgood, *J. Phys. Chem.*, 1960, **64**, 709.
54. Deuel, H., *Makromol. Chem.*, 1959, **34**, 206.

55. Grubner, O., and E. Smolkova, *"Gas Chromatography,"* 3rd Conf. Anal. Chem., Prague, Sept. 1959.
56. Vyakhirev, D. A., and A. I. Bruk, *Zhur. Fiz. Khim.*, 1959, **33**, 1309.
57. Greene, S. A., and H. E. Roy, *Anal. Chem.*, 1957, **29**, 569.
58. Glemser, O., and G. Rieck, *Angew. Chem.*, 1957, **69**, 91.
59. Turkel'taub, N. M., O. V. Zolotareva, A. G. Latukhova, A. I. Karymova and E. Kalnina, *Zhur. Anal. Khim.*, 1956, **11**, 159.
60. Crespi, V., and F. Cevolani, *J. Inst. Petrol.*, 1959, **45**, 137A.
61. Yu, W-L., *Acta Focalia Sinica*, 1957, **2**, 352.
62. Gregg, S. J., and R. Stock, *Trans. Faraday Soc.*, 1957, **53**, 1355.
63. White, D., *Nature*, 1957, **179**, 1075.
64. White, D., and C. T. Cowan, *Trans. Faraday Soc.*, 1958, **54**, 557.
65. White, D., and C. T. Cowan, *Gas Chromatography*, 1958, Butterworths, London (editor, D. H. Desty), p. 116.
66. Hughes, M. A., D. White and A. L. Roberts, *Nature*, 1959, **184** 1796.
67. Krejci, M., K. Tesarik and J. Janak *2nd International Symposium* I.S.A., Lansing, Mich., June, 1959, Preprints, p. 105.
68. Glueckauf, E., and G. P. Kitt, *Vapour Phase Chromatography*, 1957, Butterworths, London (editor, D. H. Desty), p. 422.
69. Thomas, C. O., and J. A. Smith, *J. Phys. Chem.*, 1959, **63**, 427.
70. Moore, W. R., and H. R. Ward, *J. Amer. Chem. Soc.*, 1958, **80**, 2909.
71. Van Hook, W. A., and P. H. Emmett, *J. Phys. Chem.*, 1960, **64**, 673.
72. Smith, H. A., and P. P. Hunt, *J. Phys. Chem.*, 1960, **64**, 383.
73. Hunt, P. P., and H. A. Smith, *J. Phys. Chem.*, 1961, **65**, 87.
74. Furuyama, S., and T. Kwan, *J. Phys. Chem.*, 1961, **65**, 190.
75. Eggertsen, F. T., H. S. Knight and S. Groennings, *Anal. Chem.*, 1956, **28**, 303.
76. Grubner, O., and E. Smolkova, "Gas Chromatography," 3rd Conf. Anal. Chem., Prague, Sept. 1959.
77. Quinn. C. P. (Ph. D thesis, Cambridge, 1961).
78. Norrish, R. G. W., and J. H. Purnell, *Proc. Roy. Soc.*, 1958, **A243**, 435.
79. Hara, N., H. Shimada, A. Ishikawa and K. Dohi, *Bull. Japan Petrol. Inst.*, 1960, **2**, 33.
80. McKenna, T. A., and J. A. Idleman, *Anal. Chem.*, 1960, **32**, 1299.
81. Percival, W. C., *Anal. Chem.*, 1957, **29**, 20.
82. Sokol, L., *Chem. Listy*, 1958, **52**, 1726.
83. Brenner, N., E. Cieplinski, L. S. Ettre and V. J. Coates, *J. Chromatog.*, 1960, **3**, 230.
84. Rysselberge, J. van, *Ind. chim. belge*, 1959, **24**, 1023.
85. Lichtenfels, D. H., S. A. Fleck, F. H. Burow and N. D. Coggeshall, *Anal. Chem.*, 1956, **28**, 1376.
86. Mackay, D. A. M., D. A. Lang and M. Berdick, *Drug and Cosmetic Ind.*, 1960, **86**, p. 46 et seq.
87. Janak, J., and J. Novak, *Chem. Listy*, 1957, **51**, 1832.
88. Ray, N. H., *Analyst*, 1955, **80**, 853.
89. Martin, R. L., *Anal. Chem.*, 1960, **32**, 336.
90. Kerr, J. A., and A. F. Trotman-Dickenson, *Trans Faraday Soc.*, 1959, **55**, 572.
91. Harris, W. E., and W. H. McFadden, *Anal. Chem.*, 1959, **31**, 114.
92. Whitham, B. T., *Nature*, 1958, **182**, 391.
93. Hunter, I. R., K. P. Dimick and J. W. Corse, *Chem. and Ind.*, **1956**, 294.
94. Drawert, F., and G. Kupfer, *Angew. chem.*, 1960, **72**, 33.
95. Langer, S. H., P. Pantages and I. Wender, *Chem. and Ind.*, **1958**, 1664.

96. Zlatkis, A., and J. F. Oro, *Anal. Chem.*, 1958, **30**, 1156.
97. Ralls, J. W., *J. Agr. Food Chem.*, 1960, **8**, 141.
98. Ralls, J. W., *Anal. Chem.*, 1960, **32**, 332.
99. Schepartz, A. I., and P. E. McDowell, *Anal. Chem.*, 1960, **32**, 723.
100. Hall, W. K., and P. H. Emmet, *J. Amer. Chem. Soc.*, 1957, **79**, 2091.
101. Emmett, P. H., R. J. Kokes and H. H. Tobin, *U.S.* **2**, 905, 536.
102. Hall, W. K., D. S. MacIver and H. P. Weber, *Ind. Eng. Chem.*, 1960, **52**, 421.
103. Littlewood, A. B., C. S. G. Phillips and D. T. Price, *J. Chem. Soc.*, 1955, 1480.
104. Drew, C. M., and J. R. McNesby, *Vapour Phase Chromatography*, 1956, Butterworths, London (editor, D. H. Desty), p. 213.
105. Greene, S. A., M. L. Moberg and E. N. Wilson, *Anal. Chem.*, 1956, **28**, 1369.
106. Ryce, S. A., and W. A. Bryce, *Anal. Chem.*, 1957, **29**, 925.
107. Harrison, G. F., P. Knight, R. P. Kelley, and M. T. Heath, *Gas Chromatography*, 1958, Butterworths, London (editor, D. H. Desty), p. 216.
108. Kogler, H., *Chem. Tech.* (*Berlin*), 1957, **9**, 400.
109. dal Nogare, S., and W. C. Safranski, *Anal. Chem.*, 1958, **30**, 894.
110. Zhukhovitskii, A. A., B. A. Kanzanskii, O. D. Sterligov and N. M. Turkel'taub, *Doklady Akad. Nauk. U.S.S.R.*, 1958, **123**, 1037.
111. dal Nogare, S., and J. C. Harden, *Anal. Chem.*, 1959, **31**, 1829.
112. dal Nogare, S., and W. E. Langlois, *Anal. Chem.*, 1960, **32**, 767.
113. Sullivan, J. H., J. T. Walsh and C. Merritt, *Anal. Chem.*, 1959, **31**, 1826.
114. Habgood, H. W., and W. E. Harris, *Anal. Chem.*, 1960, **32**, 450.
115. Turner, N. C., *Natl. Petrol. News*, 1943, **35**, R234.
116. Turner, N. C., *Oil Gas J.*, 1943, **41**, 48 et seq.
117. Turkel'taub, N. M., V. P. Shuartsman, T. V. Georgievskaya, O. V. Zolotereva, and A. I. Karymova, *Zhur. Fiz. Khim.*, 1953, **27**, 1827.
118. Turkel'taub, N. M., *Neftyanoe Khoz.*, 1954, **32**, 72; *Anal. Khim. Akad. Nauk. U.S.S.R.*, *Inst. Geokhim. i Anal. Khim.*, 1955, **6**, 146.
119. Sventsitskii, E. I., N. I. Lulova, A. I. Tarasov and E. I. Zemskova, *Zavodskaya Lab.*, 1956, **22**, 1399.
120. Turkel'taub, N. M., and A. A. Zhukhovitskii, *Geol. Nefti.*, 1957, **1**, 54; *Zavodskaya Lab.* 1957, **23**, 1120.
121. Turkel'taub, N. M., *Zhur. Anal. Khim.*, 1958, **13**, 43.
122. Vyakhirev, D. A., and L. E. Reshetnikova, *Zhur. Priklad. Khim.*, 1958, **31**, 802.
123. Vyakhirev, D. A., M. I. Otasheva and L. E. Reshetnikova, *Trudy Khim. i Khim. Tekhol.*, 1958, **2**, 334.
124. Nerheim, A. G., *Anal. Chem.*, 1960, **32**, 436.
125. Glueckauf, E., *Gas Chromatography*, 1958, Butterworths, London, (editor, D. H. Desty), p. 89.
126. Glueckauf, E., and G. P. Kitt, *Disc. Faraday Soc.*, 1949, **7**, 199.
127. Purnell, J. H., and M. S. Spencer, *Nature*, 1955, **175**, 988.
128. Knox, J. H., *Chem. and Ind.*, **1959**, 1085.
129. Porath, J., *Arkiv. Kemi.*, 1954, **7**, 535.
130. Keulemans, A. I. M., and H. G. Voge, *J. Phys. Chem.*, 1959, **63**, 476.
131. Pratt, G. L. (Ph.D. Thesis, Cambridge, 1960).
132. Grant, D. W., *Gas Chromatography*, 1958, Butterworths, London (editor, D. H. Desty), p. 153.
133. McWilliam, I. G. (see ref. 132), p. 163.
134. Lovelock, J. E., and S. R. Lipsky, *J. Amer. Chem. Soc.*, 1960, **82**, 431.
135. Lee, E. H., and G. D. Oliver, *Anal. Chem.*, 1959, **31**, 1925.
136. Krejci, M., and J. Janak, *Chemie* (*Prague*) 1958, **10**, 264.

137. Zhukhovitskii, A. A., and N. M. Turkel'taub, *Zavodskaya Lab.*, 1958, **24**, 796.
138. Grant, D. W., and G. A. Vaughan, *J. Appl. Chem.*, 1960, **10**, 181.
139. Brace, R. O., see *Principles and Practice of Gas Chromatography*, 1959, Wiley, New York (editor, R. L. Pecsok), p. 145.
140. Davison, W. H. T., S. Slaney, and A. L. Wragg, *Chem. and Ind.*, **1954**, 1356.
141. Angelis, G. de, P. Ippoliti, and N. Spina, *Ricerca Sci.*, 1958, **28**, 1444.
142. Lehrle, R. S., and J. C. Robb, *Nature*, 1959, **183**, 1671.
143. Janak, J., "Gas Chromatography," *3rd Conf. Anal. Chem.*, Prague, Sept. 1959.
144. Legate, C. E., and H. D. Burnham, *Anal. Chem.*, 1960, **32**, 1042.
145. Wilzbach, K., and P. Riesz, *Science*, 1957, **126**, 748.
146. Dudenbostel, B. F., and W. Priestley, *Ind. Eng. Chem.*, 1956, **48**, 55A.
147. Wachi, F. M., *Diss. Abstr.*, 1959, **20**, 53.
148. Juvet, R. S., and F. M. Wachi, *Anal. Chem.*, 1960, **32**, 290.
149. DeBoer, F. E., *Nature*, 1960, **185**, 915.
150. Hanneman, W. W., 137*th Ann. Mfng. Amer. Chem. Soc.*, 1959, *Chem. Eng. News*, 1960, **38**, 114.

14
NON-ANALYTICAL
APPLICATIONS

PREPARATIVE CHROMATOGRAPHY

The application of gas chromatography to preparative chemistry is already well advanced but, with few exceptions, in comparison with analytical work, the results are not striking. On the other hand, even relatively inefficient units provide separations which would be very difficult to achieve by distillation or other methods. For example, the technique has proved immensely valuable already in the fluorocarbon field. The most popular approach has been that of using wide columns (0.5 to 4 in.) with appropriate scaling-up of ancillary apparatus. Several other methods have also been studied, for example, parallel column systems have been proved successful while, in a somewhat different aspect, a number of so called "continuous chromatographs" have been devised. The only really worthwhile continuous method has, however, involved a counter-current system and is, thus, not truly chromatographic. The distinction is more or less academic and so will be ignored in the subsequent discussion.

LARGE DIAMETER COLUMNS

Columns which were perfectly packed and ideally operated should show no variation in H with changing diameter. Instances where such results have been obtained were quoted earlier (p. 182) but, in general, it is found that increase in column diameter beyond about 10 mm. leads to a considerable increase in H. In the first instance this must be attributed to gross overloading of the columns used. It was shown earlier that analytical columns (ca. 5 mm. diameter) become seriously overloaded at sample sizes greater than about 1 to 5 μl. of liquid. Simple extrapolation then suggests that, at best, a 25-mm. column should be able to handle only about 0.1 ml. and a 75-mm. column only about 1 ml. In almost all the work described in the literature, minimum sample sizes of about 1 ml. are common, even for quite small diameter columns, while, in some instances, as much as 10 ml. of liquid has been injected into 30-mm. columns. In such circumstances, not only must the column be overloaded in terms of the solute/solvent ratio, but the feed volume must also be well in excess of the theoretically tolerable maximum. It is not, therefore, surprising that the usual efficiencies for wide columns (ca. 6 mm.) are only about one-tenth those for analytical columns.

The only explanation of this widespread tendency to overloading is the desire to deal with fairly substantial quantities of material in reasonable periods of time. This underlines the fact that on the preparative scale, if no other, theoretical plates per unit time (u/H) are more significant than plates (L/H) alone (1). Thus, the approach to faster analysis discussed earlier is particularly pertinent here, since it is clear from the literature that considerable reductions in elution time would be possible in most published examples of preparative work. The speeding up of elution would permit more frequent separation of much smaller quantities and the higher efficiencies resulting would permit the use of shorter columns, which, in turn, would speed up the process. Alternatively, of course, more difficult separations than are now dealt with might be attempted.

In addition to the above, which are purely points of technique, certain band spreading processes which may be insignificant in analytical columns can be anticipated to arise in wide columns through the greater probability of inhomogeneities in the radial distribution of (a) the packing, (b) the solvent and (c) the injected solute vapour. Their effects may be eradicated during elution in narrow columns through radial diffusion but some evidence to the contrary exists (p. 198) In the situation that uniform mixing through these processes in the column is unlikely, it is clear that any radial non-uniformity in the concentration of vapour established during injection will persist throughout the column, while even if there is uniform injection, radial non-uniformity of solvent or of carrier gas flow pattern caused by packing irregularities will have the same effect.

These problems have recently been the subject of theoretical study by Golay (2). He considered, first, the consequences of the fact that in any column there is a packing gap at the wall which is about half a particle diameter (d_p) in size and through which the carrier velocity is greater than the average for the column. He concluded that H is only affected when the column diameter is much greater than the theoretical plate height ($d \gg H$) and so, in analytical columns the wall gap effect can be ignored. The

contribution to the theoretical plate height when $d \gg H$ is an amount extra
to that of the usual rate processes, which is given by

$$H = \frac{(ad_p)^2 u_o}{8 D_g^{\,o}}$$
(14.1)

$D_g^{\,o}$ and u_o have their usual significance while a represents the ratio of the
cross-section of the gap at the wall to that of the average inter-particle
channel. It thus lies between about 3 and 6 as we go from well to badly
packed columns. According to Golay the net increase in H that is to be
expected from the occurrence of the wall effect cannot be greater than 40
per cent.

Golay has considered also the more important problem of the effect of
radial inhomogeneities arising from solvent or solute maldistribution or a
macroscopic non-uniform velocity profile. The theory does not distinguish
between these and so relates to one or all occurring simultaneously. He
characterised the effects by assuming that the passage of molecules over a
distance L down one side of a column was paralleled by transport of identical
molecules a distance $(1 + \epsilon)L$ down the other side. This process was shown
to contribute to the theoretical plate height according to the expression

$$H = \frac{\epsilon^2 \, d^2 u_o}{D_g^{\,o}}$$
(14.2)

where d is the column diameter. The contribution of inhomogeneities to H
is likely in badly made columns to be greater than that of the wall effect,
but, in contrast, because ϵ can take the value zero, its contribution can be
eliminated. The attainment of the condition $\epsilon = 0$ is bound up with the
care exercised in column preparation and sample injection and the probable
route to this end was discussed at some length earlier (p. 167). The reduction of wall effects can best be achieved by the use of solid support of the
smallest d_p and of minimum size spread, since the latter must lead to the
most regular packing and the lowest a. Thus the conclusions to be drawn
from the earlier discussion and Golay's work are, first, that wide columns
must be operated according to exactly the same rules of procedure as
analytical columns (p. 202), and, secondly, that column preparation techniques need to be more refined as diameters are increased. In these conditions wide column efficiencies certainly not less than two-thirds those
achieved with analytical columns should be attainable, and so preparatory
columns of 500 theoretical plates per foot should be realisable.

An interesting practical point put forward by Golay is that even if ϵ
cannot be reduced to vanishing proportions, the effects of all column inhomogeneities can be much reduced, if not eliminated, by frequent "remixing" of the gas phase as it passes through the column. In effect, this
means the use not of a uniform column but of one constructed from a series

of short lengths connected by very narrow tubing. The length of these connexions should be such that every molecule spends enough time therein to travel radially the equivalent of several diameters. It is possible that if its connectors were sufficiently narrow, mixing through turbulent flow could be achieved. Golay has calculated the conditions for improvements in column performance to be observed and found these to be that

$$d_p < 4\epsilon d$$

Since d_p is unlikely to be bigger than 0.05 cm. we see that when $d = 50$ mm. ϵ is only about 2×10^{-4}. Thus, differences in solute velocity along the two sides of a column in excess of only 0.02 per cent would lead to loss of efficiency. Thus, the use of connecting mixers is probably always worthwhile.

The only comprehensive experimental investigation of the effect of inhomogeneities on wide column efficiency is that of Huyten, van Beersum and Rijnders (3) who concentrated their study on the non-uniform velocity profile. The method adopted was to saturate a column with ammonia vapour, which was unsorbed, and then, on elution, to trap this in a short, detachable end section containing phosphoric acid. The packing in this section could be cut out in uniform sections and each titrated for unreacted acid. Pronounced radial maldistribution of ammonia was observed in all the experiments and the mode of packing was shown to affect this considerably. The suggestion made earlier re column packing methods (p. 242) was confirmed since it was found that the greatest uniformity of carrier flow and the highest column efficiency followed packing during which only beating of the column was employed; vibration in every case reduced the efficiency, the indications being that this resulted from the occurrence of large gaps at the wall. Measurements of the apparent H at various points along the radius of the column showed that H at the walls was frequently as much as five times H at the centre of the column while the over-all column value was more than twice as great. In summarising their results, the authors recapitulated Golay's recommendation of the use of mixing vessels along the column length while, in addition, they suggested that it would be very profitable to collect column effluents in two parts; an outer part for recirculation and an inner part for use. They quoted preliminary results obtained in this way which showed a 4 in. diameter column to be capable of giving about 300 theoretical plates per ft. Such values are indeed encouraging and substantiate the view stated earlier that very much higher efficiencies than are usual may readily be attainable at the expense of relatively little effort.

PARALLEL COLUMNS

The possibilities inherent in the use of parallel arrays of columns of small diameter were pointed out early (4) but it is only recently, with the emergence of a successful commercial instrument (5) that attention has been focussed on this approach. The scaling up of column cross-sectional areas (capacities) in this way is attractive for the wall effect is eliminated and, to a large extent, so too is any contribution to H from a non-uniform solute velocity profile. It is obviously essential to the success of the method that the maxima of peaks eluted from the individual columns be exactly superimposed in time, since otherwise this is equivalent to solvent inhomogeneity in a wide column. This condition is realised by ensuring that all columns contain exactly the same *weight* of solvent and that gas flow rates through each are the same for given values of p_i and p_o. The former is achieved by carefully making up the individual column packings separately while minor flow differences can be balanced out by the incorporation at column inlets of calculated lengths of capillary or, more elaborately, by separate flow control. The evidence is now clear that column construction procedure can be systematised such that columns of reproducible H can be made up quite easily (see e.g. 10). Thus, a properly balanced array of parallel columns should show the same efficiency as any individual column. This has been shown to be the case (5) in numerous instances. For example, an eight column assembly ($d = \frac{5}{8}$ in.) gave precisely the same H (2.6 mm.) with a 1-ml. liquid sample of aromatics as did a single $\frac{5}{8}$-in. column with a 0.125-ml. sample. Even at this sample size the columns were overloaded and extrapolation suggests that $H = 2$ mm. could easily have been attained if desired. The solid support used had $d_p \simeq 0.25$ mm. and so it is clear that, with a finer support, a theoretical plate height in the region of 1.0 to 1.5 mm. should be readily possible. This suggestion is supported by the author's finding (4) that an assembly of eight highly efficient columns, equivalent in cross-section to a 1-in. diameter column, gave in a few instances theoretical plate heights as low as 0.6 mm.

It seems certain that at this time the parallel column approach offers the simplest route to high efficiencies for scaled-up systems. The results quoted earlier, however, indicate that future developments with wide columns may render these equally effective.

CONTINUOUS CHROMATOGRAPHY
The Counter-current Method. The most successful and comprehensive studies in this field are those of Benedek, Szepesy and their associates (6 to 8). Their approach is to use a counter-current technique in which packing falls against an up-stream of carrier, sample being continuously injected at the centre. The method is thus a form of frontal analysis. Adjustment of the rate of fall of the packing, which is the critical parameter and which should be as small as possible, is made such that in a binary mixture one component

travels up the column with the carrier while the other travels downward with the packing. Recovery of the top and bottom fractions is followed by (*a*) removal of the carrier from the top fraction, and (*b*) extraction of the second component from the bottom fraction.

The process (*a*) is apparently best achieved with a second column while (*b*) is achieved by heating. The theoretical principles involved have been discussed in great detail (6 to 8) and are relatively simple. The only complications introduced arise from competitive sorption of the mixture components, but static measurements of sorption isotherms for the appropriate mixtures permits more or less precise calculation of the operating variables. The extension of the method to the continuous separation of an *n*-component mixture would require only the use of $n/2$ columns in cascade, the top fraction from column 1 going into column 3, and so on. No work along these lines has yet been reported but application of the established theory (6 to 8) indicates no snags other than the rather severe mechanical ones associated with construction and operation of the column system and fraction rectification units. The excellent capabilities of the method are illustrated by the fact that a unit for the recovery of acetylene from the products of the partial combustion of methane, capable of processing nearly a million cubic feet a day, has been operated successfully (7) while, in pilot plants CH_4/C_2H_2 mixtures (11) and *cis* and *trans* but-2-enes (12) have been adequately dealt with. In the latter instance the column was operated with a longitudinal temperature gradient to facilitate both separation and rectification.

The Skarstrom "Drier." One of the pressing problems in many areas is the provision of large supplies of highly pure gas, usually air. A simple chromatographic solution to this problem has been provided by Skarstrom (9) in brilliant fashion. His "drier" comprises a pair of identical columns, usually containing either alumina or silica gel. On starting up, one of these is fed directly from the gas supply and, for a time, the emerging gas is free of all impurities which are more strongly adsorbed. However, since the process occurring is again frontal analysis, these impurities must eventually break through at their input concentrations. Before this occurs the input gas is, therefore, switched to the other column, the effluent from which is split, part being taken for use and the residue being fed back as a purge flow to the already saturated first column and thence to waste. The latter can be completely denuded of adsorbed impurities by a fraction of the total gas purified since their rate of removal is governed only by their saturation vapour pressures and hence the flow rate, while the pressures in the two columns can, of course, be adjusted to any value. Thus, for example, if the purifying column is operated at 10 atm. and the purging column at 2 atm. only 20 per cent of the purified gas is needed to provide equal volume flow through both columns. If the splitting ratio is slightly greater than the operating pressure ratio, the purging flow is greater than the purifying flow and so there is little fear of inadequate purging and the wastage still need not be high. When impurities are due to break through the second column, the roles of the columns are reversed and it in turn is purged. By continual switching of columns very highly pure gas can be obtained in almost any amount, since the columns can be built to almost any size. A fairly rapid rate of switching (ca. 3 min.) has been found helpful since it keeps the columns short and, also, the heat evolved during sorption is not removed rapidly and so becomes available to speed up the purge rate.

It is usually found on start-up that a conditioning period is necessary, since adsorbed water or other materials must be removed from the adsorbents. This may be as long as twenty days but at this point the water content of the purified gas is below 1 p.p.m. Even after a few hours the water content of air can be reduced to 10–100 p.p.m. After protracted use in optimum conditions of one model of the drier, air containing water, CO_2 and hydrocarbons amounting to no more than 0.05 p.p.m. has been obtained. Experiments have shown that the machine operates successfully over the ranges −30 to 80°C. and 15–3500 p.s.i. It is, therefore, extremely versatile and can be used in almost any circumstances to purify any gas, provided the contaminants are more strongly adsorbed.

PURITY OF SEPARATED MATERIALS

Band Overlap in Batch Methods. It was pointed out in Chapter 7 that once material is introduced into a chromatographic column it cannot subsequently be completely removed. Thus, there must always be some degree of peak overlap even though this may not be apparent from a chromatogram. It is important to be able to estimate the resulting impurity of fractions obtained gas chromatographically or, alternatively, to compute the efficiency (N) required to give material of desired purity. The method of achieving this is due to Glueckauf (13) and involves calculation of the overlap area for a pair of solutes for any degree of peak separation. He starts by considering the amount of solute, Δm, contained in any part of a band in a column (that is, under any section of the elution peak). This is given by equation 7.21 as

$$\Delta m = m \left[0.5 - A_\epsilon \left(\frac{N - M}{M^{1/2}} \right) \right]$$

provided the feed volume requirement (p. 112) is met. If now we define the impurity content of any band by

$$\eta_1 = \frac{\Delta m_2}{m_1 - \Delta m_2} \simeq \frac{\Delta m_2}{m_1}$$

where the subscript 2 denotes the contaminating solute, we find that for any pair of solutes eluted and cut in such a way as to be equally impure ($\eta_1 = \eta_2$), equation 7.21 gives

$$\frac{m_2}{m_1}\left\{0.5 - A_\epsilon\left[N_2^{\frac{1}{2}}\frac{V_{R_2}' - V}{(V_{R_2}'V)^{\frac{1}{2}}}\right]\right\} = \frac{m_1}{m_2}\left\{0.5 - A_\epsilon\left[N_1^{\frac{1}{2}}\frac{V_{R_1}' - V}{(V_{R_1}'V)^{\frac{1}{2}}}\right]\right\}$$

The solutions of this equation in the condition that the column is equally efficient for both solutes ($N_1 = N_2 = N$) are

$$\eta_1 = \eta_2 = \eta = \frac{2m_1m_2}{m_1^2 + m_2^2}\left(0.5 - A_\epsilon\left\{N^{\frac{1}{2}}\frac{[(V_{R_2}')^{\frac{1}{2}} - (V_{R_1}')^{\frac{1}{2}}]}{(V_{R_1}'V_{R_2}')^{\frac{1}{4}}}\right\}\right)$$

$$(14.3$$

and that the volume flow through the column when the cut between the two fractions (V_c) should be made is

$$V_c = (V_{R_1}'V_{R_2}')^{\frac{1}{2}} + \left[\left\{\frac{2V_{R_1}'V_{R_2}'}{N(V_{R_2}' - V_{R_1}')}\right\}\left\{\frac{m_1^2 - m_2^2}{m_1^2 + m_2^2}\right\}\right] \quad (14.4)$$

The retention volumes are introduced in place of N and M by the method used earlier (p. 103). From equation 14.3 it is seen that the lowest purity materials are obtained when $m_1 = m_2$ since the function $m_1m_2/(m_1^2 + m_2^2)$ is then a maximum. In this condition, equation 14.4 gives the optimum cut point as the geometric mean peak retention volume

$$V_c = (V_{R_1}'V_{R_1}')^{\frac{1}{2}}$$

On the other hand, when $m_1 \neq m_2$ it is seen that the cut must be made nearer to the smaller peak since when $m_1 > m_2$,

$$V_c > (V_{R_1}'V_{R_2}')^{\frac{1}{2}}$$

while, when $m_1 < m_2$ the second bracketted term is negative, and

$$V_c < (V_{R_1}'V_{R_2}')^{\frac{1}{2}}$$

Most often, columns are not equally efficient for all solutes, and in this situation the theory is rather more complex. In this case it is found that

$$\eta_1 = \eta_2 = \eta = \frac{2m_1m_2}{m_1^2 + m_2^2}\left[0.5 - A_\epsilon\left\{\tilde{N}^{\frac{1}{2}}\frac{V_{R_2}' - V_{R_1}')}{(V_{R_2}' + V_{R_1}')}\right\}\right] \quad (14.5)$$

where $\tilde{N}$ is the arithmetic mean column efficiency $(N_1 + N_2)/2$. The optimum cut point for equal purity of fractions is then

$$V_c = \frac{V_{R_1}' + V_{R_2}'}{2}\left[1 + \frac{N_2}{2V_{R_2}'}\left(\frac{V_{R_2}' - V_{R_1}'}{V_{R_1}' + V_{R_1}'}\right)^2\left(\frac{m_1^2 - m_2^2}{m_1^2 + m_2^2}\right)\right] \quad (14.6)$$

In this situation it is seen that when $m_1 = m_2$, V_c is the arithmetic mean peak retention volume. Again, however, it is predicted that for $\eta_1 = \eta_2$ but $m_1 \neq m_2$ the cut should be made closer to the minor peak. The values of η

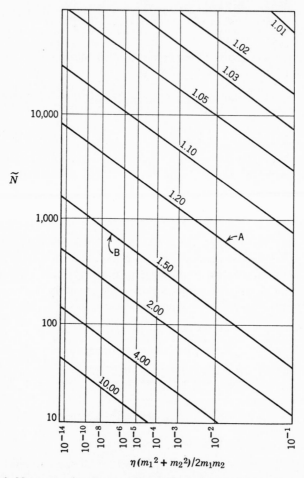

FIG. 1. Nomogram for the calculation of the purity of eluted bands as a function of the arithmetic mean column efficiency $\tilde{N}$, component mass ratio and retention volume ratio α (1.01 to 10). *By courtesy of the Faraday Society.*

given by equations 14.3 and 14.5 differ little and so it is possible to construct a graph, which is adequate whether $N_1 = N_2$ or not, from which the purity of cut fractions can be computed if retention volume ratios and mean column efficiencies are known.

Such a plot is shown in Figure 1, $\tilde{N}$ being plotted against the bracketed term of equation 14.5 for a wide range of values of α. To illustrate the use of this diagram consider the point marked A. This point corresponds to the elution of a pair of substances of $\alpha = 1.20$ from a column having a mean efficiency of about 900 theoretical plates. The relevant value of $\eta (m_1^2 + m_2^2)/2m_1m_2$ is about 6×10^{-3}. If $m_1 = m_2$, this value corresponds to η, which means that, if the cut were made at the V_c indicated by equation 14.6, each major fraction would contain 0.6 per cent of the other component. If, on the other hand, $m_1 = 10m_2$ and V_c were appropriately displaced, $\eta = 1.2 \times 10^{-3}$ and each major fraction would contain only 0.12 per cent of the other component. The importance of having large values of α is clearly shown if we now refer to the point B in the diagram. This relates to elution of a pair of solutes of $\alpha = 1.50$ from a column giving again $\tilde{N} = 900$ and it is seen that the small change in α from 1.20 has reduced η nearly a millionfold.

The discussion up to this point has been based on the idea of cutting between peaks in such a way that each is equally impure and that all the eluted material is recovered. Evidently, if desired, the cut can be made nearer to the peak maximum of one component in order to obtain this in higher purity than is calculable from equation 14.6. If a middle fraction can be wasted, both peaks may be cut in this way. At the present time, preparative column efficiencies are relatively so low as to justify this procedure, which is widely practised. With the probable future increase in efficiencies, however, it should become unnecessary, and then the Glueckauf theory will provide the means to calculate in advance the experimental requirements, and subsequently to specify the purity of the recovered materials.

Solvent Volatility. This attains greater significance in preparative than in analytical applications of chromatography since in the latter it affects mainly detector stability and response, whereas in the former it may lead to considerable contamination of products. We can estimate the volatility limit which is likely to be tolerable by assuming reasonable experimental parameters. Suppose the sample used contained 1 g. of component 1 and 0.1 g. of component 2. If the gas flow corresponding to elution of each peak (i.e. base width) were 2 l. and the vapour pressure of the solvent were 10^{-1} mm. Hg (at, say, 80°C.) about 0.2 ml. (N.T.P.) of solvent vapour would contaminate each fraction. At a solvent molecular weight of 400 this would mean that the major fraction would contain 0.4 per cent and the minor fraction 4 per cent by weight of solvent. Reconsidering the first example (point A on Figure 1) of the last section, which is very typical of present-day standards, $\eta = 0.12$ per cent when $m_1 = 10m_2$ and we see, therefore, that contamination by the solvent would indeed be very significant in the specified conditions. It seems certain, therefore, that at this time no solvent of $p^0 > 10^{-3}$ mm. Hg at the chosen column temperature should be used, since even at this level contamination by solvent is comparable with that result-ing from peak overlap for simple separations.

EXPERIMENTAL REQUIREMENTS

The general requirements and procedures for preparative scale work have already been shown to be very similar to those for analytical studies, and so

TABLE 1

SOLUTE TYPES ISOLATED WITH WIDE, PREPARATIVE COLUMNS AND SOLVENTS USED

Solutes	Solvents	Reference
Terpenes	Emulphor-O Dinonyl phthalate Silicone	14, 15, 16
Hydrocarbons Naphthenes	Silicone Dicyanomethyl nitropentane Dinonyl phthalate Tetraisobutene	18, 19, 20, 23
Aliphatics	Silicone Apiezon-L Polypropylene glycol esters α, β-dinaphthyl sulphone	17, 21, 22, 24
Aromatics	Silicone Dinonyl phthalate	15, 20
Fluorocarbons	Dibutyl phthalate Dinonyl phthalate	25–28
Aldehydes	"Tide"	29, 30
Alkyl esters of fatty acids	Apiezon-L Polyethylene glycol esters	31,32
Pyrazolines, nicotines pyridines, pyrindines	Dinonyl phthalate Reoplex	33, 34, 35

do not require recapitulation. In so far as experimental requirements differ, for example, in the arrangements for injection of sample and trapping of eluted materials, it is a difference in degree and not in kind. These matters were discussed in detail earlier (p. 243, 260). The one practical point of importance yet to be made is in connection with the choice of detector.

This, in preparative work, is not primarily determined by sensitivity and so is in some respects rather wider than in analytical work. Thus, such devices as the dielectric constant and simple β-ray detectors, for example, may well be very suitable, particularly because they are relatively flow insensitive. Carrier flows are very high with wide columns and serious difficulties may be experienced with, for example, katharometers, when several litres of gas per minute are passed through them. Flow sensitive detectors should, thus, be avoided unless arrangements are made to take only a small proportion of the total effluent through the detector.

In conclusion, we may consider the types of purification described in the literature at this time. Table 1 lists these under general solute type headings and also tabulated are the solvents found to be useful.

It is noticeable that, again, the solvents listed in Chapter 12 predominate. In the cases quoted column diameters were all greater than 12 mm., the average being 25 mm., while in several instances (26, 27) they were as great as 75 mm. The minimum column length used was 2 m. and the longest recorded (21) was 8 m. Sample sizes dealt with range from about 0.5 to 50 g. (26) with 1 to 5 g. as the normal charge. In several cases (for example, 14, 35) as many as five components have been trapped out in a multiple collector unit in a single run. This approach is obviously very profitable and is clearly the best way to utilise gas chromatography. There can be little doubt that many more compounds than are listed in the literature have been purified by gas chromatography. This may be anticipated because numerous commercial instruments are available and also because preparative work merely mirrors analytical achievements at a lower level of efficiency and workers are likely then to be reluctant to publish.

It goes without saying that the next few years will see considerable development of both the batch and "continuous" approaches to preparative chromatography and, in the field of difficult separations it is not inconceivable that they may supplant distillation even on economic grounds.

PHYSICO-CHEMICAL STUDIES

The possibility of using gas chromatography for physico-chemical studies was emphasised in a number of the earliest publications (36, 41) although up to this time it has been little used. The types of study which are feasible fall, broadly, into one of two classes. The first, based on the evaluation of thermodynamic data, activity coefficients and the determination of partition isotherms, bears on the mechanism of sorption processes. The second, which is founded on the rate theory, involves the attempted evaluation of inter-diffusion coefficients from bandwidth/gas velocity relationships. The former has received almost all of the attention yet given to this aspect of chromatography because, on the whole, the theory of retention is more firmly founded than that of band broadening while, in addition, the derivation of the necessary information from chromatograms is very much simpler.

Thus, while the applicability of gas chromatography to the study of solution and adsorption phenomena is fairly well established and now requires only exploitation, further work is undeniably needed before diffusion measurements can be conducted with confidence. There is, however, every hope that this situation will develop and even if, at best, derived coefficients are only approximate, the approach will still have value, since conventional methods for the study of diffusion are both time consuming and require elaborate apparatus. The last statement embodies what is perhaps the most attractive aspect of gas chromatography in relation to physical studies; the great rapidity with which experimental information can be amassed with relatively simple apparatus.

THE MEASUREMENT OF ACTIVITY COEFFICIENTS

The measurement of specific retention volumes or partition coefficients by the elution technique allows calculation of activity coefficients through equations 10.8 and 10.12. Since these activity coefficients must be taken to correspond to those for infinite dilution, because otherwise it is difficult to specify the relevant concentration, it is essential, in practice, that sample sizes be kept to a minimum. Specification of a maximum sample size is difficult, but it is generally conceded that at no point in the column should the solute concentration exceed 0.5 to 1.0 moles per cent (48). In conjunction with the theoretical demand for injection of sample into the first theoretical plate of the column, this imposes quite serious restrictions on sample size. Unless small samples can be conveniently dealt with it is necessary to measure γ as a function of sample size and to extrapolate to γ_0. Occasionally, partition isotherms are linear beyond 1 mole per cent and in such systems the problem is less significant.

Since γ_0 is calculated from V_g, the weight of solvent in the chosen column must be known with accuracy. If direct weighing is either precluded or unreliable, the simplest course is to compare a known V_g for some standard material with its V_R for a given column. This approach demands close temperature and flow control, but this is no great drawback, since these are the requirements for worthwhile measurement of γ in any case. Finally, for the most precise work, fugacities should be used instead of saturation vapour pressures, but, as pointed out earlier, this is possible only in the limited number of cases where fugacities have been directly measured or where the virial coefficients of the equation of state of the vapour (equation 2.26) are known.

The theory of retention advanced in Chapter 10 and used extensively up to this point has implicitly been taken as correct. The numerous illustrations of the various log retention volume plots shown earlier clearly lend weight to this view, but no evidence has yet been presented to show that any V_g determined at some temperature for a given system by one worker is identical with that measured by another. As would be expected, this is the case, and furthermore, that V_g is independent of solid support identity and dimensions, column dimensions and the identity (for gas liquid chromatography) and rate of flow of the carrier gas has been amply demonstrated. Porter, Deal and Stross (41) for example, showed that with all the systems they studied, a fourfold carrier velocity change, a sixfold change of column length, a fivefold variation in p_i/p_o, or change of carrier gas had no effect on V_g. The only known source of uncertainty in V_g measurement derives from the possibility of adsorption by uncovered solid support; a problem which was discussed earlier and so needs no recapitulation. It is generally accepted that above 15 per cent w/w solvent/support in packed columns, V_g is usually independent of solvent/support ratio and so is reliable for measurement of γ_0 (33). Often, of course, lower ratios can be tolerated, particularly if treated supports or such things as metal helices are used. It should be pointed out in passing that reproducibility of V_g data with a given packing is no proof of the inertness of the support, since the adsorptive properties of the latter are themselves consistent.

A much more important question than their reproducibility is whether or not gas chromatographically determined values of γ_0 correspond to the true thermodynamic values which would be found in static experiments. A number of direct comparisons of results obtained by chromatographic and static methods have been made (37, 41–43, 48) and in each case have shown excellent agreement. Perhaps the most impressive test is the most recent, in which the results of a comprehensive static investigation of the solubility of benzene and cyclohexane in di-n-nonyl phthalate (43) were compared (50) with the gas chromatographic data (45) and found to agree as closely as could be expected. A further point of interest deriving from these studies (43) is that distribution of the phthalate on Celite in the static work was shown to speed up equilibration enormously.

Martin, however, (44) has recently presented evidence indicating that, in some systems, V_g increases with increasing solvent/support ratio. This is the converse of the effect of solid support adsorption. Martin explained his results by assuming that increasing solvent/support ratio was equivalent to increasing the liquid surface area and, hence, that "adsorption" at the solvent surface, as well as solution in the bulk liquid, determined the retention volume. This situation seems unlikely on general grounds, but should this interpretation prove correct and the phenomenon be found general, it is clear that gas chromatography can offer little in the study of solution processes.

However, it must be remembered that the bulk of the evidence is against the above view and that, even in the polar solute/polar solvent type systems which Martin described as exhibiting the effect most strongly, the phenomenon has never previously been observed (see, for example, 41, 42). There

TABLE 2

ACTIVITY COEFFICIENTS AT INFINITE DILUTION, γ_0

| | Hexadecane | | 1,2,4-Trichloro- |
	25°	40°C.	benzene, 30°C.
Methanol	71.5	44	
Ethanol	47	30.5	
n-Propanol	31.5	19.5	
Isopropanol	26.5	18.5	
Acetaldehyde	7.3	6.1	
Acetone	6.3	5.1	
Ethyl formate	3.7	3.2	
Methyl acetate	3.6	3.1	
n-Pentane	0.89	0.86	2.97
Cyclopentane	0.71	0.71	2.11
2-Methyl pentane	0.85	0.88	3.11
2,2-Dimethyl pentane	0.94	0.90	3.45

may, thus, be other explanations of the results. For example, no static measurements were made for comparison and it is conceivable that the systems studied may have had complex partition isotherms. At this time, therefore, it seems eminently reasonable to accept that gas chromatographically measured activity coefficients are both reproducible and correspond to the thermodynamic values.

Experimental Data. The range of values of γ_0 encountered in practice is very wide, as may be gauged from the data in Table 2, which are taken from the work of Kwantes and Rijnders (48).

It is seen that γ_0 ranges between about 0.7 and 70. Higher values are common while some, as low as 0.01, have been reported (54) for systems in which compound formation is considered to occur. The data in the table illustrate the very marked positive deviations of solutions of oxygenated compounds in n-hexadecane and that solutions of hydrocarbons, on the other hand, are not far from ideal although there is some differentiation between aliphatic and naphthenic hydrocarbons. Included also in the table are data for hydrocarbon elution from the highly polar solvent 1,2,4-

trichloro-benzene (48) which show, in this instance, that the solutions deviate positively.

Discussion of reasons for the type and magnitude of the deviations observed is hardly profitable at this time, since there have been few attempts to reconcile the results with theory. However, such developments can be confidently expected. There have, on the other hand, been several attempts at empirical correlation of gas chromatographic activities with solute and solvent structure, the primary aim being the development of a system for the prediction of partition coefficients. Success in this enterprise would go far towards eliminating time-wasting preliminary study. The earliest work in this direction was that of Pierotti, Deal, Derr and Porter (47) who studied a wide variety of systems comprising paraffins, alkanones and alcohols eluted from solvents of differing polarity. The basis of their method of representing the data in terms of molecular structures was outlined in Chapter 2 and it is sufficient here to remember that they proposed that, for any solute and solvent, $\log \gamma_0$ could be represented as the sum of the contributions of a number of structural interaction energy terms. Their experimental evidence substantiated this view reasonably well, and there is little doubt that further study of this sort would be profitable.

More recently, Kwantes and Rijnders (48) have made a comprehensive study of some hydrocarbon/n-paraffin systems. They found that over a temperature range of 30–110°C., activity coefficients for a given system were virtually constant and, further, that for a given solvent, γ_0 was the same for all paraffin homologues, and also for related compounds such as benzene, toluene and p-xylene, and cyclopentane, cyclohexane and their methyl derivatives. Figure 2 illustrates in abbreviated form some of their results, γ_0, averaged for the various compound types over the whole temperature range, being plotted against the carbon number of the paraffin solvents (C_8 to C_{38}). Interpretation of the curves lies outside the scope of this discussion, but the curves for n-paraffin and naphthene solutes are of the form predicted by the Flory-Huggins equation and $\gamma_0 \rightarrow 1$ when the solvent carbon number approaches that of the solute. The aromatic curve is interesting in that at high solvent carbon numbers the solutions show negative deviation but at low solvent carbon numbers they deviate positively.

A point which should be borne in mind in discussions such as this is that activity coefficients between 0.25 and 1, could merely reflect the use of molar rather than volume fractions in the derivation of the basic retention equations. Evidently, the derivation of equation 10.8 and those following, could have been based on the concepts of the Miller-Guggenheim or Flory-Huggins theories (equations 2.22 through 2.25). That this procedure may in some instances be appropriate is suggested by recent studies (43) with solutions of benzene and cyclohexane in either di-*n*-nonyl phthalate or squalane. In every case it was found that the results were better accounted for by the Flory-Huggins approach than by that based on conventional theory. Further evidence for this point of view comes from the work of

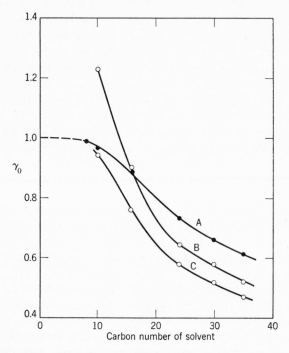

FIG. 2. Illustration of the effect of carbon content of paraffin solvent molecule on γ_0 for: A, aliphatics; B, aromatics; C, naphthenes.

Langer and the author (49) who found that differences in γ_0 for individual aromatic solutes eluted from a number of solvents were, at least to some extent, reconciled by use of volume, as opposed to molar, fractions in computing the results. This aspect of retention theory is in its infancy and little more can be said than that it demands exploration.

THE EVALUATION OF THERMODYNAMIC QUANTITIES

The differential molar heat of sorption can be calculated by measurement of V_g or K at several temperatures, followed by application of equation 10.12 or 10.14. The difference between this quantity and the latent heat of vaporisation at the appropriate temperatures gives the partial molar excess enthalpy. The free energy of sorption can be calculated from the retention volume for a single temperature and so, since

$$\Delta G^s = \Delta H^s - T \Delta S^s$$

the entropy of sorption is calculable. If the activity coefficients are known the same calculations can be made to obtain the partial molar excess quantities directly, since for solutions, for example,

$$\Delta G^m = 2.3RT \log \gamma_0 = \Delta H^m - T\Delta S^m$$

and

$$\frac{\partial \Delta G^m}{\partial T} = -\Delta S^m \qquad \frac{\partial (\Delta G^m/T)}{\partial (I/T)} = \Delta H^m$$

In general the partial excess quantities met with in gas chromatography, especially ΔH^m, are small in comparison with the corresponding quantities for sorption. Hence, few have been directly evaluated and it is true to say that for most systems, accuracies considerably higher than are now common will be necessary if worthwhile information is to be obtained from V_g measurements. This is illustrated by the data in Table 3 which lists most of the values of ΔH^m either quoted or calculable from data to be found in the literature. It is seen that only in a few cases, notably with alcohols as solutes, is ΔH^m greater than about 1 kcal. per mole. This may be compared with the corresponding values of ΔH^s which lie between 6 and 12 kcal. per mole. The derived quantity is thus sufficiently small to be susceptible to considerable error. In fact, apart from the data of Adlard, Khan and Whitham (45) none of the data in the table are likely to be more accurate than about ±300 cal. per mole and so, in many cases, ΔH^m might well be zero. With such systems it is evident that extreme experimental precautions are needed and also that fugacity corrections are probably essential if the results are to carry much weight.

There appear to be no instances of the quotation of gas chromatographically measured partial excess free energies and entropies except in so far as it has several times been suggested that $\Delta H^m = 0$ (43, 45, 49) when

$$\Delta G^m = RT \ln \gamma_0 = - T \Delta S^m$$

and so, the listing of γ_0 and T is equivalent to that of ΔG^m and ΔS^m. For what it is worth, Table 4 lists some values deduced from graphically illustrated data for γ_0 (47) for systems for which ΔH^m (41) was listed in Table 3. The fact that the figures are somewhat inconsistent is to be attributed to the inconsistencies of ΔH^m evident in Table 3 but they serve to show the orders of magnitude involved. The negative entropies, which correspond to an increased order over that to be expected in an ideal solution, are not in agreement with the predictions of the Flory-Huggins theory.

THE DETERMINATION OF PARTITION ISOTHERMS

Although the elution technique has on occasion been used to measure gas solid adsorption isotherms (59) it is not well suited to this. Frontal analysis, on the other hand, can be used to evaluate the relevant partition

TABLE 3
PARTIAL MOLAR HEATS OF MIXING (ΔH^m, cal./mole) MEASURED GAS CHROMATOGRAPHICALLY

Solute	Tricresyl Phosphate	Silicone 702	Di-isodecyl Phthalate	Squalane	Medicinal Paraffin	Di-nonyl Phthalate	Polyethylene Glycol Cresyl Ether	Cobalt Stearate
Methanol	—	—	3240					
Ethanol	1200	3400	4610 (?)		200			2000
n-Propanol	500	.2900	1410		220			
n-Butanol	—	—	1800		200			
Me. Acetate	-400	200						
Et. Acetate	-500	0						
n. Pr. Acetate	-900	-300						
Benzene	-800	-800				0	0	
Toluene	-1100	-900	-400			0	1500	
Cyclohexane			-1330 (?)	-580				
Me. Cyclohexane			-120	-500				
Et. Cyclohexane			-580	—				
	(ref. 38)	(ref. 38)	(ref. 41)	(ref. 41)	(ref. 46).	(ref. 45)	(ref. 42)	(ref. 54)
n-Pentane			—	-720	-60			
n-Hexane			-930	-600	-70			600–1100
n-Heptane			-170	-540	-70			
1-Hexane					-200			
1-Heptene					-270			
Methylene chloride					-650			
Chloroform					-900			
Carbon tetrachloride					-900			

TABLE 4
PARTIAL MOLAR EXCESS FREE ENERGIES AND ENTROPIES

	Squalane		Di-isodecylphthalate	
Solute	$-\Delta G^m$ cal. mole^{-1}	$-\Delta S^m$ cal. mole^{-1} deg^{-1}	$-\Delta G^m$ cal. mole^{-1}	$-\Delta S^m$ cal. mole^{-1} deg^{-1}
$n\text{-}C_5H_{12}$	450	0.72	—	—
$n\text{-}C_6H_{14}$	330	0.72	140	2.85
$n\text{-}C_7H_{16}$	295	0.65	45	0.55

isotherms, and thus the activity coefficients over a wide range of concentrations. To date, with the exception of a few isolated experiments (42) this approach has not been adopted in gas liquid chromatography. There have, however, been several studies of gas solid systems in this way (51 to 53). In each case the results have been excellent and examples of some of the isotherms obtained are shown in Figures 1 and 2 of Chapter 11. The method seems particularly suited to adsorption studies with adsorbents of low activity or area (52, 53). The relative simplicity of the technique makes it very attractive and there seems no reason why it should prove less satisfactory for solution studies, where the much more comprehensive information obtainable would make it more useful than the elution method.

DETERMINATION OF PHYSICAL PROPERTIES
The possibility of using gas liquid chromatographic retention data for the measurement of saturation vapour pressures, boiling points and latent heats of vaporisation was pointed out early (39, 40). Measurement of the first quantity depends upon the finding of family retention plots (p. 211) for homologues or compounds related to that under study. $\text{Log } p^0$ can then be read off at the appropriate value of $\log V_g$ for the substance studied. The method is, of course, relative, but might well be of value for high molecular weight materials, which were available in small amount or in low purity. Family plots, so far as can be said at present, are most likely, although not by any means exclusively to be found with non-polar materials such as the hydrocarbons. An example of the precision possible is the prediction (40) from a family plot based on ethane and propane, that p^0 for n-butane at 21°C. would be 1642 mm. Hg., the accepted value being 1634 mm. Hg. Again, the boiling points of a number of 1 and 2-olefins were predicted by comparison with the retention characteristics of the hexenes and found to agree with the literature values to within about 2°C.

In the particular case where $\Delta H^m \simeq 0$ it is clear that the heat of sorption derived from $\log V_g / T^{-1}$ plots is equal, though of opposite sign, to the molar latent heat of vaporisation at the mean elution temperature. If this condition is fulfilled by several members of a series of compounds with a given solvent, it can be assumed that it applies also to others. It is not, of course, necessary to measure V_g since only the slope of a plot is used to deduce ΔH^v and so any measure of retention can be used. An added possibility is that, for a given solute, measurements might be conducted with numerous solvents. If then several equal values of $\Delta H_e{}^s$ were found it would be a reasonable supposition that in these cases $\Delta H^m \simeq 0$ and that $\Delta H_e{}^s = \Delta H^v$. In this approach no other series members would be required to characterise the chromatographic system, and so the method would be quite general. The probable accuracy of ΔH^v measured by gas chromatography is unlikely to be greater than about 300 cal./mole, unless many precautions are taken, but this compares reasonably with the capabilities of at least the simplest conventional techniques.

SOLVENT MOLECULAR WEIGHTS

If activity coefficients were always unity, gas chromatographic retention measurements with solutes of known physical properties would provide a means to evaluate the molecular weight of the solvent, M_l (see equation 10.7). It is not often that $\gamma_0 = 1$ but, even so, in some instances a reasonable estimate of M_l may be made. It is not inconceivable that a broad study might lead to the finding of standard procedures whereby M_l might be calculable from V_g data. Even if this never becomes possible, it is clear that V_g measurements for standard solutes can be used to identify solvents with reasonable certainty.

STUDIES OF COMPLEX FORMATION

The use of gas chromatography in the study of complex formation in solution was initiated by Phillips and his co-workers (54). They employed columns containing the molten stearates and oleates of Mn, Co, Ni, Cu and Zn and in the elution of a wide variety of volatile organic compounds. In such systems it is not possible to evaluate equilibrium constants from solubility data and so the results were discussed in terms of "retardation factors." These were measured by plotting retention times (relative to mesitylene) for homologues in the form of log/log plots, the reference solvent, chosen for its non-polar character, being Apiezon-M grease. The log/log plots for all the series of compounds studied were linear and the retardation factor for any series was taken as the slope of the plot.

The linearity of the original plots clearly implies a linear increase in the free energy of solution with increasing molecular weight of solute (cf. p. 27). Analysis of the derived retardation factors revealed a number of other interesting features. For example, for secondary and tertiary amines with the stearates of Mn, Co and Zn the retardation factors were found to be proportional to the basic dissociation constants of the amines. The extent to which primary amines deviated from this rule was indicative of hydrogen bond formation, while the low retardation factors for pyridine homologues were consistent with steric interference. Again, it was found for all the chemical types studied that the variation of retardation factor with the identity of the metal in the solvent molecule paralleled closely the variation of complex stabilities found in studies in aqueous solution.

Measurements of heats of solution showed that these, like the free energies, varied linearly with solute molecular weight for any homologous series. Clearly, therefore, this must also be true of the entropies of solution and it was shown (54) that a plot of ΔH^s against $T \Delta S^s$ was linear in all cases. This kind of relationship has previously been noted on numerous occasions in conventional studies of vaporisation from both pure liquids and solutions (see e.g. 56). Heats of mixing were found to be about 1 kcal./mole for hydrocarbon solutes and 2 kcal./mole for alcohols. These results underline what was said earlier about the probable magnitude of ΔH^m in ordinary gas chromatographic solutions since here, well defined compounds are supposed to form.

More recently (55) the same approach has been used in studies involving salicylaldimines of Ni, Pd, Pt and Cn and glyoximes of Ni, Pd and Pt. Here again valuable information was derived from retardation factors. A particular merit of the approach was found to be its capability of giving results for systems in which interactions were very weak and also where components were readily hydrolysed. These are features which make the conventional approach difficult and there thus seems little doubt that gas chromatography will provide a valuable new technique for the study of organometallic complexes.

A somewhat different approach to the study of complexing in solution is that adopted by Langer, Zahn and Pantazoplos (58). These workers studied the elution of aromatics from columns containing one or other of several n-alkyl tetrahalophthalate esters. They inferred complex formation from the fact that, for example, m-xylene was eluted before p-xylene although it has the lower saturation vapour pressure, and also from ultra-violet spectroscopic studies and the finding that hexamethylbenzene, for instance, forms solid complexes. Their method of evaluating the relative complexing power of a given solvent for various solutes was based on a slight modification of the theory advanced in Chapter 2 to account for partition co-efficients in systems where the distributed species has a different molecular weight in the two immiscible phases. Langer et al. showed simply that the apparent (measured) activity coefficient, g, is related to the true coefficient for the uncomplexed solute γ_0 by

$$g = (1 - c)\gamma_0$$

where c is the fraction of solute in solution which is complexed. It was shown earlier (p. 12) that the calculation of an equilibrium constant for a reaction in solution requires information obtained at a variety of solute concentrations. Thus, elution gas chromatography cannot in the ordinary way provide enough data. Langer et al. overcame this problem by assuming that γ_0 was the same for all aromatics. They were then able to compute relative values of c for all the solutes. The results obtained in this way, although perhaps only semi-quantitative, were certainly consistent with the hypothesis of charge transfer interactions.

The discussion of Chapter 2 indicates how the above approach might be modified to permit absolute evaluation of c and, hence, of equilibrium constants. In order to get around the difficulty of studying the effect of variation of solute concentration, a mixed column containing a second solvent, in which complexing was unlikely, and which was immiscible with the first solvent, might be used. The two liquids would somehow have to be brought into intimate contact in the column but, if this condition could be achieved, the theory of Chapter 2 would be directly applicable and retention data for a given solute obtained at different solvent/solvent ratios should yield equilibrium constants. Whether or not this approach can be developed there can be no doubt that gas chromatography presents considerable opportunities in the study of complex formation and occasionally some feature may make the study of a system much simpler. As an example, we may consider in some detail results obtained with the one system with which it has so far proved possible to determine an equilibrium constant for a complexing reaction directly from gas chromatographic results.

The Reaction of Ammonia with Silver Nitrate. Du Plessis and Spong (57) found that columns of silver nitrate dissolved in benzyl cyanide absorbed ammonia samples irreversibly when new. This they very reasonably attributed to the reaction

$$AgZ + x\mathrm{NH}_3 = AgZ(\mathrm{NH}_3)_x$$

the use of AgZ in the equation being dictated by the observation of some decomposition of the nitrate. After the loss of a number of samples, ammonia vapour could be eluted in the usual way, and this was taken to indicate completion of the above reaction throughout the column. However, the peak shape then obtained depended very markedly on sample size. With very small samples of ammonia, normal peaks were observed; greater samples gave flat-topped peaks of constant height but of a width which was dependent on sample size. With even larger samples, a normal elution peak appeared ahead of the plateau.

Figure 3 illustrates the elution pattern observed in this condition. The explanation of these phenomena offered by Du Plessis and Spong is that the following equilibrium occurs in the conditioned column

$$AgZ(NH_3)_x + yNH_3 \rightleftharpoons AgZ(NH_3)_{x+y}$$

At any given temperature this equilibrium is characterised by the dissociation pressure p of the back reaction and so, if the injected sample of ammonia is so small that the pressure p is never achieved anywhere in the

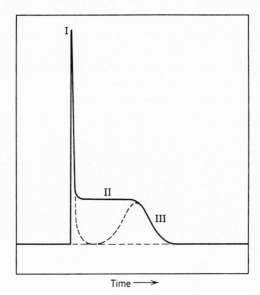

Time $\longrightarrow$

FIG. 3. Elution peak obtained with a large sample of ammonia vapour taken through a conditioned (ammonia saturated) column containing $AgNO_3$ + benzyl cyanide. I, elution peak for ammonia and chemically equilibrated solvent; II, plateau corresponding to saturation of solvent; III, tail of true elution peak of ammonia from unreacted solvent.

column, the elution is normal (zone III) and the retention volume depends upon the normal partition coefficient plus the equilibrium constant. If the injected sample is sufficiently big to maintain the pressure p for some distance through the column then a plateau (zone II) corresponding to this concentration is observed. The plateau height is, of course, limited by the pressure p, but its width may increase in the forward direction (its tail is always that of zone III) up to the point where the whole column is filled by ammonia at this pressure. Any increase in sample size above this level will lead to the excess travelling as a true elution peak which moves ahead of the plateau; the retention volume of this peak being determined only by the partition coefficient for ammonia dissolved in the chemically equilibrated solvent.

By apportioning the areas on the chromatogram between the various zones and knowing the size of injected sample and free gas space, p could be calculated and, knowing the weight of silver nitrate in the column, so also could y. In experiments conducted over a wide range of sample sizes, solvent/support ratios and column lengths, it was found that $y = 0.5 \pm 0.05$, a result which must be regarded as confirmation of the basic arguments. The method could obviously be extended to determine ΔH for the equilibrium and is also likely to be applicable in the study of the formation of other complexes. It must be emphasised that the peculiar form of the chromatograms, which provides both the clue and the key to the understanding of the processes occurring, is only likely to be observed with very lean columns, a fact which may explain why such anomalies have not been reported by others using silver nitrate columns.

THE MEASUREMENT OF INTERDIFFUSION COEFFICIENTS

It has been apparent for some years that gas chromatography might provide a means to determine interdiffusion coefficients in the gas phase, if not those in solution. Until relatively recently the several attempts at the evaluation of D_g data have been only partially successful. This was a consequence of the use of the simplified van Deemter equation in the analysis of the results and the confusion about carrier gas velocity. Even so, with the assumption of not unreasonable values of the labyrinth constant γ, more or less correct values of D_g have been obtained by some workers (25, 59). The earlier discussion shows clearly, however, that the extended rate equation must be used if worthwhile diffusional data are to be obtained. Attempts along these lines have recently been described (60, 61, 62). The earliest work (62) involved elution of hydrogen in nitrogen through unpacked tubes and yielded an interdiffusion coefficient good to about 5 per cent. The later studies (60, 61) were more comprehensive and were conducted in three groups:

a. Elution of permanent gases from open tubes.

b. Elution of unsorbed permanent gases from solvent containing packed columns.

c. Elution of sorbed gases from the packed columns.

In the experiments in (*a*), the appropriate form of the extended rate equation was the simplified expression

$$H = \frac{B_o}{u_o} + \frac{r_0^2 u_o}{24 D_g^{\,o}}$$

since $k' = 0$. The second term contributed less than 1 per cent of H at the velocities employed and so could be ignored. Some of the results obtained (60) for diffusion in nitrogen are listed in Table 5.

TABLE 5
INTERDIFFUSION COEFFICIENTS FOR SOME PERMANENT GASES IN
NITROGEN AT 1 ATM. AND 51°C.; MEASUREMENTS MADE BY ELUTION
FROM OPEN TUBES

Diffusing Species	Range of u_0 cm. sec.$^{-1}$	$D_g{}^o$ cm.^{2} sec.$^{-1}$	$D_g{}^o$ (lit.) cm.^{2} sec.$^{-1}$
H_2	0.85–1.56	0.892 ± 0.016	0.909
O_2	0.72–1.42	0.263 ± 0.003	0.244
CO_2	0.73–1.40	0.188 ± 0.003	0.194

For the analysis of the results of the experiments listed under (b) the rate equation must be extended to

$$H = A + \frac{2\gamma D_g{}^o}{u_o} + \frac{\chi d_p{}^2 u_o}{24 D_g{}^o}$$

Again, by working at velocities of 1 cm. sec.$^{-1}$ or less the last term was rendered negligible. The method of evaluating A and the evidence relating to the magnitude of γ were described earlier (p. 159). The indications were that $\gamma \simeq 1$ and assuming this to be true, the data for B_o (60) can be used to compute $D_g{}^o$ directly. The results for a series of columns of different d_p, each consisting of polyethylene glycol/Sil-O-Cel (20 per cent w/w) are then as shown in Table 6.

The last group of experiments (61) which were made with systems of type (c) employed the same set of columns and conditions as above, but the eluted gases were acetone and benzene vapours. In this case the complete extended rate equation (equation 8.40) had to be used to evaluate B_o each time. Again the evidence favoured the view that $\gamma \simeq 1$ and using this

TABLE 6
INTERDIFFUSION COEFFICIENTS OF HYDROGEN AND CARBON
DIOXIDE IN NITROGEN AT 1 ATM. AND 51°C.; MEASUREMENTS
MADE IN PACKED COLUMNS

Diffusing Species	Column d_p cm.	$D_g{}^o$ cm.^{2} sec.$^{-1}$		$D_g{}^o$ (open tubes) cm.^{2} sec.$^{-1}$	$D_g{}^o$ (lit.) cm.^{2} sec.$^{-1}$
H_2	0.032	0.860 ⎤			
	0.016	0.925 ⎥ 0.877		0.892	0.909
	0.010	0.875 ⎦			
CO_2	0.032	0.167 ⎤			
	0.016	0.190 ⎥ 0.176		0.188	0.194
	0.010	0.172 ⎦			

value for our present purposes we get the diffusion coefficients listed in Table 7.

Consideration of the data in the three tables shows that with each type of system very reasonable agreement with the literature data, which were obtained by conventional techniques, was achieved. When hydrogen was involved, either as the eluted sample or as carrier, the agreement was in fact excellent as, for example, is seen from Table 7, where the data agree exactly. This situation almost certainly arises because, when hydrogen is involved,

TABLE 7

MEAN INTERDIFFUSION COEFFICIENTS FOR ACETONE AND BENZENE VAPOURS IN HYDROGEN AND NITROGEN AT 1 ATM. AND 51°C.; MEASUREMENT BY ELUTION FROM SEVERAL PACKED COLUMNS OF DIFFERENT d_p EACH CONTAINING POLYETHYLENE GLYCOL/Sil-O-Cel, 20 PER CENT w/w

| Diffusing Species | Hydrogen | | Nitrogen | |
	$D_g{}^o$ cm.^{2} sec.$^{-1}$	$D_g{}^o$ (lit.) cm.^{2} sec.$^{-1}$	$D_g{}^o$ cm.^{2} sec.$^{-1}$	$D_g{}^o$ (lit.) cm.^{2} sec.$^{-1}$
Acetone	0.468	0.467	0.115	0.120
Benzene	0.412	0.411	0.093	0.105

diffusion is a maximum and the measurements become more accurate thereby. On the whole, the data presented show two things, first that the plate and rate concepts are realistic and, secondly, that there is every prospect of establishing gas chromatography as a technique for the measurement of interdiffusion coefficients in the gas phase.

Turning now to interdiffusion in solution. It is a simple matter to calculate the quantity $d_f{}^2/D_l$ accurately if C_l can be reliably computed from theoretical plate height data. The remaining problem is that of determining d_f. In packed columns this clearly presents difficulties but in open tubes (capillaries) a reasonable estimate at least may be made. There are numerous values of C_l in the literature for packed columns but virtually none for capillaries. We can therefore at this time discuss only packed column data. Using results obtained with the simplified van Deemter equation should give results not greatly in error but those derived with the use of the extended rate equation are likely to be better. The only ones available as yet (61) relate to the diffusion of acetone and benzene in polyethylene glycol at 51°C. For columns of d_p in the range 0.010–0.016 cm. it was found that $d_f{}^2/D_l$ was 0.0225 for acetone and 0.055 for benzene. These results give D_l(benzene)/D_l(acetone) = 0.5 since d_f must be the same for both solutes.

This is encouraging since a similar ratio is found for diffusion of these substances in simpler solvents. There is little point in attempting a more detailed breakdown, but if we estimate d_f at 10^{-4} cm., we find that $D_l \simeq 4 \times 10^{-7}$ cm.^{2} sec.$^{-1}$, a not unreasonable figure. If means to measure d_f are found it thus seems likely that diffusion coefficients in solution may be measured chromatographically.

REFERENCES

1. Purnell, J. H., *Ann. N.Y. Acad. Sci.*, 1959, **72**, 614.
2. Golay, M., *2nd International Symposium I.S.A.*, Lansing, Mich., June, 1959, Preprints, p. 5.
3. Huyten, F. H., W. van Beersum and G. W. A. Rijnders, *Gas Chromatography*, 1960, Butterworths, London (editor, R. P. W. Scott), p. 224.
4. Purnell, J. H., *J. Roy. Inst. Chem.*, 1958, **82**, 586.
5. Johns, T., M. R. Burnell and D. W. Carle, *2nd International Symposium I.S.A.*, Lansing, Mich., June, 1959, Preprints, p. 82.
6. Benedek, P., L. Szepesy et al., *Acta Chim. Acad. Sci. Hung.*, 1958, **14**, 3; 19; 31; 339; 353; 359.
7. Freund, M., P. Benedek and L. Szepesy, *Vapour Phase Chromatography*, 1957, Butterworths, London (editor, D. H. Desty), p. 359.
8. Benedek, P., L. Szepesy and S. Szepe, *Gas Chromatography*, 1958, Academic Press, New York (editor, V. J. Coates et al.), p. 225.
9. Skarstrom, C. W., *Ann. N.Y. Acad. Sci.*, 1959, **72**, 751.
10. Bohemen, J., Ph.D. Thesis, Cambridge, 1960. See also references 60 and 61.
11. Kapfer, W. H., M. Malow, J. Happel and C. J. Marsel, *A.I.Ch.E. Journal*, 1956, **2**, 456.
12. Pichler, H., and H. Schulz, *Brennstoff-Chem.*, 1958, **39**, 148.
13. Glueckauf, E., *Trans. Faraday Soc.*, 1955, **51**, 34.
14. Teisseire, P., *Recherche*, 1959, **9**, 10.
15. Theimer, E. T., *Drug and Cosmetic Ind.*, 1959, **85**, 754; 824; 830.
16. Stadler, P. A., and P. Oberhausli, *Helv. Chim. Acta*, 1959, **42**, 2597.
17. Benson, R. E., and R. V. Lindsay, *J. Amer. Chem. Soc.*, 1959, **81**, 4250.
18. Williams, J. K., and W. H. Sharkey, *J. Amer. Chem. Soc.*, 1959, **81**, 4269.
19. Criegee, R., and K. Noll, *Annalen*, 1959, **627**, 1.
20. Catalette, G., J. P. Beaufils, B. Gras and J. E. Germain, *Bull. soc. chim. France*, **1960**, 6.
21. Whitham, B. T., *Vapour Phase Chromatography*, 1957, Butterworths, London (editor, D. H. Desty), p. 194.
22. Skell, P. S., and R. G. Allen, *J. Amer. Chem. Soc.*, 1959, **81**, 5383.
23. Doering, W., and T. Mole, *Tetrahedron*, 1960, **10**, 68.
24. Sokol, L., *Coll. Czech. Chem. Commun.*, 1960, **25**, 906.
25. Reed, T. M., J. F. Walter, R. R. Cecil and R. D. Dresdner, *Ind. Eng. Chem.*, 1959, **51**, 271.
26. Evans, D. E. M., W. E. Massingham, M. Stacey and J. C. Tatlow, *Nature*, 1958, **182**, 591.
27. Coe, P. L., C. R. Patrick and J. C. Tatlow, *Tetrahedron*, 1960, **9**, 240.
28. Serpinet, J., *Chim. anal.*, 1959, **41**, 146.
29. Matthews, J. S., F. H. Burow and R. E. Snyder, *Anal. Chem.*, 1960, **32**, 691.
30. Pichat, L., J. Clement and C. Baret, *Bull. soc. chim. France*, **1959**, (2), 329; (4), 580.

31. Howard, G. A., and R. Stevens, *Chem. and Ind.*, **1959**, 1518.

32. Böttcher, C. J. F., F. P. Woodford, C. C. Romeny-Wachter, E. B. Van Houte and C. M. Van Gent, *Lancet*, **1959**, (1), 1378.

33. McGreer, D. E., *J. Org. Chem.*, 1960, **25**, 852.

34. Abramovitch, R. A., A. D. Notation and G. C. Seng, *Tetrahedron*, 1959, **9**, 1.

35. Lochte, H. L., and A. G. Pittman, *J. Amer. Chem. Soc.*, 1960, **82**, 469.

36. James, A. T., and A. J. P. Martin, *Biochem. J.*, 1952, **50**, 679.

37. Bradford, B. W., D. Harvey and D. E. Chalkley, *J. Inst. Petrol.*, 1955, **41**, 80.

38. Littlewood, A. B., C. S. G. Phillips and D. T. Price, *J. Chem. Soc.*, **1955**, 1480.

39. Hoare, M. R., and J. H. Purnell, *Research*, 1955, **8**, S41.

40. Hoare, M. R., and J. H. Purnell, *Trans. Faraday Soc.*, 1956, **52**, 222.

41. Porter, P. E., C. H. Deal and F. H. Stross, *J. Amer. Chem. Soc.*, 1956, **78**, 2999.

42. Anderson, J. R., and K. H. Napier, *Australian J. Chem.*, 1957, **10**, 250.

43. Ashworth, A. J., and D. H. Everett, *Trans. Faraday Soc.*, 1960, **56**, 1609.

44. Martin, R. L., *Anal. Chem.*, 1960, **32**, 336.

45. Adlard, E. R., M. A. Khan and B. T. Whitham, *Gas Chromatography*, 1960, Butterworths, London (editor, R. P. W. Scott), p. 251.

46. Purnell, J. H., *Vapour Phase Chromatography*, 1957, Butterworths, London (editor, D. H. Desty), p. 6.

47. Pierotti, G. J., C. H. Deal, E. L. Derr and P. E. Porter, *J. Amer. Chem. Soc.*, 1956, **78**, 2989.

48. Kwantes, A., and G. W. A. Rijnders, *Gas Chromatography*, 1958, Butterworths, London (editor, D. H. Desty), p. 125.

49. Langer, S. H., and J. H. Purnell (unpublished data).

50. Khan, M. A., *Gas Chromatography*, 1958, Butterworths, London (editor, D. H. Desty), p. 135.

51. James, D. H., and C. S. G. Phillips, *J. Chem. Soc.*, **1954**, 1066.

52. Bohemen, J., S. H. Langer, R. H. Perrett and J. H. Purnell, *J. Chem. Soc.*, **1960**, 2444.

53. Perrett, R. H., and J. H. Purnell, *J. Chromatog.* (in press).

54. Barker, D. W., C. S. G. Phillips, G. F. Tusa and A. Verdin, *J. Chem. Soc.*, **1959**, 18.

55. Cartoni, G. P., R. S. Lowrie, C. S. G. Phillips and L. M. Venanzi, *Gas Chromatography*, 1960, Butterworths, London (editor, R. P. W. Scott), p. 273.

56. Butler, J. A. V., *Chemical Thermodynamics*, 1955, Macmillan, London, p. 367.

57. Du Plessis, L. A., and A. H. Spong, *J. Chem. Soc.*, **1959**, 2027.

58. Gregg, S. J., and R. Stock, *Gas Chromatography*, 1958, Butterworths, London (editor, D. H. Desty), p. 90.

59. de Wet, W. J., and V. Pretorius, *Anal. Chem.*, 1958, **30**, 325.

60. Bohemen, J., and J. H. Purnell, *J. Chem. Soc.*, **1961**, 360.

61. Bohemen, J., and J. H. Purnell, *J. Chem. Soc.*, **1961**, 2630.

62. Giddings, J. C., and S. L. Seager, *J. Chem. Phys.*, 1960, **33**, 1579.

INDEX